SYMPOSIA OF THE
SOCIETY FOR EXPERIMENTAL BIOLOGY

NUMBER XXII

Other Publications of The Company of Biologists

JOURNAL OF EXPERIMENTAL BIOLOGY
JOURNAL OF CELL SCIENCE
JOURNAL OF EMBRYOLOGY AND EXPERIMENTAL MORPHOLOGY

SYMPOSIA

The Journal of Experimental Botany
is published by the Oxford University Press
for the Society for Experimental Biology

SYMPOSIA OF THE
SOCIETY FOR EXPERIMENTAL BIOLOGY

NUMBER XXII

ASPECTS OF
CELL MOTILITY

Published for the Company of Biologists on behalf
of the Society for Experimental Biology
ACADEMIC PRESS INC., PUBLISHERS
NEW YORK, NEW YORK
1968

Published by the Syndics of the Cambridge University Press
Bentley House 200 Euston Road, London, N.W. 1

The Symposia of the Society for Experimental Biology
are published in the U.S.A. by: Academic Press Inc.
111 Fifth Avenue, New York, N.Y. 10003

Printed in Great Britain
at the University Printing House, Cambridge
(Brooke Crutchley, University Printer)

2390

CONTENTS

The solubility properties of the fragments, obtained from the myosin molecule by the controlled digestion with proteolytic enzymes, reflect in a striking way differences in the relative ability of different parts of the molecule to interact with each other and with the aqueous medium. For example, the light-meromyosin component (Szent-Györgyi, 1953), de-

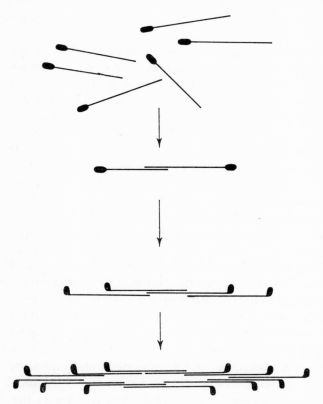

Fig. 1. Scheme showing mechanism of formation of fibrous aggregates from myosin monomers. After Huxley (1963).

rived from the tail of the molecule, possesses the solubility properties of myosin itself in that at ionic strengths corresponding to that in the cell, i.e. < 0·3, the molecules show a greater tendency to interact with each other rather than pass into solution. This, of course, is an important property, for at the ionic strength of the cytoplasm the strong interactions between the tails of the myosin molecules in the A filament provide the filament with the strength required to transmit tension. In contrast heavy meromyosin (Szent-Györgyi, 1953), subfragment 1 (Mueller & Perry, 1962) and subfragment 2 (Lowey, Goldstein & Luck, 1966) are all soluble at low physiological ionic strengths, indicating that under these conditions there is a relatively stronger interaction with the aqueous medium than between the molecules themselves. Thus those parts of the molecule upon which the biologically active centres are localized do not interact strongly either with the body of the A filament composed of the tails of the myosin molecules or with the head region, a significant property if this part of the molecule is flexible, thus enabling the cross-bridges to move during contraction (Reedy, Holmes & Tregear, 1965; Huxley, 1967).

It is a matter of importance for the understanding of the molecular mechanism of contraction to determine how many myosin molecules are associated with each cross-bridge. In view of the known properties of myosin systems on aggregation, there would appear to be little doubt that the projections of A filaments are formed by the head regions of the myosin molecules, where it is known that the biologically active centres concerned in ATP hydrolysis and actin combination are localized. What is less certain is the number of molecules associated with each bridge, or indeed whether other protein material is also present there as well as in the body of the A filament (see Perry, 1967, for discussion).

To determine the number of myosin molecules per cross-bridge it is necessary to have good quantitative data for the protein composition of the myofibril. The information is difficult to obtain with precision because of the problems involved in estimating myofibrillar proteins. This is due mainly to the ease with which they interact with other proteins, some of which have as yet to be well characterized, to form complexes which are not broken down during the extraction procedures used for estimation. A new approach to this problem has recently been made using the 3-methyl histidine and amino acid content of isolated myofibrils, purified actin and myosin (Perry & Harris, 1967). The calculation made from these data depends on the assumption that there is no 3-methyl histidine in the myofibril other than that due to actin and myosin. It is known that this amino acid is not present in tropomyosin (Johnson, Harris & Perry, 1967).

Preliminary determinations by this method indicate that the isolated rabbit myofibril contains 55% myosin, a figure which is in good agreement with those that have been arrived at in the past based on other possibly less precise methods of determination.

The myofibrillar–nuclear fraction, separated by the differential centrifugation technique, represents approximately 20·6 mg. nitrogen/g. wet wt. of rabbit longissimus dorsi muscle (Perry & Zydowo, 1959). Helander (1961), using extraction techniques, estimated the myofibrillar fraction of rabbit skeletal muscle as 19·5 mg. nitrogen/g. wet wt., a value which was reduced when exercise was restricted. Thus there is considerable agreement with the experimentally determined value for the nitrogen represented by the myofibrillar fraction, which for the purposes of the calculation below is taken as 20 mg./g. wet wt. of rabbit skeletal muscle. The value is probably an upper one; certainly that determined by the probably more specific method of morphological fractionation will give a high figure, for the myofibrillar fraction determined in this way will also contain stroma, nuclei and fragments of the sarcoplasmic reticulum adhering to the myofibrils. Taking the myofibrillar content of myosin as 55 %, the nitrogen content of myosin as 16·7 %, a molecular weight of 500,000 and the figure of $2·4 \times 10^{14}$ A filaments per ml. of rabbit muscle (Huxley, 1963), each A filament can be calculated to contain 330 myosin molecules. This is significantly greater than the 200–220 cross-bridges observed (Huxley, 1963), and gives a 'molecular weight' of the A filament, if it consists solely of myosin, of 165×10^6. The calculations using 3 methyl histidine require the assumption that myosin and actin together represent 75 % of the myofibril and will no doubt need to be modified when this figure can be revised.

If each cross-bridge represents a myosin molecule, the A filament would possess a molecular weight of $100–110 \times 10^6$, whereas Huxley (1963) estimated it to be about 160×10^6 from its dimension in the electron microscope. This appears to be a considerable discrepancy, part of which may be accounted for by the appreciable amount of protein present in the myofibril in addition to actin, myosin and tropomyosin, possibly representing up to 25 % of the whole, part of which must be in the A filament. One such component might be involved in regulating the aggregation of myosin molecules to form the A filaments of constant width and length.

In insect flight muscle the relationship between the number of cross-bridges and myosin molecules appears to be different from that in rabbit skeletal muscle. Chaplain & Tregear (1966) have concluded from analytical and electron-microscope data that there are three myosin molecules per cross-bridge of the A filament from flight muscle of the water-bug, *Lethocerus cordofanus*. This difference is perhaps surprising in view of the general similarity of the size of the cross-bridges in the two systems, but may be a special requirement for the much reduced I band movement which occurs in insect flight muscle. On simple mechanical grounds it would appear at first sight to present little advantage to group together the biologically active heads of three myosin molecules in view of the stereochemical problems which may be involved in interacting with actin monomers on the neighbouring I filament.

Although in the past there has been considerable discussion about the true value of the molecular weight of myosin, the data at present available suggest that it is probably close to 500,000 (see Perry, 1967, for review).

This is a large molecule containing about 5,000 amino acid residues and which if it possessed a unique structure would be very much larger than most enzymes. Considerable evidence exists, however, for the presence of sub-units in the myosin molecule, for in the presence of dissociating agents the standard myosin preparations can be resolved into high and low molecular-weight fractions (see Perry, 1967). The high molecular-weight component representing the major fraction has a molecular-weight of about 200,000–260,000 and probably is produced by the dissociation of the molecule into the two main chains of which it is composed. These chains appear to be identical as judged from studies of the tryptic peptides (Landon & Perry, 1963, Perry & Landon, 1964; Perry, 1967; Weeds & Hartley, 1967). The smaller fraction of much lower molecular weight represents about 10–15% of the original myosin and consists of components of molecular weight estimates of which have varied from 15,000 to 30,000. From myosin of rabbit skeletal muscle several different small molecular-weight components can be identified (Gerschman, Dreizen & Stracher, 1966; Dreizen, Gerschman, Trotta & Stracher, 1967; Locker & Hagyard, 1967 a, b; Gaetjens, 1967) and some variation in the composition of those components occurs between myosin isolated from different sources. It is difficult as yet to decide whether this low-molecular-weight component is an integral part of the myosin molecule and essential for its biological activity or is simply due to contaminating proteins that are not readily removed from myosin, which, like all myofibrillar proteins, is notoriously difficult to purify by conventional procedures. The fact that the amounts of low-molecular-weight material obtained on treating the molecule with dissociating agents can be reduced after rigorous purification, and the often extreme complexity of the low-molecular-weight-fraction when examined by gel electrophoresis, suggest that the latter explanation may be correct. It must be concluded, however, that as yet there are not enough data to make a final decision as to the functional or structural significance of the low-molecular-weight components in myosin.

In addition to the highly specific way the myosin molecule undergoes aggregation to produce the A filament, it also possesses two unusual properties which are intimately associated with the contractile process.

In the first place myosin can act as an enzyme and hydrolyse ATP and secondly it interacts with actin to form the complex, actomyosin, which can be dissociated by ATP and other polyphosphate compounds. Thus it is able to act enzymically on the substrate which modifies its interaction with the other main myofibrillar protein component.

The enzymic property has certain unusual features in that whereas Mg^{2+} is usually the most effective activating divalent cation in enzymic systems involving ATP as a substrate, Ca^{2+} and not Mg^{2+} activates the ATPase of myosin. In the presence of actin, however, the enzymic characteristics are in some way changed so that Mg^{2+} can then catalyse the hydrolysis of ATP. The enzymic activity in the presence of actin has another unusual feature in that actin modifies events about the enzymic centre of myosin so that when the relaxing-factor-protein system is present the Mg^{2+}-activated ATPase becomes susceptible to control by changes of Ca^{2+}. Thus although the Mg^{2+} concentration remains constant in the range $5-10 \times 10^{-3}$M alteration of the Ca^{2+} concentration in the range $10^{-5}-10^{-7}$M effectively changes the enzymic activity from the high and low rates of ATP hydrolysis which correspond to the contracting and resting states of muscle respectively.

Thus by the release of Ca^{2+} into the muscle cytoplasm in response to the electrical stimulus arriving at the muscle, the enzymic activity of the myofibril is regulated in the space of milliseconds. This is a unique situation for which the interaction of actin at the enzymic centre is responsible.

The fact that actin modifies the enzymic character of myosin implies that this protein in some way interacts with the enzyme. It is important to decide whether this enzymic effect is a consequence of the interaction with actin which leads to physical changes in the system, i.e. the well-known increase in viscosity and light scattering. Until recently it has always been assumed that Mg^{2+}-activated ATPase was a property of the acto-myosin complex and that the activity of the enzymes necessitated the strong interaction between the two proteins that was responsible for the viscosity and light-scattering changes occurring when the proteins were combined. Thus it was concluded that any set of conditions that broke the interaction caused the enzymic characteristics of the system to change to those of myosin itself, i.e. activated by Ca^{2+} but not by Mg^{2+} (Szent-Györgyi, 1951; Hasselbach, 1952). Studies with heavy meromyosin, however, indicate that this may not be the case, for under conditions of low ionic strength where acto-heavy-meromyosin, unlike actomyosin, is soluble and amenable to study by physicochemical methods, the system is Mg^{2+}-activated whereas viscosity and light-scattering measurements indicate that in the classical sense the system is dissociated (Leadbeater & Perry, 1963; Perry & Cotterill, 1965; Eisenberg & Moos, 1967). These results, interpreted at their face value and extrapolated to the actomyosin system, imply that although the classical strong interaction between myosin and actin is not made evident by the usual physical measurements, actin is still able to interact with the enzymic centre of myosin in view of the strong Mg^{2+}-activation of the ATPase.

The direct evidence for the localization of the centres concerned with biological activity on the myosin molecule comes principally from the studies of fragments obtained from myosin by proteolytic degradation. Both actin-combining and ATPase activities are associated with sub-fragment I (Mueller & Perry, 1962; Jones & Perry, 1966), a particle of molecular weight about 130,000, which is obtained by the progressive tryptic digestion of heavy meromyosin. A knowledge of the number of the active centres per molecule is obviously essential for a description of the contractile process but unfortunately the information at present available lacks precision. In the past the centres for ATP hydrolysis and actin com-bination have often been considered to be identical, but there is now considerable evidence to suggest that this assumption may not be correct, a situation which has led to ambiguity in the interpretation of the results obtained.

The two activities can be modified independently, for example with thiol reagents (Bárány & Bárány, 1959; Perry & Cotterill, 1964; Kaldor, Gitlin, Westley & Vock, 1964) and, although subfragment I combines readily with actin, it differs from myosin and heavy meromyosin in that its ATPase is not very significantly activated by Mg^{2+} in the presence of actin (Jones & Perry, 1966).

Although the evidence suggests that different centres are involved, the events occurring at them must be closely related in the contractile cycle. It is not clear how this is accomplished but some type of allosteric relation-ship which ensures that combination at one centre produces effects at the other could readily be visualized. Despite the evidence for two types of site, there have been no reports of fragments, isolated by the use of proteo-lytic enzymes, possessing either enzymic or actin-combining activity, apart from the work of Nankina, Kofman, Chernyak & Kalamkarova (1964), which has not yet been confirmed. The observation that on elution of pre-parations of subfragment I from DEAE cellulose and Sephadex the peaks of ATPase activity and of protein separated by actin combination are not always coincident (Jones & Perry, 1966) is possibly relevant in this connexion.

The evidence regarding the number of centres of each type is much more equivocal. If the molecule is composed of two similar chains the possibility exists of there being two enzymic and two actin-combining centres. Values obtained for the ATP and pyrophosphate-combining centres range from 1 to 2 (Gergely & Kohler, 1957; Tonomura & Morita, 1959; Nanninga & Mommaerts, 1960) but, as it is not always clear whether the enzymic or actin combining centres are being determined in these studies, it is diffi-cult to make a final decision on the number of sites of each type per mole-cule. It might be concluded from actin-combination studies in which each myosin molecule combines with approximately two actin monomers, that there are two centres for actin combination, provided that stereochemical considerations are not important and all the monomer units in F actin are equally available for combination. Such a view is supported, although not necessarily confirmed, by the recent electron microscope evidence, which indicates that the head of the myosin molecule consists of two globular regions (Slaytor & Lowey, 1967).

There is now good evidence that the breakdown of ATP accompanies contraction (Davies, 1965) and that the myofibrillar system has the enzymic capacity to liberate inorganic phosphate at the rate it is produced *in situ*. In vertebrate muscle at $37°$ C inorganic phosphate is produced at the rate of $1-10 \times 10^{-4}$ mole/g. per min. during tetanus (Mommaerts, 1950). When measured *in vitro* under conditions comparable to those presumed to exist *in vivo*, myofibrils from rabbit muscle split inorganic phosphate from ATP at an average rate comparable to that at the lower end of this range, when measured over an interval greater than 1 min. The actual rate would probably be much increased if it were measured over a short time scale comparable to that associated with a single contraction–relaxation cycle. During such a period the high initial rate, which is several times the steady rate reached after some seconds (Weber & Hasselbach, 1954; Tonomura & Kitagawa, 1957), probably applies. This possibility, coupled with the probability that the full activation of the enzyme will apply in the thiol environment in the cell, implies that the values of myofibrillar ATPase determined in the usual type of *in vitro* experiment do not adequately reflect the *in vivo* potential of the myofibril to hydrolyse ATP. In addition the fact that the total rate of inorganic phosphate production measured in whole muscle no doubt includes, in addition to the myofibrillar contribution, the inorganic phosphate liberated by the calcium-pump system of the vesicles, further suggests that the myofibrillar ATPase is fully capable of liberating inorganic phosphate from ATP at the rate observed in intact muscle.

A direct role of the ATPase of myosin in the contractile response is also supported by the correlation between the specific enzymic activity of myosin and the maximal speed of shortening of the muscle from which it is derived (Bárány, 1967). The correlation is not only observed between muscles from different species but also between muscles within the same species. For example, the specific enzymic activity of myosin isolated from the red, slow flight muscles of the pigeon is lower than that of the myosin from the fast white muscles of the leg of the same animal (Maddox & Perry, 1966). Quite apart from the enzymic differences, there is evidence of structural differences such as give rise, for example, to differences in susceptibility to tryptic digestion (Gergely *et al.* 1965; Bárány, Bárány, Reckard & Volpe, 1965; Maddox & Perry, 1966).

These findings indicate that the enzymic properties of the myosin molecule may vary according to the activity pattern of the muscle from which it is derived and imply that a mechanism exists which ensures that the myosin type appropriate to the activity pattern of the tissue is produced by a particular muscle type in a given species. Investigations reported elsewhere (Kendrick-Jones & Perry, 1965, 1967 a, b) have indicated that the enzymic composition of muscle both *in vivo* and *in vitro* can be modified by an adaptive response to activity. Although direct experimental evidence for this type of adaptation is as yet not available in the case of myosin, it is conceivable that similar processes apply in selecting the myosin type appropriate to the tissue function.

The problem has been approached by a study of myogenesis with particular emphasis on the nature of the myosin associated with different stages of development of skeletal muscle in the usual laboratory animals (Perry & Hartshorne, 1962; Trayer & Perry, 1966). Myosin from foetal muscle tends to be contaminated with more protein impurity than the adult form, but if care is taken to remove the contaminants by fractionation on DEAE cellulose it can be shown that the earlier the stage of development of the muscle the lower the specific activity of the purified myosin obtained from it. With increasing age the specific enzymic activity approaches the adult value, the precise age at which this occurs depending on the species (Fig.2). In general, in those animals born highly developed, such as the guinea-pig or chicken, the adult value is reached immediately at birth or hatching or very soon after it. On the other hand, in those species which are less developed at birth and which spend a considerable part of the neonatal life in comparative inactivity, the specific activity of the myosin ATPase does not reach the adult value until later (Fig. 2).

Foetal muscle can in general be regarded as a more primitive tissue with a slower speed of shortening and more comparable to red adult muscle than white adult muscle. The latter is the most highly specialized form of muscle, with a rapid contractile response and a high dependence on anaerobic metabolism for ATP production. Thus as development and specialization occur in muscle the tissue responds by increasing the amount and at the same time by modifying the quality of the myosin so that its biological properties are more appropriate to the function of the muscle; that is, it hydrolyses ATP at a more rapid rate as the speed of contraction increases with development.

The mechanism of this unique response in the major protein component of the contractile system is not clear, but the specialization which occurs must clearly affect the type of myosin molecule which is being synthesized. The changes observed may be explained, as has been suggested elsewhere

PLATE I

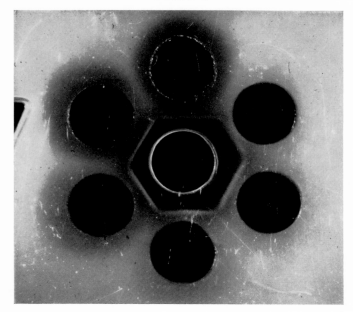

(a)

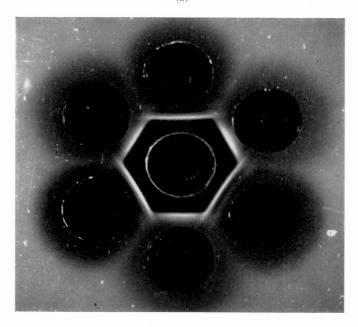

(b)

Immunochemical differences between foetal and adult forms of myosin from rabbit skeletal muscle (Trayer & Perry, unpublished.) (a) Ouchterlony plates of adult myosin antibody and adult myosin. Centre well contains undiluted fowl antiserum raised against adult rabbit myosin purified by DEAE chromatography and precipitation with LiCl and $(NH_4)_2SO_4$. Outer wells contain homologous antigen at concentrations of 8·6, 4·3, 2·2, 1·1, 0·54, 0·27 mg./ml. distributed in a clockwise direction with the most concentrated solution in the uppermost well. (b) Ouchterlony plates of adult myosin antibody and adult and foetal myosins. Centre well contains fowl antiserum raised against adult rabbit myosin purified by DEAE chromatography. Adult and foetal myosins (8 mg./ml.), both purified by DEAE chromatography, arranged alternately in the outer wells with the uppermost well containing adult myosin.

(Trayer & Perry, 1966), by assuming that myosin exists as isoenzymes which have considerable biological and structural differences. Thus by repression or stimulation of the appropriate genes an isoenzyme complement would be obtained which is appropriate to the function of the particular type of muscle cell, whether it be of the foetal, slow or fast type. The concept of the isoenzyme pattern of a cell changing in development is now widely accepted, but one of the special features of the myosin system is the large difference in specific enzymic activity which apparently exists between the different forms of myosin.

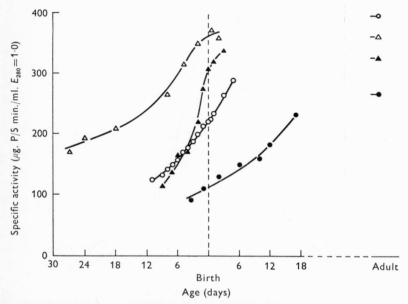

Fig. 2. Change in specific ATPase activity of purified myosins prepared from mixed skeletal muscle at different stages of development. Assays carried out in 5 mM ATP, 5 mM-CaCl$_2$, 50 mM tris-HCl buffer, pH 8·2, 0·2 M-KCl. Adult values (averages of at least three preparations indicated by symbols in top right-hand corner of figure). From Trayer & Perry (1966). O, Rabbit; △, guinea pig; ▲, fowl; ● rat.

Myosin isoenzymes have not yet been directly demonstrated, for the standard electrophoretic methods used require that the protein be in solution. This occurs only at fairly high ionic strength with myosin and thus the system is not very amenable to study by these methods. Considerable evidence, however, now exists for structural differences between the foetal and adult forms of myosin from rabbit skeletal muscle. In particular the two forms show differences in susceptibility to succinylation, tryptic digestion and to reaction with 5-5′-dithiobis (2-dinitrobenzoic acid) (Trayer, Perry & Teale, 1967). The environment around the tryptophan residues appears to be more hydrophobic in the case of foetal myosin as judged by the reduced quantum yield of the fluorescence obtained on excitation at 290 mμ (Fig. 3). The observation that the difference in quantum yield disappears when both proteins are treated with urea implies it is related to differences in tertiary structure in the two proteins.

The range of properties which differ in the foetal and adult forms of rabbit myosin indicate considerable structural differences between the two

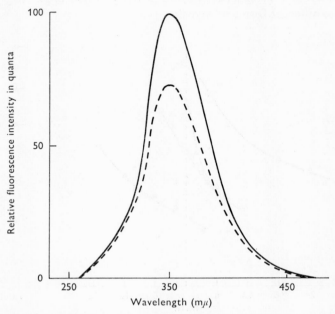

Fig. 3. Fluorescence spectra of tryptophan residues in myosins from rabbit adult and 28-day-old foetal muscle. Myosin, purified by chromatography on DEAE cellulose, in 0·5 M-KCl, 25 mM tris-HCl buffer, pH 7·6. E_{280} = 0·2 in each case. Excited at 290 mμ ———, Adult myosin; – – –, foetal myosin.

proteins and these would be expected to be apparent by immunochemical procedures. With the Ouchterlony procedure both foetal and adult myosin from rabbit skeletal muscle react with antibody to adult rabbit myosin raised in the fowl (Plate 1). The cross-over of the precipitin lines indicates however that the two myosins are not immunochemically identical.

Adult rabbit myosin has been shown to contain a small but significant amount of material which by comparison with similar studies on actin has been provisionally identified as 3-methyl histidine (Johnson *et al.* 1967). This amino acid, which has not so far been identified in proteins other than actin, is localized in the subfragment I portion of the myosin molecule and all the evidence at present indicates that it exists in peptide form.

The amount of 3-methyl histidine in myosin from adult rabbit muscle is somewhat variable, possibly due to difficulties in the assay procedure, and in myosin isolated from rabbit longissimus dorsi it averages out at 1·6 residues per 500,000 (Table 1). Surprisingly, myosin from the 28-day-old foetus does not contain any significant amount of 3-methyl histidine but the value rises to the adult level in the first few weeks of neonatal life (Trayer, Harris & Perry, 1967).

Table 1. *3-Methyl histidine content of myosin and actin isolated from rabbit skeletal muscle*

Myosin preparations purified by DEAE chromatography
(Perry, 1960; Trayer & Perry, 1966)

Protein	Age of animal	No. of different preparations	3-Methyl histidine (residues/10^5 g)
Myosin*	Adult	5	0·327 ± 0·033
	28-day foetus	5	Not detectable
Actin†	Adult	5	2·10 ± 0·04

* Trayer, Harris & Perry (1967). † Johnson, Harris & Perry (1967).

In this respect myosin appears significantly different from actin with respect to its 3-methyl histidine content, for this amino acid is present in both foetal and adult forms of rabbit actin. In view of the possible similarities between foetal myosin and that present in red muscle it is of interest that 3-methyl histidine is present also in myosin isolated from cardiac muscle. Although the number of estimations carried out is limited it may be significant that the values so far obtained are somewhat lower than those obtained from myosin from white rabbit muscle.

These preliminary results suggest that in the myosin of rabbit skeletal muscle the 3-methyl histidine content increases as the specific ATPase of the myosin rises. Clearly, 3-methyl histidine is not essential for the ATPase activity of myosin, for the protein obtained from the 28-day-old rabbit foetus has 60% of the adult ATPase activity and no conclusion can be made as to whether the increase in specific enzymic activity in neonatal life is related to the increase in 3-methyl histidine content. As yet it is too early to attach any biological significance to the methylation of specific residues of the histidine in actin and myosin. It may be important, however, that the only other protein in which appreciable amounts of another *N*-methylated amino acid occur—in this case *N*-methyl lysine—is flagellin (Ambler & Rees, 1959), which is a main component of the contraction protein system of the flagella of *Salmonella typhimurium*.

The presence of this residue in the myofibrillar protein may be related to the fact that muscle tissue is unique in that it contains the *N*-methyl histidine peptide, anserine, although here the methylation occurs in the 1 rather than the 3 position in the imidazole ring of histidine. An under-standing of the role of the methylation of histidine is further complicated by the fact that the two major proteins of the contractile system are methy-lated at different stages of myogenesis. It would appear that different methylation systems are required for actin and myosin, since the histidine in the former protein is methylated before birth whereas the system for anserine formation is not significantly active in the rabbit until some time after birth.

In summary, myosin is an impressive example of a molecule effectively designed for its biological role. By its ability to interact both with actin and with itself it can develop and transmit tension along the myofibril. Its bifunctional property is the key to the transduction process and the events at the enzymic centre can be controlled through the relaxing-factor-protein system with a precision unusual in biology. In addition to the demands made on the molecule by these complex functions, mechanisms exist in the cell to modify the structure of the molecule and hence its enzymic be-haviour in response to the particular requirements of the activity pattern of the cell. Few other protein molecules have the capacity to function so effectively under such demanding conditions.

REFERENCES

AMBLER, R. P. & REES, M. W. (1959). *Nature, Lond.* **184**, 56.

BÁRÁNY, M. (1967). In *The Contractile Process*, p. 197. *J. gen. Physiol.* **50** (Supplement).

BÁRÁNY, M. & BÁRÁNY, K. (1959). *Biochim. biophys. Acta* **35**, 293.

BÁRÁNY, M. & BÁRÁNY, K., RECKARD, T. & VOLPE, A. (1965). *Archs Biochem. Biophys.* **109**, 185.

BETTEX-GALLAND, M. & LUSCHER, E. F. (1965). *Adv. Protein Chem.* **20**, 1.

CHAPLAIN, R. A. & TREGEAR, R. T. (1966). *J. molec. Biol.* **21**, 275.

CONOVER, T. E. & BÁRÁNY, M. (1966). *Biochim. biophys. Acta* **127**, 235.

DAVIES, R. E. (1965). The role of ATP in muscle contraction. In *Muscle*, p. 49. Ed. W. M. Paul, E. E. Daniel, C. M. Kay and G. Monckton. London: Pergamon Press.

DREIZEN, P., GERSCHMAN, L. C., TROTTA, P. P. & STRACHER, A. (1967). In *The Contractile Process*, p. 85. *J. gen. Physiol.* **50** (Supplement).

EISENBERG, E. & MOOS, C. (1967). *J. biol. Chem.* **242**, 2945.

GAETJENS, E. (1967). In *The Contractile Process*, p. 113. *J. gen. Physiol.* **50** (Supplement).

GERGELY, J. & KOHLER, H. (1957). Light scattering studies on the stepwise forma-tion and dissociation of actomyosin. *Conf. on Chem. Muscular Contraction*, Tokyo, p. 14. Tokyo: Igaku Shoin, Ltd. (1957).

GERGELY, J., PRAGAY, D., SCHOLZ, A. F., SIEDEL, J. C., SRETER, F. A. & THOMPSON, M. M. (1965). In *Molecular Biology of Muscular Contraction*, p. 145. Ed. S. Ebashi *et al.* Tokyo: Igaku Shoin.

GERSCHMAN, L. C., DREIZEN, P. & STRACHER, A. (1966). *Proc. natn. Acad. Sci. U.S.A.* **56**, 966.
HAMOIR, G. & LASZT, L. (1962). *Nature, Lond.* **193**, 682.
HANSON, J. & LOWY, J. (1964). *Proc. R. Soc.* B **160**, 523.
HASSELBACH, W. (1952). *Z. Naturf.* **7***b*, 163.
HELANDER, E. A. S. (1961). *Biochem. J.* **78**, 478.
HOFFMAN-BERLING, H. (1960). In *Comparative Biochemistry*, vol. 11, p. 341. Ed. M. Florkin and H. S. Mason. New York and London: Academic Press.
HUXLEY, H. E. (1963). *J. molec. Biol.* **7**, 281.
HUXLEY, H. E. (1967). In *The Contractile Process*, p. 71. *J. gen. Physiol.* **50** (Supplement).
JOHNSON, P., HARRIS, C. I. & PERRY, S. V. (1967). *Biochem. J.* **105**, 361.
JONES, J. M. & PERRY, S. V. (1966). *Biochem. J.* **100**, 120.
JOSEPH, R. & HARRINGTON, W. F. (1966). (Personal communication.)
KALDOR, G., GITLIN, J., WESTLEY, F. & VOCK, B. W. (1964). *Biochemistry* **3**, 1137.
KAMINER, B. & BELL, A. L. (1966). *Science, N.Y.* **151**, 323.
KENDRICK-JONES, J. & PERRY, S. V. (1965). *Nature, Lond.* **208**, 1068.
KENDRICK-JONES, J. & PERRY, S. V. (1967*a*). *Nature, Lond.* **213**, 406.
KENDRICK-JONES, J. & PERRY, S. V. (1967*b*). *Biochem. J.* **103**, 207.
LANDON, M. & PERRY, S. V. (1963). *Biochem. J.* **88**, 9P.
LEADBEATER, L. & PERRY, S. V. (1963). *Biochem. J.* **87**, 233.
LOCKER, R. H. & HAGYARD, C. J. (1967*a*). *Archs Biochem. Biophys.* **120**, 454.
LOCKER, R. H. & HAGYARD, C. J. (1967*b*). *Archs Biochem. Biophys.* **120**, 241.
LOWEY, A. G. (1952). *J. cell comp. Physiol.* **40**, 127.
LOWEY, S., GOLDSTEIN, L. & LUCK, S. (1966). *Biochem. Z.* **345**, 248.
MADDOX, C. E. R. & PERRY, S. V. (1966). *Biochem. J.* **99**, 8P.
MOMMAERTS, W. F. H. M. (1950). *Muscular Contraction.* New York: Interscience.
MUELLER, H. & PERRY, S. V. (1962). *Biochem. J.* **85**, 431.
NANKINA, V. P., KOFMAN, E. B., CHERNYAK, V. YA. & KALAMKAROVA, M. B. (1964). *Biokhimiya* **29**, 424.
NANNINGA, L. B. & MOMMAERTS, W. F. H. M. (1960). *Proc. natn. Acad. Sci. U.S.A.* **46**, 1166.
NEEDHAM, D. M. & SHOENBERG, C. F. (1964). *Proc. R. Soc.* B **160**, 517.
OHNISHI, T. & OHNISHI, T. (1962). *J. Biochem.*, *Tokyo* **52**, 230.
PERRY, S. V. (1960). *Biochem. J.* **74**, 94.
PERRY, S. V. (1967). *Prog. biophys. molec. Biol.* **17**, 325.
PERRY, S. V. & COTTERILL, J. (1964). *Biochem. J.* **92**, 603.
PERRY, S. V. & COTTERILL, J. (1965). *Nature, Lond.* **206**, 161.
PERRY, S. V. & HARRIS, C. I. (1967). (To be published.)
PERRY, S. V. & HARTSHORNE, D. J. (1962). In *The Proteins of Developing Muscle*, p. 491. Prague: Czechoslovak Academy of Sciences. Ed. E. Gutman and P. Hnik.
PERRY, S. V. & LANDON, M. (1964). In *Biochemistry of Muscular Contraction*, p. 36. Ed. J. Gergely. Boston: Little Brown and Co.
PERRY, S. V. & ZYDOWO, M. (1959). *Biochem. J.* **72**, 682.
REEDY, M. K., HOLMES, K. C. & TREGEAR, R. T. (1965). *Nature, Lond.* **207**, 1276.
SLAYTOR, H. S. & LOWEY, S. (1967). *Proc. natn. Acad. Sci. U.S.A.* **58**, 1611.
SZENT-GYÖRGYI, A. (1951). *Chemistry of Muscular Contraction*, 2nd ed. New York: Academic Press.
SZENT-GYÖRGYI, A. G. (1953). *Archs Biochem. Biophys.* **42**, 305.
TONOMURA, Y. & KITAGAWA, S. (1957). *Biochim. biophys. Acta* **26**, 15.

TONOMURA, Y. & MORITA, F. (1959). *J. Biochem. (Tokyo)* **46**, 1367.
TRAYER, I. P., HARRIS, C. I. & PERRY, S. V. (1968). *Nature, Lond.* **217**, 452.
TRAYER, I. P. & PERRY, S. V. (1966). *Biochem. Z.* **345**, 87.
TRAYER, I. P., PERRY, S. V. & TEALE, F. W. J. (1967). *Abstr. 7th Int. Congr. Biochem. (Tokyo)*, p. 943.
TS'O, P. O. P., EGGMAN, L. & VINOGRAD, J. (1956). *J. gen. Physiol.* **39**, 801.
WEBER, A. & HASSELBACH, W. (1954). *Biochim. biophys. Acta* **15**, 237.
WEEDS, A. G. & HARTLEY, B. S. (1967). *J. molec. Biol.* **24**, 307.

THE ROLE OF ACTIN–MYOSIN
INTERACTION IN CONTRACTION

By ANDREW G. SZENT-GYÖRGYI

Department of Biology, Brandeis University, Waltham, Massachusetts

The present dogma of muscle contraction is founded principally on two tenets: (1) that contraction is the result of an interaction between actin, myosin and adenosinetriphosphate (ATP), and (2) that contraction proceeds by a sliding mechanism which does not involve a permanent change in the length or configuration of the component protein molecules.

The first of these statements describes the components of the simplest contractile system. The second one tells us something about how the system may operate and tells us a great deal about how it may not. It establishes certain boundaries and welcome restrictions about our speculations in describing contraction.

In the first part of this contribution the consequences of these statements will be discussed in somewhat general terms with particular emphasis on how they may affect the design and interpretations of biochemical approaches. The second part will describe some of our recent experimental work, illustrating our attempts to approach a solution to these problems.

The sliding-filament theory together with its experimental foundations and consequences have been described and discussed in detail by Hanson & H. E. Huxley (1955), H. E. Huxley (1960), and A. F. Huxley (1957). The importance of the cyclic interactions was particularly emphasized by Podolsky (1962). The early experimental work on the actomyosin system and glycerol extracted muscles is described by Albert Szent-Györgyi (1951), and by H. H. Weber & Portzehl (1952, 1954). More recent experiments are summarized in a number of books (Bourne, 1960; Gergely, 1964; Paul, Daniel, Kay & Monckton, 1965; Ebashi, Oosawa, Sekine & Tonomura, 1965; Stracher, 1967) and reviews (Carlson, 1963; Gergely, 1966; Hasselbach, 1964; Wilkie, 1966; Perry, 1967; Pringle, 1967).

GENERAL CONSIDERATIONS
Some aspects of contraction in muscle

Synthetic and natural contractile polymers shorten and develop tension as a consequence of the shortening of the long-chain molecules and there is a good correlation between the work produced and the change in the

2

chemical activity of the active groups and of the reactants which participate in and induce shortening (Kuhn *et al.* 1960; Katchalsky, Oplatka & Litan, 1966). The mechanical state and chemical activity in such systems are closely coupled. The conformational changes are on the whole intramolecular. Shortening represents the shortened state of the molecules and the system is essentially a one-component system.

In muscle at least two proteins are required for contraction. For activity, sites on actin need to interact with sites on myosin. That such an interaction indeed occurs is supported by biochemical and structural evidence. The differences in the mechanical properties of resting and active muscle can readily be described in terms of the presence and absence of interactions between actin and myosin. Neither of these proteins alone is 'contractile' when incubated with ATP. Early studies have demonstrated that the reactions, which are taken as test-tube analogues of contraction, require actomyosin and do not proceed with myosin or actin alone. The activation of the ATPase activity of myosin upon actomyosin is an important regulatory function of actin and indicates how the dependence of energy mobilization on work may be achieved in muscle. The separate localization of actin and myosin on different filaments, and the presence of cross-bridges as indicated by the X-ray diffraction and electron microscope evidence which describe the positions of the cross-bridges in various states of the muscle, suggest a structural basis for these interacting sites (Elliott, 1964; Reedy, Holmes & Tregear, 1965; H. E. Huxley, 1967).

A detailed description of the interaction between actin and myosin is, then, a necessary prerequisite for a better understanding of the contractile process. Even now when information is so fragmentary, several features of muscle behaviour may be pointed out. A two-component system allows a clear-cut separation between the state of rest and the state of activity. In the resting state actin and myosin do not interact and that is why muscle at rest is highly extensible and readily undergoes passive length changes. Activation consists of cross-link formation between actin and myosin; the cross-links in the presence of ATP undergo a series of steps leading to contraction. The presence of ATP is required both for rest and contraction. Its removal leads to rigor in which state cross-links are formed though they cannot undergo the steps leading to contraction. ATP is an essential component of the system and also serves as an energy source. This dual role of ATP is of paramount importance. The actomyosin formed is both the contractile unit and a potent ATPase. The correlation between work performed and energy mobilization in muscle may thus be explained by cross-link formation between actin and myosin.

The fact that active sites of two different proteins have to interact imposes geometric constraints on the system. Interaction between actin and myosin depends on the alignment and position of the active sites, determining load–velocity relationships. In conditions where contraction occurs, both *in vitro* and *in vivo*, actin and myosin are present in highly organized filaments. Experimental analysis of contraction has been restricted to such systems. Ways of describing the nature and the steps involved in the interaction of actin and myosin are therefore limited.

While one may have considerable assurance that the simplest contractile system of muscle consists of actin, myosin and ATP, and it is only the actomyosin–ATP system which 'contracts', it is also possible that the individual proteins change in their conformation and structure in the presence of ATP. Indeed, specific interactions between actin and ATP and between myosin and ATP are much sought after. If conformational changes resulting from the action of ATP on these proteins could be demonstrated, this would be a considerable advance in our understanding of muscle contraction.

Consequences of the sliding mechanism of contraction

The sliding-filament theory is founded on a detailed study of the fine structure of muscle, the description of band pattern in terms of the component proteins and the changes in muscle structure measured at different muscle lengths. Accordingly, muscle changes its length by changing the relative position of actin and myosin filaments. Muscle shortens without an over-all permanent contraction of the 'contractile' molecules. Dimensional changes of muscle are not accompanied by a shortening or extension of the individual molecules or of their filamentous aggregates. The cross-bridges which occupy a central position in the contraction process and are thought to mediate sliding, represent the heavy meromyosin (HMM) end of the myosin molecule (H. E. Huxley, 1963) and contain the active centres involved in ATPase activity and in the combination with actin. The sequence of events in this region of the molecule involves the hydrolysis of an ATP molecule resulting in the sliding of actin filaments with respect to myosin filaments. The change in sarcomere length during a twitch is considerably greater than can be expected from the movement of a single cross-bridge. Therefore each cross-bridge may react a number of times during a single twitch. The extent of shortening in such a system depends on the number of interactions which take place in series; tension depends on how many cross-bridges exert a pull on the filaments added up in parallel at any given moment. The making and breaking of the cross-bridges is a necessary consequence of the sliding filament model. Thus the reaction sequence of cross-bridge interaction must be cyclic. The contraction cycle which one seeks to understand is not the twitch of a single fibre but the cycle of reactions at a single cross-bridge.

The conformational change, if any, responsible for sliding is a part of a repetitive cycle reaction sequence and is *perforce* a transitory event. The simple correlations between length and conformational changes, characteristic for the contraction of most polymer systems and so helpful in describing the structural changes responsible for shortening, break down in the case of muscle. Length of muscle is no reflexion of the conformational state of the macromolecules and it is fruitless to try to assess such changes from comparisons of muscles at various lengths. If there is a conformational change responsible for sliding, it is present only during the process of contraction. Somewhat ironically, it is not possible now to define the structural changes which are responsible for muscle contraction. In fact it is still somewhat a matter of faith that such a change really occurs. It has only recently been established that the position of the cross-bridge depends on the state of the muscle and it is different in rest, in rigor and during contraction (Reedy *et al.* 1965; H. E. Huxley, 1967).

A search for conformational change will have to take into account the following features. The change will be transitory but it is not quite clear how transitory. The lifetime of a cycle in shortening muscle is not known but it is unlikely to be longer than a millisecond. Moreover, X-ray diffraction evidence indicates that in actively contracting muscle relatively few of the cross-bridges are attached to actin, they spend most of their time 'searching' for attachment sites and once they have found them they do not stay attached very long (H. E. Huxley, 1967). The altered conformation may exist only for a small fraction of the lifetime of the cycle. The structural change may be restricted to a relatively narrow region of the molecule, e.g. if the change involves a change in the angle of attachment the region involved would be quite small. X-ray studies further indicate that the cross-bridges move asynchronously (H. E. Huxley, 1967). In skeletal muscle, both *in vivo* and *in vitro*, once the cycle begins it proceeds to completion and at any given time during activity the cross-bridges will be going through their various conformational states and their various reactions asynchronously. In essence we are dealing with a mixed population of cross-bridges and at present it is not yet possible to say what type of movement they perform, what the conformational changes are, or what type of mechanisms lead to these movements. We are still uncertain as to the nature of the chemical reactions which start the machinery and keep it going, and also, therefore, what is the mechano-chemical coupling. Indeed, our knowledge about interaction of ATP and the various components of the contractile system is still rather fragmentary. While such asynchrony ensures a smooth continuous movement, it does not make the studies directed to define the structural changes very much easier. If the cross-bridges represent a mixed population in contracting muscle, only a small fraction of them being in the same phase of their reaction sequence, it is difficult to see how present techniques of fine structural investigations can describe this sequence. It may be possible that in insect flight muscle the cross-bridges act more synchronously (Pringle, 1967). It is still to be seen how far such hopes will be fulfilled.

Considerations of the cyclic reaction mechanism

Many of the problems imposed by the cyclic nature of the reaction sequence in establishing the nature of the conformational change hold true for the other steps of the system. These are also part of transitory, repetitive cycles proceeding in asynchrony. This is a limitation which one's approach has to overcome in order to understand the chemical steps making up the cycle. To do that, it may be of some help to describe the requirements for such repetitive cyclic reactions in muscle.

The reaction cycle of an actin–myosin interaction in its simplest form must involve the following steps: (1), making a link between actin and myosin; (2) the structural change which pulls the actin filament; (3), hydrolysing ATP coupled to the structural change; and (4), breaking the link between actin and myosin.

The mechano-chemical coupling—that is, the coupling between the steps associated with movement and the ones associated with energy mobilization in a cycle or in a number of cycles—must be good. The over-all efficiency of muscle function which includes activation, contraction and relaxation of an intact muscle may be around 25%. The efficiency of the cycle at an actin–myosin interacting site will be higher, perhaps 50% or better. The number of mistakes allowed per cycle, where energy is dissipated without effective movement, is small. An uncompleted cycle is a relatively rare event. The system has a built-in spontaneity. There is a relatively early stage in the cycle which represents a point of no return. Once this state is reached the cycle will have the tendency to proceed to completion unless interfered with. To do this the cycle must involve a reaction which is essentially irreversible and which prevents the system from retracing its steps. The X-ray diffraction evidence indicating that the cross-bridges spend only a short time attached to actin would be in line with such an assumption. Also, there must be a close correlation between the cycle and ATP hydrolysis. Phosphate liberation, in fact, may be one of the steps of the cycle. ATP hydrolysis is of course an irreversible step, but it is not necessarily the point of mechano-chemical coupling. Energy transfer must precede the hydrolytic step and a number of intermediate reactions may also take place. Measurement of ATP hydrolysis has not revealed much, as yet, of the reaction sequence within the cycle. The required close association of hydrolysis with the cycle and the measurements which show that dephosphorylation of ATP serves to balance energy expenditure (Davies, 1964) are of great significance, although a reaction is not necessarily cyclic because it depends on the hydrolysis of ATP. It is unlikely that ATP hydrolysis is the act which ensures that the cycle proceeds to completion. The point of no return is likely to follow closely that of link formation between actin and myosin, and it is rather the structural change which pushes the reaction sequence in one direction. One may imagine, for instance, that the structure associated with actomyosin-ATP is different from actomyosin-ADP. If the 'contracted' bridge position corresponds to actomyosin-ADP and this form of actomyosin link is broken by ATP, the result will be a cyclic reaction scheme. The initial state, unattached myosin and actin sites, is regained without retracing any of the preceding steps.

There are several ways in which cyclic reaction schemes can be designed, and it would be pertinent to know how to design experiments to decide among the various possibilities. The individual steps of each cycle should be demonstrated and analysed and the following approaches may be useful. (a) The cycle may be blocked at a specific point, in the hope that as time proceeds the reactions at the various interacting sites will all be blocked, and the interacting components may all be found to be in synchrony for structural and chemical analysis. Such a desirable situation may be achieved perhaps by using specific reagents which interfere with the enzymic steps or conformational changes, or it may be achieved by the *in vitro* modification of actin or myosin which produces a protein which can undergo only part of the reaction sequences. I do not know of any successful experiment in this direction, but essentially this type of event takes place in the two extreme cases where reaction is blocked. These states are rest and rigor *mortis*. In the former the reaction is blocked by the absence of calcium ions and in the latter the system is blocked due to the absence of ATP. In both cases the cross-bridges are in phase and permit a fine structural and chemical analysis. (b) A second, rather indirect, approach, but one which I think is feasible, is to look for a transitory change in the activity of certain groups, bound co-factors and so on, and to see how these changed reactivities are correlated with contraction proper and how far they are ATP-dependent. Then one may try from the observed data to deduce some of the changes which may take place in the system. (c) Thirdly, one may want to study the reactions between the individual molecules, molecular aggregates, or fragments of the molecules, with ATP and related nucleotides to see how far a specific reaction can be obtained, and how far these reactions are altered when myosin and actin are allowed to interact. (*d*) Finally, one may look for structural alterations induced by ATP *in vitro* on the isolated components.

The interaction of ATP with actin, myosin, meromyosins and other fragments will have to be reinvestigated. It is a rather sobering consideration that the structural alteration involved in a cross-bridge movement is possibly not more than the nodding of the HMM heads if translated to the level of an individual myosin molecule. Demonstration of this type of change challenges present techniques. It is doubtful if one can decide on the basis of available evidence whether the position of HMM has changed relative to the rest of the molecule in the presence of ATP or whether a loss of rigidity at a restricted region of the molecule is caused by ATP; these are the types of changes one may expect to imitate possible cross-bridge movements. If the cross-bridges have to 'search' for actin sites, this portion of the movements should take place in isolated myosin preparations. The present evidence which indicates that myosin and actin alone are not 'contractile' does not exclude the possibility that they exhibit an ATP-dependent partial reaction.

Some of these approaches have met with a limited degree of success. In the remainder of my chapter I show examples of them in greater detail.

In discussing some of the experiments I will proceed along the following lines. First we will look for a changed reactivity in some of the protein groups. Second, we will try to see if reagents, or procedures which modify the proteins, block the cycle at a particular point. Finally, we will see if an effect of ATP interaction with the individual proteins can be demonstrated and how this ATP interaction with myosin, HMM and so on, is changed by combination with actin.

ACTIN, MYOSIN AND ADENOSINETRIPHOSPHATE INTERACTIONS

Reactivity of actin-bound nucleotides

Actin is set apart from other proteins by the following characteristics: polymerizability and the polymerization process; its interaction with nucleotides and the dependence of this interaction on the monomeric and polymerized states; the activation of the myosin ATPase, and complex formation with myosin. One wonders how these unique properties relate to the contraction process.

The polymerization of monomeric units having a molecular weight of *ca.* 60,000 proceeds with great precision. In F-actin the monomers are assembled into filaments which consist of two strands twisted in a helical fashion (Hanson & Lowy, 1963). The polymerization process also alters the relationship of actin to its nucleotides. Globular actin contains ATP, fairly tightly bound to the globular units. During polymerization and usually only then, ATP is dephosphorylated. The fibrous form of actin contains ADP as bound nucleotide (Straub & Feuer, 1950). The availability of ADP bound to F-actin is different from that of ATP bound to G-actin. For instance, the ATP bound to G-actin is readily available for exchange reactions with ATP in the medium (Martonosi, Gouvea & Gergely, 1960). The ATP present in G-actin preparations can also serve as a co-factor in various coupled enzymic reactions. The ADP in F-actin preparations is not available for exchange (Martonosi, Gouvea & Gergely, 1960), or it exchanges very slowly (Moos, Estes & Eisenberg, 1966) and it will not participate as a co-factor in coupled enzymatic reactions. The presence of bound ATP is not always necessary for the polymerization reaction and experiments using G-ADP actin (Hayashi & Rosenbluth, 1960; Gruhoffer & Weber, 1961) or nucleotide-free actin (Kasai, Nakano & Oosawa, 1964) indicate that polymerization can occur with these preparations. The association of nucleotides with the two forms of actin is clearly different. The ADP associated with F-actin is protected to a greater degree by the protein conformation. The bound ADP can be made available in a number of ways, including sonication (Asakura, 1961) and high temperatures (Asai & Tawada, 1966). It was proposed that an intermediary state of actin is formed which was designated as 'f-state' (Asakura, Taniguchi & Oosawa, 1963). Under these conditions actin becomes an ATPase and each mole of actin may hydrolyse a number of moles of ATP.

In the ionic conditions which prevail in muscle one would expect the actin to be present in the fibrous form. Indeed both the electron-microscopic evidence and the X-ray diffraction data support this contention. The bound ADP content of muscle corresponds to its actin content (Perry, 1952; Biro & Muhlrad, 1960; Seraydarian, Mommaerts & Wallner, 1962). ADP is the only bound nucleotide present in muscle in significant quantity. One may try to see then how much change there is in the availability of bound nucleotides during contraction, or during superprecipitation of actomyosin, the *in vitro* analogue of contraction. Secondly, one may try to see how much the change of availability of nucleotide depends on superprecipitation, and finally how the events accompanying the change in availability indicate cyclic reactions.

It is easy to prepare actomyosin in which the ADP bound to the F-actin component is specifically labelled. G-actin is incubated with tritium-labelled

ATP, the free nucleotide is removed with ion-exchange resin and the actin is allowed to polymerize. The polymerized actin is mixed with myosin, and the actomyosin is reprecipated several times. Such a preparation contains 1 mole of labelled ADP per mole of actin. The bound ADP is protected and the specific activity stays constant during reprecipitations and washings. The bound ADP does not catalyse creatine liberation in a system which contains phosphocreatine, creatine kinase and actomyosin. If such a preparation is suspended in a solution which contains ATP labelled with

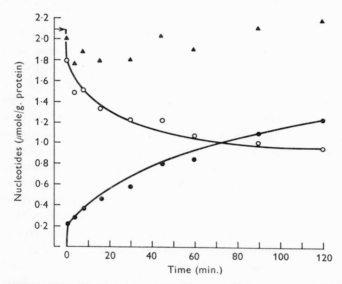

Fig. 1. ADP exchange on actomyosin. Actomyosin, 0·11 %, containing [³H]ADP bound on actin, suspended in a medium consisting of: 36 μg./ml. creatine kinase, 40 mM-NaCl, 20 mM imidazole-HCl (pH 7·0), 4·3 mM-MgCl₂, 10 mM phosphocreatine, and 0·04 mM [¹⁴C]ATP at 23° C. At various times aliquots were withdrawn and the suspension was centrifuged and washed 7–8 times with 30 vol. 40 mM-NaCl–10 mM phosphate buffer (pH 7·0) to remove free nucleotides. Radioactivity was counted in a scintillation counter in double-labelling conditions. Ordinate: bound ADP in the precipitate. Arrow, [³H]ATP at zero time; ○, [³H]ADP; ●, [¹⁴C]ADP; ▲, total ADP. (A. G. Szent-Györgyi & Prior, 1966.)

carbon-14, an exchange between the bound ADP and the ATP of the medium can readily be detected (A. G. Szent-Györgyi & Prior, 1966). Such an experiment is shown in Fig. 1. On this graph the tritium label represents the original ADP content of actin and the carbon label represents the newly incorporated ADP. It may be noted that the tritium-labelled nucleotides represent those sites of actin which have not undergone an exchange reaction, while the carbon-labelled sites represent sites which have undergone at least one exchange reaction. The experiment shows that as time proceeds there is a loss, or a release, of the original bound ADP from the actin component and at the same time there is an incorporation of ADP from the ATP of the solution. That the newly incorporated nucleotide is ADP was established independently by paper chromatography. The total nucleotide content stays fairly constant, indicating that the release and incorporation reactions can go hand in hand. The conditions of the reactions were such that superprecipitation was completed within a few seconds while the exchange reaction continues for many minutes. We have interpreted the reaction approximately as follows. The exchange reaction is a consequence of the increased availability of the bound nucleotide of actin as a result of some type of conformational change of actin. This exchange occurs as a result of an interaction between actin and myosin; that is, it takes place on actin sites which have reacted with myosin sites. The cycles of interaction continue after superprecipitation, or at least visible signs of it, has gone to completion for as long as ATP is present and available. The change of conformation of actin is not specified; it may be so large as to involve a separation of the monomers within the strand at the site of interaction or it may be restricted to a small area near the bound nucleotide.

It is of some interest to find out how much the exchange of the actin-bound nucleotide depends on superprecipitation or on contraction. The exchange reactions require the presence of ATP and it is therefore important that the control in such a study should be an actomyosin preparation which does not superprecipitate in the presence of ATP. There are various ways of preventing the onset of contraction while still keeping the actomyosin system so bonded together that actin will not pass into solution at the lower ionic strength employed. Perhaps the most intriguing system is the one which was first described by Ebashi (1963). Studies in a number of laboratories have established that the activation of muscle is the result of the appearance of ionized calcium in the cytoplasm. Ebashi (1963) has shown that in the presence of one or more protein factors, which probably include tropomyosin and other components, the presence of calcium is required both for the superprecipitation and for the ATPase activation by actin. Thus if the actomyosin suspension is incubated in the presence of 10^{-4}–10^{-3} M EGTA, an agent which strongly chelates calcium, superprecipitation does not take place provided the actomyosin system contains these additional protein factors. Addition of calcium in concentrations of about 10^{-5} M activates the system which then superprecipitates and hydrolyses ATP at a high speed (A. Weber & Herz, 1962). Figures 2 and 3 show the effect of calcium on a purified actomyosin preparation to which the calcium-sensitizing factor has been added, and also on the behaviour of myosin B, an actomyosin extracted from muscle with the factor. The turbidity change which is used here as a measure of superprecipitation

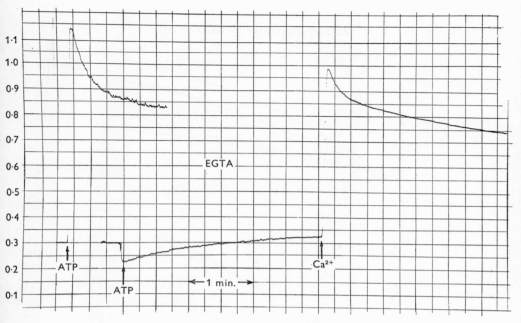

Fig. 2. Calcium dependence of superprecipitation of actomyosin in presence of 'calcium sensitizing factor'. To 0·2 % G-actin solution, containing [³H]ATP, ½ vol. crude 'calcium sensitizing factor' extract of Ebashi & Ebashi (1964) was added. The actin was polymerized in 0·1 M-NaCl and mixed with 6 times its weight of purified myosin. The resulting actomyosin was reprecipitated 3 times. Turbidity changes measured at 600 mμ in a Zeiss spectrophotometer equipped with a stirrer at 23° C. in 40 mM-NaCl, 20 mM imidazole-HCl (pH 7·0), 4 mM-MgCl₂, 36 μg./ml. creatine kinase, 10 mM phosphocreatine and 0·5 mM-ATP. EGTA and CaCl₂ in 1 mM final concentrations where indicated.

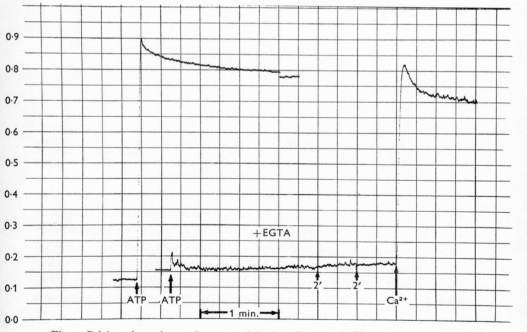

Fig. 3. Calcium dependence of superprecipitation of myosin B. Three times reprecipitated myosin B. Turbidity changes and conditions as in Fig. 2.

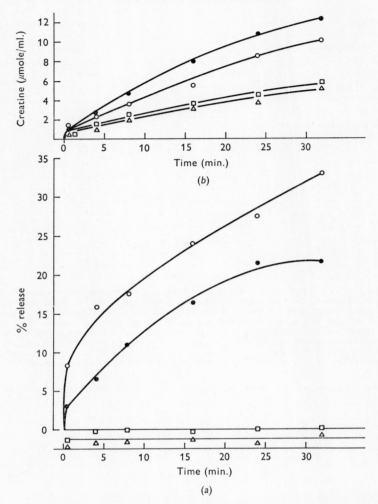

Fig. 4. Dependence of the release of actin-bound nucleotides on superprecipitation. Preparation and conditions as in Fig. 2. Graph *a*: nucleotide release; graph *b*: ATPase activity measured by creatine liberation. Actomyosin (0·15 %) prepared with 'calcium sensitizing factor': ●, 1 mM EGTA and 1·1 mM-CaCl₂; □, 1 mM EGTA; △, 0·1 mM EGTA; ○, control actomyosin (0·12 %) without 'calcium sensitizing factor'.

indicates the requirement for calcium in this reaction. Measurements of the release or the exchange of the bound nucleotides show that both are similarly calcium-dependent as are the ATPase activity and superprecipitation (Figs. 4, 5). It may be noted that there is a fairly long time period during which the actomyosin system co-exists with ATP, yet the exchange takes place extremely slowly, or not at all. Such an experiment serves as a

2390

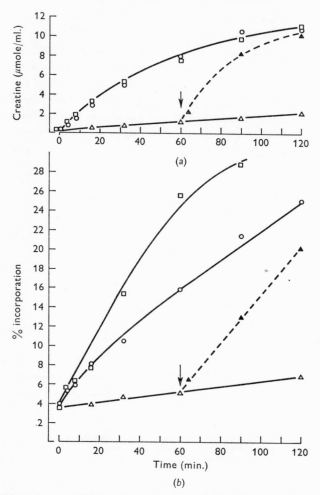

Fig. 5. Dependence of ADP incorporation on superprecipitation. Same preparation and conditions as in Fig. 3. Myosin B, 0·11 %, suspended in [³H]ATP. Graph *a*: ATPase activity; graph *b*: incorporation. □, Myosin B, nothing added; O, 1 mM EGTA and 1·1 mM-CaCl₂; △, 1 mM EGTA; ▲, 1 mM EGTA to which 1·1 mM-CaCl₂ was added at times indicated by arrow.

control and at the same time indicates the protected nature of the bound nucleotide. A similar situation has been established in a number of different ways, indicating that in normal preparations the superprecipitated state facilitates the exchange of actin-bound nucleotides.

The exchange reaction can be interrupted and restarted at any given moment, so that it is possible to determine whether the increased availability of the nucleotide is long-lasting or transitory; that is, part of some cyclic reaction. As mentioned before in the double-labelling experiments, the ^{14}C-labelled sites at any given time represent those sites at which at least one exchange reaction has taken place, while the ^{3}H-labelled nucleotides represent sites that have not undergone such exchange. If the reaction is interrupted and the nucleotides in the medium are replaced by cold ATP then the kinetics of the exchange at those sites which have already reacted can be measured independently. If these sites remain available one would expect a very rapid exchange of the carbon-labelled nucleotides with ATP. If the availability were only transitory then one would expect both the

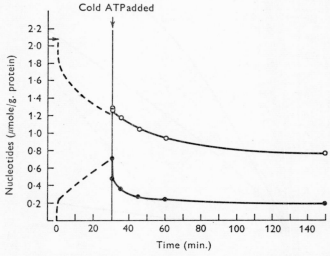

Fig. 6. Chase of labelled nucleotides from actomyosin. Portion of actomyosin of Fig. 1 removed at 30 min., washed twice and resuspended in the same medium as in Fig. 1, but containing 0·04 mM non-radioactive ATP (A. G. Szent-Györgyi & Prior, 1966). O, [3H]ADP; ●, [14C]ADP.

tritium and the carbon-labelled nucleotides to exchange at about the same speed. This experiment was performed and the results are shown in Fig. 6. They indicate that most of the sites which have already reacted exchange with the same kinetics as the unreacted sites, suggesting that under these conditions the conformational changes do not persist. Similar conclusions were drawn from the fact that the bound nucleotides in a superprecipitated actomyosin preparation, in which over one-third of the bound nucleotides has undergone an exchange, did not catalyse the liberation of creatine from phosphocreatine in the presence of creatine kinase (A. G. Szent-Györgyi & Prior, 1966). These measurements show that some conformational change can take place in actin as a result of the interaction with myosin and ATP; they do not prove, however, that the nucleotide exchange reaction is part of a normal contraction cycle or that the dephosphorylation of ATP, associated with exchange, is the mechanism of mechanochemical energy transfer. Dephosphorylation of ATP does not always accompany polymerization. G-actin preparations containing ADP, or no nucleotides, may polymerize under certain conditions in the absence of ATP.

Table 1. *Distribution of bound nucleotides during the exchange reaction*

Actomyosin, 0·1 %, containing [³H]ADP of high specific activity on actin, suspended in 40 mM-NaCl₂; 10 mM imidazole-HCl (pH 7·0) and 0·25 mM ATP. Presence of divalent ions, reaction times and temperatures are as indicated. Reaction was stopped by addition of perchloric acid. After removal of protein the extract was neutralized with KHCO₃, the supernatant concentrated and the nucleotides separated by descending paper chromatography in isobutyric acid, 0·5 M NH₄OH (5:3 v/v) system, and counted.

Conditions	Time of exchange (sec.)	[³H]AMP (%)	[³H]ADP (%)	[³H]ATP (%)	μmole/ml. Pi liberation
23°	5	0·9	98·3	0·8	0·04
	10	0·8	98·5	0·7	0·06
	15	0·8	98·5	0·7	0·06
	120	0·8	98·6	0·6	0·08
3·4 mM-MgCl₂, 23°	5	0·6	98·9	0·5	0·08
	10	0·7	98·7	0·6	0·07
	15	0·6	98·9	0·5	0·14
	120	0·7	98·9	0·4	0·21
3·4 mM-CaCl₂, 23°	5	1·3	98·2	0·5	0·06
	10	1·4	98·2	0·4	0·12
	15	1·4	98·2	0·4	0·18
	120	1·1	98·7	0·2	0·25
4 mM-MgCl₂, 15°	5	0·8	98·0	1·2	0·00
	10	0·9	97·9	1·2	0·01
	15	1·0	97·9	1·1	0·02
	120	0·9	98·1	1·0	0·24
Control, no ATP, 23°	—	1·8	97·4	0·8	—

In the reaction sequence the system requires ATP. Since ATP may be derived from exchange of the bound ADP with ATP or by rephosphorylation of the bound ADP, we explored the possibility of the formation of actin-bound ATP as a result of a transphosphorylation reaction. In the actomyosin system the extent of the phosphorylation of bound ADP can be measured with fair accuracy. If only the actin-bound ADP is labelled and this is incubated in the presence of cold ATP, any labelled ATP formed must be formed on the bound ADP. An amount of ATP formed which represents about 1 % of the total bound nucleotides can be readily detected. As Table 1 shows, there does not seem to be any accumulation of actin-bound ATP at any time during the reaction, which was carried out at varied temperatures in the presence and absence of calcium or magnesium. While these experiments cannot exclude the possibility that actin-bound ATP is formed through rephosphorylation from medium ATP, they set an upper limit to the extent of such an occurrence—about 1 % of the total number of nucleotide-binding sites at any given time. Indeed we have no evidence from these or other experiments that the actin-bound nucleotides participate in the energetics of contraction or in the transfer of mechano-chemical energy. All that these experiments indicate is that actin can undergo a conformational change.

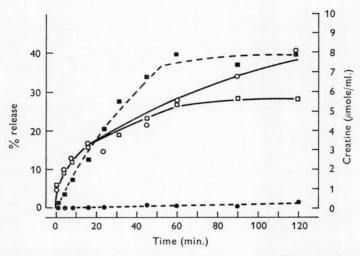

Fig. 7. Effect of modification of myosin on ADP release and ATPase activity. Myosin modified with impure *p*-nitrothiophenol according to the method of Tonomura & Kanazawa (1965): 5·3 moles of *p*-nitrothiophenol reacted with 550,000 g. myosin. Both modified and control myosin were combined with [³H]ADP containing F-actin and reprecipitated 3 times: 0·046 % modified myosin or 0·056 % control myosin in 40 mM-NaCl, 10 mM imidazole-HCl (pH 7·0), 4 mM-MgCl₂, 0·4 mM ATP, 8 mM phosphocreatine, 36 µg./ml. kinase. ○, Release; ●, ATPase of modified actomyosin; □, release; ■, ATPase of control actomyosin.

The system can be modified: for instance, Tonomura & Kanazawa (1965) showed that myosin treated with *p*-nitrothiophenol lost the initial burst of ATPase activity and superprecipitation though it still combined with actin. The preparations which we obtained using non-purified *p*-nitrothiophenol had a low ATPase activity and the modified myosin when combined with actin did not undergo superprecipitation although the release of actin-bound nucleotide was about the same as that of the control actomyosin (Fig. 7). This modified myosin could facilitate the exchange of actin-bound nucleotides without requiring the superprecipitation step. It is possible that modification produced a species of myosin which could not complete the cyclic reactions signified by superprecipitation but could only go part way.

Activation of the ATPase of heavy meromyosin by actin

Actin regulates the ATPase of actomyosin and forms a contractile complex with myosin. The HMM part of myosin reacts with actin and also has ATPase activity (A. G. Szent-Györgyi, 1953). Since the HMM portion is soluble at low ionic strengths, in contrast to myosin or light meromyosin, it is in many respects a preferable material in which to study ATP and actin interactions.

One of the interesting aspects of the trypsin fragmentation of myosin is that many of the principal properties of myosin can be recovered on one or other of the meromyosins. There are some important differences between myosin and HMM. HMM does not form filamentous aggregates, does not superprecipitate and is water-soluble. The lack of an *in vitro* demonstration of 'contractility' does not exclude cyclic interaction between HMM and actin in the presence of ATP; it may only indicate that the methods used to detect *in vitro* 'contraction' are not suitable for the measurements of changes at the level of single molecules. The HMM–actin complex is not stable in the presence of ATP and this was initially taken to mean that ATP dissociates the HMM–actin complex (A. G. Szent-Györgyi, 1953). It was of considerable interest, therefore, when Leadbeater & Perry (1963) reported that actin can activate the ATPase activity of HMM, even though their viscosity measurements were interpreted to mean that most or all of the HMM–actin complex was dissociated in the presence of ATP. This activation of ATPase might, however, be explained by a limited complex formation between HMM and actin. Some of the experiments which Eva M. Szentkiralyi (1967) has been doing in my laboratory suggest very strongly that such a complex can exist. The main difference between the actin-activated ATPase of HMM and that of myosin lies in the actin concentrations which are required for maximal effect. Myosin is activated by an amount of actin which corresponds more or less to the stoichiometric ratio (2 moles of actin per mole of myosin), while HMM requires a very large excess of actin for maximum activation. Though no more than 1 g. of actin can combine with about 3–4 g. HMM in the absence of ATP, maximum activation of HMM ATPase is not reached even at a ratio of 100 g. of actin to 1 g. of HMM (Fig. 8). A similar effect was observed by Yagi, Nakata & Sakakibara (1965), Sekiya, Takeuchi & Tonomura (1967) and by E. Eisenberg & C. Moos (personal communication). The data support the assumption that the activation of HMM ATPase is due to a complex formed between HMM and actin. In reciprocal Lineweaver–Burk plots, the activation against actin concentration gives a straight line from which an association constant and maximum velocity can be obtained (Fig. 9). It is

3

of some interest that the same amount of complex is formed if excess of HMM or excess of actin is used, calculated on a mole basis. These experiments indicate that there is 1 mole of actin for each mole of HMM in the complex but that there appears to be some steric hindrance in placing an HMM molecule on each actin monomer (Fig. 10). The kinetics of ATPase activation indicate that complex formation takes place and that an excess of one of the reactants is needed to achieve maximum complex formation.

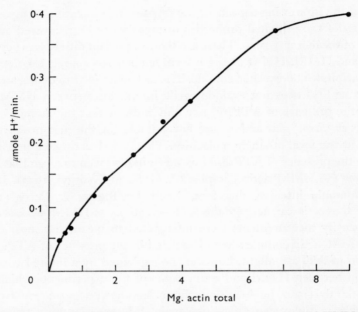

Fig. 8. Actin activation of heavy meromyosin ATPase. 0·83 mg. total HMM, 0·36 mM ATP; 2 mM-MgCl₂ at an ionic strength of 0·018, at pH 7·6; volume 10 ml. ATPase measured by proton liberation in a pH-stat. At pH 7·6 each mole of inorganic phosphate formed is equivalent with a mole of proton measured. Ordinate shows activation of ATPase above the value obtained with HMM alone, which amounted to 0·007 μmole/min.

The evidence presented suggests that the complex formed is in equilibrium with the components. The experiments do not prove, but certainly do not contradict, the hypothesis that the complex is transitory and that the local cyclic reaction sequence (or at least that part of it which takes place between the cross-bridge and actin) may also take place between actin and HMM at low ionic strength. What remains to be demonstrated is that ATP hydrolysis is coupled with the dissociation of HMM-actin. It may be of some interest to point out that the association constant between actin and HMM is not as dependent on ionic strength as is the actual ATPase activation (Fig. 11).

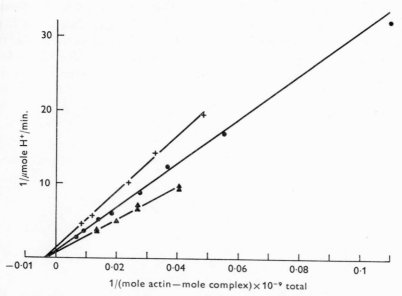

Fig. 9. Lineweaver–Burk plots of actin activated ATPase of HMM. Ionic strength 0·018, 0·36 mM ATP, 2 mM-MgCl₂. ▲ and + are the same HMM preparations but 9 days older, at 0° C. ●, Fresh preparation.

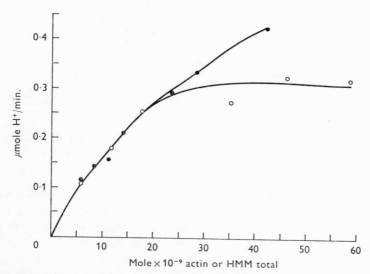

Fig. 10. Equivalence of actin and heavy meromyosin in the formation of enzymically active complex. ○, Moles of HMM added to $5 \cdot 6 \times 10^{-9}$ moles of actin; ●, moles of actin added to $5 \cdot 6 \times 10^{-9}$ moles of HMM. Ordinate: ATPase activation. Coincidence of the points shows that the enzymically active complex consists of 1 mole of actin combined with 1 mole of HMM based on molecular weights of 60,000 and 350,000 respectively. 0·36 mM ATP; 2 mM-MgCl₂.

It seems possible then that the actin and HMM complex *in vitro* reveals parts of the reactions taking place at the cross-bridge. One of the main differences between actomyosin and actin-HMM is that in the former the interacting sites are parts of filamentous aggregates. A number of reactions take place simultaneously and, by the time a cycle is completed at one

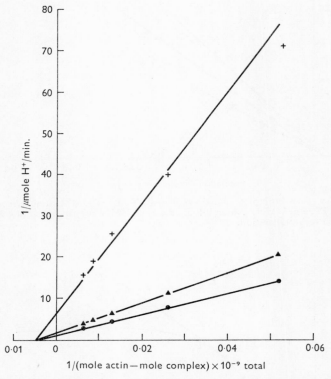

Fig. 11. Ionic strength dependence of complex formation and ATPase activity. Lineweaver–Burk plots of ATPase activation at various ionic strengths: ●, 0·01; ▲, 0·02; +, 0·07. 0·36 mM ATP; 2 mM-MgCl$_2$.

interacting site, another may start elsewhere. A cycle in this system means, first, that links are established, then that something happens on the links which leads to the sliding or relative motion of the two filaments as the result of local conformational changes, and finally that the links are broken again. When myosin filaments and actin filaments interact, probably more than one site is reacting at a given time: thus the completion of the cycle by the destruction of actomyosin cross-links will not necessarily lead to the separation of the two types of filaments. HMM does not form filamentous aggregates but individual HMM molecules react with actin filaments, and at the completion of the cycle, when the link is broken, HMM can diffuse away. Thus actin must be used in great excess to ensure maximal complex formation with HMM in the presence of ATP.

Interaction of heavy meromyosin with nucleotides

A direct demonstration that any component of myosin or actin may exist in different conformations which are dependent on ATP or ADP would be highly desirable. There is some evidence that ATP causes changes in the optical rotatory dispersion of HMM (Sekiya, Mii, Takeuchi & Tonomura, 1966) and it may change its absorption at the peptide bond in the presence of calcium ions and actin (Iyengar, Glauser & Davies, 1964) though the observations require confirmation. Recently changes in the tyrosin–tryptophan region of the spectrum have been reported by using differential spectroscopy (Morita, 1967).

The studies described here will indicate that HMM may exist in two states: one capable of a very strong ATP or ADP binding and the other in which this binding site is not functional. Combination with actin may induce a transition between the two states.

A considerable amount of nucleotide is bound by HMM after incubation with ATP or ADP and will remain with the protein even after removal of the excess nucleotide with resin treatment of gel filtration. From experiments using Sephadex treatment, a complex formation between HMM and ATP was proposed by Burton & Loewenstein (1964), who found that about 0·2 mole of ATP stayed associated with a mole of HMM and that the complex had a half-life time of about 40 min in the cold. Under our conditions both resin treatment and gel filtration experiments indicated that about 1 to 2 moles of ATP or ADP may be strongly bound by 1 mole of HMM, based on a molecular weight of 330,000 (Fig. 12). There was a considerable specificity of nucleotide binding: ATP, ADP, deoxy-ATP were bound strongly, whereas the other nucleotides GTP, GDP, UTP, CTP, ITP and AMP (adenosinemonophosphate) were bound to a much lesser extent or not at all. The very tight association indicated by these experiments should be stressed. The points measuring nucleotide and those measuring protein concentration coincide closely and the curves are not skewed in the gel filtration experiments. Experiments using both methods, resin treatment and gel filtration, indicate that the binding is strong and that the dissociation of nucleotide from the protein is limited. If there is an equilibrium, it is established rather slowly. Higher ionic strength reduces the extent of nucleotide binding. At 0·3 M-NaCl using Sephadex gel filtration the binding of nucleotides to HMM and to myosin can be compared under identical conditions (Fig. 13). In these conditions there is about 0·75 moles

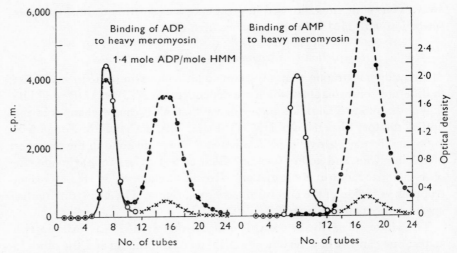

Fig. 12. ADP and AMP binding to heavy meromyosin: 14·2 mg. HMM in 3 ml. 20 mM-NaCl, 20 mM Tris-HCl (pH 7·6), 1 mM-MgCl$_2$ and 0·05 mM [^{14}C]ADP or [^{14}C]AMP applied to a 25 cm. × 1·75 cm.^{2} G-25 Sephadex column and eluted at a rate of 0·5 ml./min. at 0–20. ●, Radioactivity (broken line); ○, optical density at 280 mμ (solid line); ×, optical density at 260 mμ.

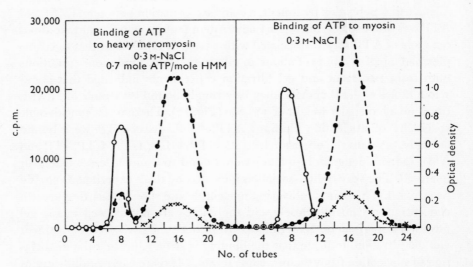

Fig. 13. ATP binding to heavy meromyosin and to myosin: 5·7 mg. HMM or 9·2 mg. myosin in 3 ml. 300 mM-NaCl, 20 mM Tris-HCl (pH 7·6), 1 mM-MgCl$_2$ and 0·05 mM [^{14}C]ATP applied to G-25 Sephadex as in Fig. 11. ●, Radioactivity (broken line); ○, optical density at 280 mμ (solid line); ×, optical density at 260 mμ.

of ADP bound per mole of HMM and none is bound to myosin. Thus there appears to be a difference between the state of HMM when attached to myosin and when it is separated. Divalent ions do not seem to be a necessary prerequisite for binding in the presence of EDTA, since ATP and ADP remain bound to HMM.

Actin interferes with the nucleotide binding of HMM. This is shown in Table 2, where the uptake of ATP, ADP and AMP on HMM in the presence and absence of actin are compared. These experiments were performed using resin for the removal of nucleotides since actin does not filter well on Sephadex gel in its fibrous form. The data indicate that ATP- and ADP-binding are reduced in the presence of actin. Figure 14 shows that as the actin concentration increases, the binding of ATP to HMM is reduced. The effect was maximal at ratios of 1 mole of actin to 1 mole of HMM.

Table 2. *The effect of actin on nucleotide binding by heavy meromyosin*

7·5 mg. HMM alone or with 2·5 mg. actin, where indicated, in 5 ml. 20 mM-NaCl, 10 mM Tris-HCl (pH 7·6) to which 0·055 mM-[^{14}C]nucleotide was used. Free nucleotide was removed from 2·5 ml. aliquots by twofold treatment with 0·1 ml. packed AG 1-x2, 200–400 mesh resin for 3 min. Nucleotide content corrected for radioactive impurities in nucleotide preparations.

Actin	Nucleotide	Mole nucleotide/mole HMM
None	ATP	1·0
+	ATP	0·4
None	ADP	1·3
+	ADP	0·6
None	AMP	0·3
+	AMP	0·4

Judging from studies on nucleotide binding, HMM may exist in two states. The effect of actin in preventing nucleotide binding may reflect an 'allosteric' interaction. There is no evidence as yet about how extensive the conformational changes are which produce the altered nucleotide interactions. The simple molar ratios between HMM, nucleotide and actin appear to be significant. The data indicating that 1 mole of nucleotide reacts with 1 mole of HMM are puzzling since the recent demonstration that HMM is built of two subunits (Slayter & Lowey, 1967). It should also be noted that the studies of the binding of ADP to HMM in equilibrium conditions have led to higher values. Young (1967) reported a binding of 3 moles and Lowey (personal communication) a binding of 2 moles of ADP by 1 of HMM. On the other hand ATPase studies indicated the presence of only one active centre in a myosin or an HMM molecule (Nanninga & Mommaerts, 1960; Kanazawa & Tonomura, 1965). Maximum shifts in the different spectra induced by ATP were observed even at ratios of 1 mole of ATP per mole of HMM (Morita, 1967). Our conditions are not equilibrium conditions and they were designed to show only an essentially stable association between nucleotide and HMM. The different values are not necessarily in contradiction with each other. It may be that the tight binding is the result of subunit interactions, a possibility which can be readily tested.

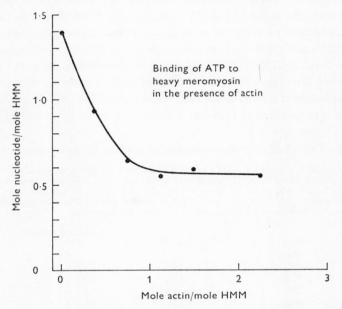

Fig. 14. Effect of actin concentration on the ATP binding of heavy meromyosin: 7·3 mg. HMM and varying amounts of actin (0–3 mg.) were mixed in 5 ml. 20 mM-NaCl, 10 mM Tris-HCl (pH 7·6) and 0·055 mM [¹⁴C]ATP at 0° C. 2·5 ml. aliquots were treated twice for 3 min. with 0·1 ml. packed AG1-x2, 200–400 mesh resin to remove free nucleotides. Protein and radioactivity were determined from the resin-free solution obtained by centrifugation. Values were corrected for the radioactive impurities not removed from the ATP preparation in absence of proteins. The correction reduced the values of bound nucleotides by about 15–30 %. Molecular weight of actin was taken to be 60,000, molecular weight of HMM was taken to be 330,000. Points represent parallel determinations. Deviation between parallel determinations were less than 0·2 mole nucleotide/mole HMM.

SUMMARY

Contraction of muscle is the result of cyclic interactions between actin, myosin and ATP. The conformational changes responsible for motion may be restricted to a small region of the molecule near the interacting sites. The structural changes and the chemical reaction sequence are part of a cycle which is transitory and repetitive and which takes place asynchronously at the various sites of interaction. Such a mechanism imposes limitations and presents challenges for both fine structural and chemical approaches.

Some experiments are described which study the chemistry of the cyclic events. By measuring the availability of actin-bound ADP, it is possible to demonstrate transitory changes in the reactivity of certain groups associated with contraction. It is also possible to show ATP-induced changes *in vitro* which depend on actin and myosin interaction. Furthermore, a transitory complex formation associated with ATPase activity between HMM and actin may be demonstrated. Thus, some aspects of the contraction cycle can be studied on the individual protein components. One conclusion from these experiments is that HMM may exist in two states with respect to nucleotide association and that the transition is regulated by actin.

The author is grateful to Dr Carolyn Cohen, Children's Cancer Research Foundation, for her interest and lively discussions. The experiments described in this paper were performed with Miss Gwen Prior and they were supported by grants from the U.S. Public Health Service, RO1 GM 14675, and National Science Foundation, GB 5368. Figures 1 and 6 have been published in the *Journal of Molecular Biology*; Figs. 8, 10 and 11 are taken from work of E. M. Szentkiralyi submitted for publication to the same journal.

REFERENCES

ASAI, H. & TAWADA, K. (1966). *J. molec. Biol.* **20**, 403.

ASAKURA, S. (1961). *Biochim. biophys. Acta* **52**, 65.

ASAKURA, S., TANIGUCHI, M. & OOSAWA, F. (1963). *J. molec. Biol.* **7**, 55.

BIRO, N. A. & MUHLRAD, A. (1960). *Acta Physiol. hung.* **18**, 96.

BOURNE, G. H. (1960). *Structure and Function of Muscle.* II. *Biochemistry and Physiology.* New York and London: Academic Press.

BURTON, P. & LOEWENSTEIN, J. M. (1964). *Biochem. J.* **90**, 70.

CARLSON, F. D. (1963). *Progr. Biophys. molec. Biol.* **13**, 261.

DAVIES, R. E. (1964). *Proc. R. Soc.* B **160**, 480.

EBASHI, S. (1963). *Nature, Lond.* **200**, 1010.

EBASHI, S. & EBASHI, F. (1964). *J. Biochem.* (*Tokyo*) **55**, 604.

EBASHI, S., OOSAWA, F., SEKINE, T. & TONOMURA, Y. (1965). Molecular biology of muscular contraction. (*Biochim. biophys. Acta* Library, vol. 9.) Tokyo.

ELLIOTT, G. F. (1964). *Proc. R. Soc.* B **160**, 467.

GERGELY, J. (1964). *Biochemistry of Muscle Contraction.* Boston: Little, Brown and Co.

GERGELY, J. (1966). *A. Rev. Biochem.* **35**, 691.

GRUBHOFFER, N. & WEBER, H. H. (1961). *Z. Naturf.* **16**b, 435.

HANSON, J. & HUXLEY, H. E. (1955). *Symp. Soc. exp. Biol* **9**, 228.

HANSON, J. & LOWY, J. (1963). *J. molec. Biol.* **6**, 46.

HASSELBACH, W. (1964). *Progr. Biophys. molec. Biol.* **14**, 167.

HAYASHI, T. & ROSENBLUTH, R. (1960). *Biol. Bull. mar. biol. Lab., Woods Hole* **119**, 294.

HUXLEY, A. F. (1957). *Progr. Biophys. biophys. Chem.* **7**, 153.

HUXLEY, H. E. (1960). In *The Cell*, vol. IV, p. 365. Ed. J. Brachet and A. E. Mirsky. New York: Academic Press.

HUXLEY, H. E. (1963). *J. molec. Biol.* **7**, 281.

HUXLEY, H. E. (1967). *J. gen. Physiol.* **50**, 71.

IYENGAR, M. R., GLAUSER, S. C. & DAVIES, R. E. (1964). *Biochem. biophys. Res. Commun.* **4**, 379.

KANAZAWA, T. & TONOMURA, Y. (1965). *J. Biochem.* (*Tokyo*), **57**, 604.

KASAI, M., NAKANO, E. & OOSAWA, F. (1964). *Biochim. biophys. Acta* **94**, 494.

KATCHALSKY, A., OPLATKA, A. & LITAN, A. (1966). In *Molecular Architecture in Cell Physiology*, p. 3. Ed. T. Hayashi and A. G. Szent-Györgyi. Englewood Cliffs, New Jersey. Prentice Hall.

KUHN, W., RAMEL, A., WALTERS, D. H., EBNER, G. & KUHN, H. J. (1960). *Adv. Polymer Sci.* **1**, 540.

LEADBEATER, L. & PERRY, S. V. (1963). *Biochem. J.* **87**, 233.

MARTONOSI, A., GOUVEA, M. A. & GERGELY, J. (1960). *J. biol. Chem.* **235**, 1700.

MOOS, C., ESTES, J. E. & EISENBERG, E. (1966). *Biochem. biophys. Res. Commun.* **23**, 347.

MORITA, F. (1967). *J. biol. Chem.* **242**, 4501.

NANNINGA, L. B. & MOMMAERTS, W. F. H. M. (1960). *Proc. natn. Acad. Sci.*, *U.S.A.* **46**, 1166.

PAUL, W. M., DANIEL, E. E., KAY, C. M. & MONCKTON, G. (1965). *Muscle*. London: Pergamon Press.

PERRY, S. V. (1952). *Biochem. J.* **51**, 495.

PERRY, S. V. (1967). *Progr. Biophys. molec. Biol.* **17**, 325.

PODOLSKY, R. J. (1962). *Fedn Proc.* **21**, 964.

PRINGLE, J. W. S. (1967). *Progr. Biophys. molec. Biol.* **17**, 3.

REEDY, M. K., HOLMES, K. C. & TREGEAR, R. T. (1965). *Nature, Lond.* **207**, 1276.

SEKIYA, K., MII, S., TAKEUCHI, K. & TONOMURA, Y. (1966). *J. Biochem.* (*Tokyo*) **59**, 584.

SEKIYA, K., TAKEUCHI, K. & TONOMURA, Y. (1967). *J. Biochem.* (*Tokyo*) **61**, 567.

SERAYDARIAN, K., MOMMAERTS, W. F. H. M. & WALLNER, A. (1962). *Biochim. biophys. Acta* **65**, 443.

SLAYTER, H. S. & LOWEY, S. (1967). *Proc. natn. Acad. Sci. U.S.A.* **58**, 1611.

STRACHER, A. (1967). *J. gen. Physiol.* **50**, No. 6, Part 2.

STRAUB, F. B. & FEUER, G. (1950). *Biochim. biophys. Acta* **4**, 455.

SZENT-GYÖRGYI, A. (1951). *Chemistry of Muscular Contraction*, 2nd ed. New York: Academic Press.

SZENT-GYÖRGYI, A. G. (1953). *Archs Biochem. Biophys.* **42**, 505.

SZENT-GYÖRGYI, A. G. & PRIOR, G. (1966). *J. molec. Biol.* **15**, 515.

SZENTKIRALYI, E. M. (1967). (Abstract.) *J. gen. Physiol.* **50**, 2494.

TONOMURA, Y. & KANAZAWA, T. (1965). *J. biol. Chem.* **240**, PC 4110.

WEBER, A. & HERZ, R. (1962). *J. biol. Chem.* **238**, 599.

WEBER, H. H. & PORTZEHL, H. (1952). *Adv. Protein Chem.* **7**, 161.

WEBER, H. H. & PORTZEHL, H. (1954). *Progr. Biophys. biophys. Chem.* **4**, 60.

WILKIE, D. R. (1966). *A. Rev. Physiol.* **28**, 17.

YAGI, K., NAKATA, T. & SAKAKIBARA, J. (1965). *J. Biochem.* (*Tokyo*) **58**, 236.

YOUNG, M. (1967). *J. biol. Chem.* **242**, 2790.

ADDENDUM
POLYMERIZATION OF MICROTUBULE PROTEIN
By R. E. STEPHENS

Department of Biology, Brandeis University, Waltham, Massachusetts, and The Marine Biological Laboratory, Woods Hole, Massachusetts

Microtubules from the outer fibres of cilia and flagella are formed from 40Å. globular subunits with a molecular weight of 60,000 having 1 mole of guanine nucleotide per mole of protein subunit and an amino acid composition resembling that of muscle actin; the monomer can be prepared from acetone powders of whole cilia or flagella and also by direct solubilization of the isolated outer fibres in urea, guanidine hydrochloride, or the organic mercurial Salyrgan (Renaud, Rowe & Gibbons, 1966; Renaud, Rowe & Gibbons, 1968; Stephens, Renaud & Gibbons, 1967; Stephens, 1968). However, when prepared by such methods, the protein monomer is apparently not polymerizable to the fibrous form.

Flagellar outer fibres were prepared from isolated sea urchin (*Arbacia punctulata*) sperm tails by selective solubilization of dynein, central pair of fibres, matrix, and membrane (Gibbons, 1965; Stephens *et al.* 1967). The final preparation consisted primarily of doublet microtubules and a small amount of membrane fragments (Plate 1). The fibres were dissolved by suspension in a solution containing 0·5% Sarkosyl detergent (Geigy Chemical Corporation, Ardsley, New York), 1 mM guanosine triphosphate (GTP), 10 mM Tris.HCl, pH 8·0, and 0·01% mercaptoethanol. After standing at 0° C. for at least 30 min., the mixture was sedimented at 35,000 g for 15 min. and the pellet of partially dissolved tubules was discarded. Under these conditions, a minimum of 90% of the protein remained in solution and in the analytical ultracentrifuge consisted of a single component with a sedimentation rate of 2·0 S (Plate 2*a*).

Negative staining of the undiluted protein in the 0·5% Sarkosyl-GTP medium indicated only small aggregates and a few 50–100Å. fibrils, neither of which were removed by the relatively brief 35,000 g centrifugation (Plate 2*b*).

When the solution of protein in detergent was diluted 1:10 with cold, CO_2-free distilled water, long fibres up to 2μ in length formed. The fibres consisted of ribbon-like arrays of linearly arranged 40Å. globular subunits, 3–5 subunits in width (Plate 3, arrows) or more densely staining aggregates of such structures.

Addition of salt to an ionic strength of 0·1 (or initial 1:10 dilution with 0·1 M-KCl) caused extensive growth and aggregation of the fibrous ribbons into more complex fibres, many of which stain in the same manner as single microtubules (Plate 4, arrows). Upon standing, many of these fibres frayed to 40Å. protofilaments similar to those originally described in sonicated sperm tails (Pease, 1963). No doublet microtubules were evident and the synthetic fibres were quite flexible, often forming knots, unlike the microtubules from which they were derived. After salt-induced polymerization of protein derived from freshly prepared outer fibres, 60–70% of the total soluble protein was recoverable in fibrous form through centrifugation at 35,000 g for 15 min.

GTP appears to be important in both the initial solubilization and in the repolymerization since, in the ultracentrifuge, the protein monomer aggregates when dissolved in the absence of nucleotide, and far less protein undergoes polymerization to either ribbon-like fibres or apparent microtubules.

'Seeding' is necessary for the reassociation. The small aggregates and fibrils present in the solubilized and centrifuged preparation provide the requisite nucleation. If the protein is freed of these aggregates by centrifugation at 15,000 g for 60 min., no appreciable amount of ordered polymerization takes place but, instead, random aggregates are found. A similar nucleation requirement has been reported for the polymerization of bacterial flagellin (Asakura, Eguchi & Iino, 1964).

Incubation of the soluble protein with 10^{-4} M colchicine, followed by dilution and addition of salt, results in fibre formation essentially identical to that observed without colchicine. This is indicative that, at least in flagellar microtubule protein, colchicine does not have a direct effect on the polymerization process.

This work was supported by National Institutes of Health grants 1-F2-GM-24,276-01 and GM-15,500-01 to the author, and by Physiology Training Grant 5-T1-265-09 to the Marine Biological Laboratory.

REFERENCES

ASAKURA, S., EGUCHI, G. & IINO, T. (1964). *J. molec. Biol.* **10**, 42.
GIBBONS, I. R. (1965). *Archs Biol. (Liège)* **76**, 317.
PEASE, D. C. (1963). *J. Cell Biol.* **18**, 313.
RENAUD, F. L., ROWE, A. J. & GIBBONS, I. R. (1968). *J. Cell Biol.* **36**, 79.
RENAUD, F. L., ROWE, A. J. & GIBBONS, I. R. (1966). *J. Cell Biol.* **31**, 92A.
STEPHENS, R. E. (1968). *J. molec. Biol.* **32**, 277.
STEPHENS, R. E., RENAUD, F. L. & GIBBONS, I. R. (1967). *Science, N.Y.* **156**, 1606.

PLATE I

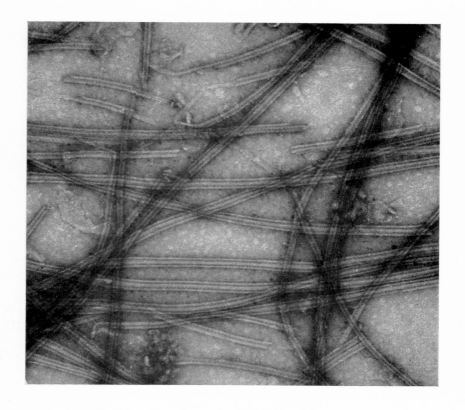

Isolated outer fibres negatively stained with 1 % uranyl acetate. × 50,000. (For explanation see p. 43.)

(*facing p.* 44)

PLATE 2

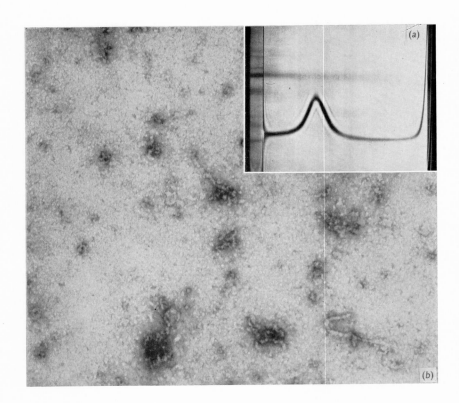

(a) Schlieren pattern of microtubule protein dissolved in 0·5 % Sarkosyl-GTP medium; (b) negatively stained solubilized protein, showing aggregates. × 50,000. (For explanation see p. 43.)

PLATE 3

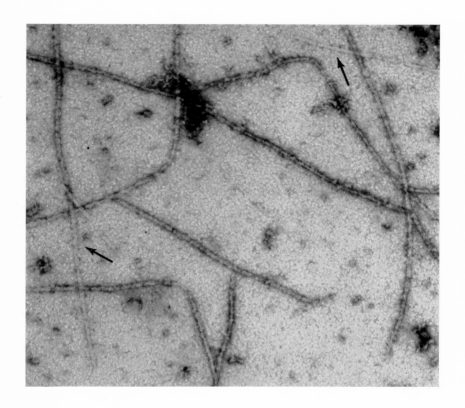

Soluble protein diluted 1:10 with distilled water, with ribbon-like fibres (arrows) and higher aggregates. × 50,000. (For explanation see p. 43.)

PLATE 4

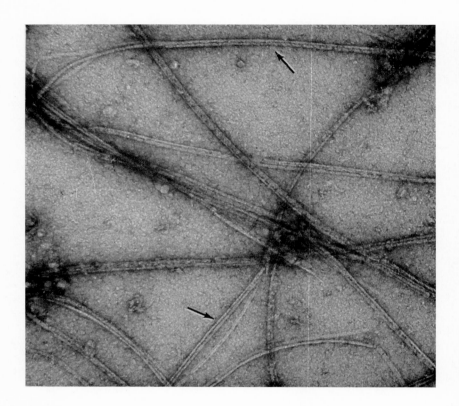

Protein diluted 1:10 with 0·1 M-KCl, showing various types of fibres and microtubule-like material. × 50,000.

CONTRACTILE MECHANISMS OF SMOOTH MUSCLE

By J. C. RÜEGG

Department of Cell-Physiology, Ruhr University, Bochum,
and Max-Planck-Institute for Medical Research, Heidelberg

The special features of smooth muscle—its ability for excessive shortening, its plasticity, its slowness as well as its economy in the maintenance of tension—are a challenge to the comparative muscle physiologist and bio-chemist. What, for instance, is the molecular basis for the extremely high holding economy in the prolonged maintenance of tension which is so striking in invertebrate 'catch muscles' and which may or may not be related to the slowness of the contraction–relaxation cycle or to the abundance of tropomyosin A (paramyosin)? Perhaps the most pertinent problem is the question of a sliding-filament mechanism in vertebrate smooth muscle, for the evidence of the possible existence of thick myosin filaments in this type of muscle is as yet fairly scanty. Considering these problems we should not forget that there is a great structural and biochemical variety of smooth-muscle types so that it may be dangerous to generalize conclusions derived from a particular type of muscle. Table 1 shows that the various kinds of muscle cells do not only differ in the degree of order in the

Table 1. *The diversity of smooth muscle*

		Proteins of myofilaments		
Type of muscle	Z-line structure	Thin filaments	Thick filaments	Examples†
Helical smooth or obliquely striated	Z-column or dense bodies	Actin (3)	Myosin and tropo-myosin-A (para-myosin)*	Earthworm body wall (1); oyster yellow adductor (4)
Invertebrate smooth, type I (paramyosin muscle)	Dense bodies	Actin (3)	Myosin, very much paramyosin	ABRM (2); oyster opaque adductor (5)
Invertebrate smooth, type II (classical smooth)	Dense bodies	Actin	Myosin	Pharynx retractor, snail (2)
Vertebrate smooth muscle	Dense bodies	Actin (3)	No thick filaments? No paramyosin	Uterus (6); taenia coli (8, 9, 10); chicken gizzard (7, 11)

* Paramyosin and tropomyosin-A are used synonymously.
† (1) Heumann & Zebe, 1967; (2) Heumann, 1967; (3) Hanson & Lowy, 1964a; (4) Hanson & Lowy, 1961; (5) Lowy & Hanson, 1962; (6) Shoenberg, 1958; (7) Shoenberg, 1968; (8) Needham & Shoenberg, 1964; (9) Elliott, 1967; (10) Lane, 1965; (11) Panner & Honig, 1967.

arrangement of myofilaments but also in the structure and composition of the thick (myosin) filaments, and in the amount of tropomyosin A (paramyosin).

A double array of discontinuous filaments is required in a sliding mechanism, but in smooth muscle it has as yet only been demonstrated in invertebrates.

1. EVIDENCE FOR A SLIDING-FILAMENT MECHANISM

In a sliding-filament mechanism of the type operating in vertebrate striated muscle, actin filaments slide relative to myosin filaments but the latter do not slide relative to each other; they remain in register during shortening. Thus the extent of possible shortening is limited, and since the degree of overlap between the sliding thick and thin filaments determines the tension, contractile tension is strictly related to length (Gordon, Huxley & Julian, 1964). The extent of shortening is also limited by the sarcomere divisions, the Z-disks into which the sliding thick filaments push at short sarcomere lengths. Yet many smooth muscles are able to shorten under tension to 20% of their rest length or less (Winton, 1926; Csapo, 1955; Hasselbach & Ledermair, 1958) and contractile tension is not always strictly related to length: the anterior byssus retractor muscle of *Mytilus* (ABRM), for instance, shows an optimum contractile tension at resting length, but this tension optimum may be shifted so as to occur at greater lengths by excessive stretching of the unstimulated muscle, 'as if the contractile material were slipping' because of its plastic properties. The effect on the tension–length relationship is reversed by contractile processes only (Abbot & Lowy, 1958*b*; see also Bandmann & Reichel (1954) for similar experiments with *Pinna* adductor muscle and Greven & Sieglitz (1951) for studies on the plasticity of vertebrate smooth muscle).

Excessive shortening in smooth muscle is structurally possible and compatible with a sliding-filament hypothesis because the thick filaments are not kept in register and because there is no structural barrier such as the Z-disks into which the thick myosin filaments would push during supercontraction. In fact, Z-disks seem to be replaced by Z-columns in obliquely striated ('smooth') muscle and by dense bodies in vertebrate smooth muscle (Shoenberg, 1958) and in invertebrate smooth muscles (Heumann & Zebe, 1967; Tina Gori, quoted by Twarog, 1967*a*).

In a sliding-filament mechanism, clearly, excessive shortening is only possible if thick filaments are allowed to slide not only relative to thin filaments but also relative to each other so that they double-overlap. Such a mechanism appears to be realized, for instance, in the earthworm body-wall muscle (Heumann & Zebe, 1967) and in the yellow adductor of oyster (cf. Hanson & Lowy, 1961) in such a way that during shortening the oblique 'striation' becomes less oblique (Fig. 1). As we have seen (Table 1), the filament arrangement of most invertebrate smooth muscle is, however, much more irregular, probably because sliding thick filaments of contracting muscle may by-pass dense-bodies and then do not only overlap each other but also change their actin partners. Under the circumstances

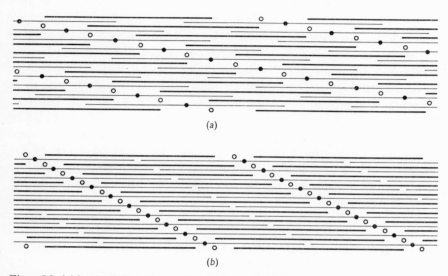

(a)

(b)

Fig. 1. Model for the sliding-filament mechanism in the obliquely striated body-wall muscle of the earthworm (cf. Heumann & Zebe, 1967). (a) Relaxed state; (b) contracted state. Note that the thick filaments do not only slide relative to thin filaments but also relative to each other (from Heumann, 1967).

the degree of actin–myosin overlap and tension cannot be so strictly related to length, as it is in vertebrate striated muscle, especially since an actin filament may be pulled out from alongside a myosin filament during extension. It may then change its partner and lie alongside another thick filament with which it may interact (cf. Lowy & Hanson, 1962). Evidence for a double overlap of thick filaments in shortened ABRM has been presented by Hanson & Lowy (1959) and by Heumann (1967), who showed that during shortening of ABRM the number of thick filaments per fibre cross-section (but not necessarily per cross-sectional area, see Hanson & Lowy, 1959) greatly increases. The mechanism of excessive shortening in these muscles may therefore be similar to that observed recently in embryonic striated muscle of insects (Osborne, 1967), where during shortening the

Z-line precursors are apparently by-passed by sliding myosin filaments which then double-overlap with myosin filaments of neighbouring sarcomeres.

While filament counts make it comparatively easy to prove sliding of thick filaments versus thick filaments (Hanson & Lowy, 1959) or of thin filaments versus thin filaments in vertebrate smooth muscle (Schoenberg, 1962; see also Lane, 1965), it is much more difficult to demonstrate that actin filaments slide relative to myosin filaments without changing their length. It could be shown, however, that the length of thick filaments does not decrease during shortening since the diameter of the discontinuous thick filaments remains constant (Hanson & Lowy, 1959; Lowy & Hanson, 1962) and since the axial periodicities remain unchanged (Selby & Bear, 1956; Millman & Elliott, 1965). Heumann (1967) has recently shown that in ABRM, I-band regions containing thin filaments not interacting with thick filaments are clearly seen in relaxed but not in tonically contracted muscle. At least in obliquely striated 'smooth' muscle the operation of a sliding filament contractile mechanism appears to be fairly well established (Hanson & Lowy, 1961; Heumann & Zebe, 1967). Perhaps one of the reasons why it is so difficult to prove a sliding-filament mechanism in the case of other smooth muscles is the lack of knowledge concerning the location of myosin.

2. PROTEIN COMPOSITION AND STRUCTURE OF MYOFILAMENTS

With the possible exception of vertebrate smooth muscle (Table 1), all other smooth-muscle types show a double array of thick and thin filaments; the latter have been identified as actin in all cases (Hanson & Lowy, 1964a; Peterson, 1963) but the structure and composition of the thick filaments is not exactly understood nor is the location of myosin really known. The thick filaments of *invertebrate smooth muscle* probably do contain myosin since they bear projections like those on the myosin filaments of vertebrate striated muscles (Hanson & Lowy, 1964c) and attempts to extract the myosin component of these muscles selectively (Khan & Johnson, 1960; but see Rüegg, 1965) apparently removed much of the thick filament substance. On the other hand, no X-ray diffraction pattern characteristic for myosin has ever been obtained from these muscles (Elliott, 1967). The wide-angle diagram derived from these muscles (type I pattern of Bear, 1945; see also Astbury, 1947) is a typical α pattern which probably originates from the presence in the muscles of large amounts of tropomyosin-A (para-myosin) which constitutes the bulk of the thick filaments (Hanson *et al.*

1957). It is interesting to note that the diameter of thick filaments is only 300 Å. in *Pecten* fast adductor and in *Helix* pharynx retractor, about 600 Å. in the translucent adductor of oysters, 1200 Å. in the opaque adductor of oysters, and 1500 Å. in *Pinna* adductor muscle (Lowy & Hanson, 1962). Since the content of tropomyosin A or paramyosin also increases in the same order from a few per cent up to 70 % of the total structural protein (cf. Bailey, 1956, 1957; Rüegg, 1961 b; Kahn & Johnson, 1960), it seems that the variation in the diameter of thick filaments is largely due to the presence of tropomyosin A, as was suggested by Lowy, Millman & Hanson (1964).

Strong evidence for the location of myosin in thick filaments comes from the fact that myosin is able to aggregate from solution into 'thick' filaments which are structurally identical with the thick filaments of vertebrate striated muscle (Huxley, 1963). In the absence of ATP, purified myosin from a *vertebrate smooth muscle* (bovine uterus, see Hanson & Lowy, 1964 b) also aggregates into thick filaments bearing the projections characteristic for myosin. Similar filaments have been observed by Shoenberg (1968) in homogenates of aged extracts of uterus muscle prepared in the presence of high Mg^{2+}-concentrations, and by Kaminer (1967) at slightly acid pH. While this evidence is suggestive it is now crucial to know whether the filaments observed in homogenates or extracts pre-exist in the intact muscle or whether they form after extraction. Indeed, the evidence for the pre-existence of thick myosin filaments in the intact vertebrate smooth muscle cell is as yet fairly poor.

The thick filaments which were sometimes observed by Choi (1962) and by Needham & Shoenberg (1964) in various vertebrate smooth muscles are far too few in number to account for the mass of myosin known to be present in these muscles (Shoenberg et al. 1966). In most of the published electron micrographs of vertebrate smooth muscle one type of filament only is seen and this appears to be actin (Hanson & Lowy, 1964 a). Further evidence for the absence of myosin filaments in vertebrate smooth muscle may be summarized as follows:

(1) An X-ray diffraction pattern attributable to myosin could not be obtained (Elliott, 1964, 1967).

(2) The form and intrinsic birefringence of vertebrate smooth muscle (Fischer, 1944) does not decrease after extracting myosin, but it does decrease under ionic conditions which are likely to extract tropomyosin B (Seidel & Weber, 1967).

(3) Actin and myosin may be extracted at low ionic strength with a relaxing solution (containing 5 mM Mg-ATP and EGTA) (Shoenberg et al. 1966) in which the myosin filaments of striated muscle are known to be

4

stable (Huxley, 1963). These low ionic strength extracts (cf. Laszt & Hamoir, 1961) contain the total smooth muscle myosin (Rüegg, Strassner & Schirmer, 1965) but not aggregated into filaments (Shoenberg *et al.* 1966), while actin is always filamentous. The myosin component is dispersed and exists in the form of dimers or trimers as suggested by ultra-centrifugation studies (Schirmer, 1965), showing also that the myosin dissociates reversibly into monomers of 6 S at high ionic strength. But since native myosin filaments could sometimes be observed in smooth-muscle extracts, one wonders whether the easy extraction and solubilization of smooth-muscle myosin is not an artifact.

It might well be that the myosin filaments (if indeed there are any in vertebrate smooth muscle) may be extremely labile (cf. Hanson & Lowy, 1964*b*) and perhaps easily solubilized in minced muscle, either because of their *in vitro* combination with a 'solubilizing factor' or because of the loss of divalent cations such as calcium (cf. Filo, Bohr & Rüegg, 1963) or magnesium (cf. Shoenberg, 1968).

The possible combination of extracted actomyosin with a solubilizing factor was further considered by Schirmer (1965) and by Weber & Rüegg (1966) when they discussed the insolubilization of actomyosin in the presence of Mg-ATP at low ionic strength. This could be achieved without loss of biological activity by rigorous purification, by slight acidification, by treatment with 10 mM calcium chloride or simply by ageing. But as yet no direct evidence has been obtained for the action of a solubilizing factor. In particular, it seems unlikely that native tropomyosin (Ebashi, Ebashi & Maruyama, 1964) or tropomyosin B, which is so plentiful in these smooth muscles (Tsao, Tan & Peng, 1956), is involved in solubilization (Schirmer, 1965). But even if the high solubility of extracted actomyosin were not an artifact, i.e. if the *in vitro* action of a solubilizing factor could not be established, it is unlikely that *all* the myosin is dissolved *in situ* in the living smooth muscle cell. In fact, the solubility of freshly extracted actomyosin has never been found to be higher than 3–5 mg./ml., while its concentration within the cell is about 20 mg./ml. These solubility measurements (Schirmer, 1965) were made in a 'relaxing medium' containing 5 mM Mg-ATP and 4 mM EGTA and the actomyosin estimates were made on extracts from gravid uterus (Needham & Williams, 1963*a*) or from arteries (Rüegg *et al.* 1965), after correcting for contaminants such as the water soluble proteins associated with actomyosin (Needham & Williams, 1963*a*), the 'extraglobulins' (Rüegg *et al.* 1965) or tropomyosin B (Schirmer, 1965). It was assumed that the extracellular space was about 50% (Weber & Rüegg, 1966; see also Norman, Rondell & Bohr, 1959) and that about half of the tissue was collagen, i.e. NaOH insoluble protein.

In spite of the negative evidence mentioned (see also Panner & Honig, 1967), we conclude, therefore, that within the vertebrate smooth-muscle cell myosin does form some kind of organized structure which, perhaps because of its great lability, has so far eluded morphological characterization by birefringence studies, X-ray diffraction measurements or by electron-microscope techniques. Functional studies on the 'isolated' contractile apparatus do indeed support this conclusion since they show that even the details of the contractile mechanism and of the interaction of myosin and actin filaments are very much the same in vertebrate smooth and striated muscle.

3. INTERACTION OF MYOSIN AND ACTIN FILAMENTS IN CONTRACTION

Contractile proteins. Purified actin and myosin from invertebrate smooth muscle (Rüegg, 1961 a) or vertebrate smooth muscle (Needham & Williams, 1963 b) combine with each other to form synthetic actomyosin when mixed in a proportion of about 4:1. At low (physiological) ionic strength these synthetic actomyosin gels split ATP by the actin-magnesium-activated ATPase after addition of ATP, and the gel volume decreases. This shrinking process is probably fundamentally related to the smooth-muscle contractile process (Schirmer, 1965). In this respect it seems quite irrelevant whether both actin and myosin are prepared from the same smooth muscle or whether one of the contractile proteins is derived from smooth muscle and the other from striated muscle (Schirmer, 1965).

These findings strongly suggest that the fundamental contractile process is very much the same in striated and unstriated muscle despite the fact that the myosin components of the two muscle types do somewhat differ. The protein extracted from vertebrate smooth muscle (tonomyosin) has a greater solubility (Hamoir & Laszt, 1962a), a higher content of negatively charged amino acid residues (Huriaux, Péchère & Hamoir, 1965) and a more heat-stable ATPase than myosin from striated muscle (Hamoir & Gaspard-Godfroid, 1964). Smooth-muscle actin, on the other hand, resembles striated-muscle actin more closely in its amino acid composition (Carsten, 1965), its solubility properties, in its ability to polymerize reversibly from the globular G-form to the fibrillar F-form (Carsten, 1965; Rüegg et al. 1965) and in its great affinity for tropomyosin B (Schirmer, 1965), which is so abundant in the smooth muscles of arteries (Hamoir & Laszt, 1962b) and uterus (Tsao et al. 1956; Needham & Williams, 1963a; Jaisle, 1960, 1962).

In contrast to purified 'synthetic' actomyosin the solubility properties and contractile properties of freshly prepared crude actomyosin from vertebrate smooth muscle are strikingly different from those of striated muscle actomyosin. Unlike the latter the smooth-muscle protein does not 'superprecipitate' at low ionic strength after the addition of ATP; instead it dissolves (Laszt & Hamoir, 1961) even with optimal activation by calcium and magnesium ions (Schirmer, 1965). Unlike skeletal-muscle actomyosin, its calcium-activated ATPase activity is increased by raising the ionic strength to o·5 mM (Needham & Cawkwell, 1956; Schirmer, 1965). To distinguish the easily soluble actomyosin of smooth muscle from the classical type, it has been called 'tonoactomyosin' on the assumption that it may be associated with smooth-muscle tone (Laszt & Hamoir, 1961). Evidence is accumulating, however, that most if not all of the special features of smooth-muscle actomyosin may be due to impurities rather than to intrinsic properties. *In vitro*, actin–myosin interaction and Mg-activated ATPase may be inhibited (even in the presence of calcium ions) by some kind of inhibitor (see Schirmer, 1965; Weber & Rüegg, 1966), similar perhaps to those described recently by Hartshorne, Perry & Schaub (1967) in skeletal muscle. It is interesting that ATPase activity of smooth-muscle myofilaments and of trypsin-treated actomyosin (Needham & Williams, 1959) is much higher than that of freshly prepared crude actomyosin and that the capacity for superprecipitation of this preparation greatly increases after ageing or purification (Schirmer, 1965). It is imperative therefore to complement the '*in vitro* studies' on the interaction of extracted actin and myosin with studies on the actin–myosin interaction *in situ*, i.e. in extracted fibres.

Glycerol-extracted smooth-muscle fibre bundles. Contractile structures of all types of smooth muscle and striated muscle contract under nearly identical conditions when they have been functionally isolated by extraction of the soluble components with 50% glycerol. Contraction as well as relaxation occur only in the presence of ATP; contractile tension is maximal when the calcium ion concentration is about 10^{-5} M, and relaxation is complete at free calcium concentrations below 10^{-7} M (Filo, Bohr & Rüegg, 1965; Schädler, 1967). The magnesium requirement, however, is much higher (about 5 mM in the presence of 5 mM ATP; see Hasselbach & Ledermair, 1958) than in skeletal muscle, insect flight muscle, heart muscle, or the ABRM (Table 2), even with an optimal supply of free calcium (Filo *et al.* 1965). As in striated muscle, an increase in calcium concentration (by means of calcium-EGTA buffers) increases the contractile tension, an effect which is paralleled by an increase in the magnesium (actin)-activated ATPase activity, so that the ATPase increase is linearly related to tension (Schädler, 1967). In myofibrils of skeletal muscle the calcium activation of ATPase activity is more or less paralleled by an increase in the calcium binding (Weber, Hertz & Reiss, 1964): maximally 1–2 moles of calcium are bound per mole of myosin, suggesting that with calcium saturation all the contractile sites, and, at the concentration required for half activation, 50% of the sites, may be activated by calcium ions and reacting with actin. It is likely that the 'sites' in question are identical with the cross-bridges

Table 2. *Differences in the calcium and magnesium requirement for contraction in extracted fibre-bundles from various types of muscle*

Muscle	Free calcium concentration (M) for half-maximal activation of tension or ATPase*	Mg concentration (mM) (total) for half-maximal calcium activation*
Rabbit skeletal	$\sim 10^{-6}$ (1)	< 0·1 (2)
Insect fibrillar	$\sim 10^{-7}$ (3)	< 0·1 (5)
Dog heart	$\sim 10^{-6}$ (3)	1–2 (6)
Invertebrate smooth (ABRM)	$\sim 10^{-6}$ (3)	< 0·1 (6)
Vertebrate smooth		
Pig arteries	$\sim 10^{-6}$ (2)	3–4 (2)
Taenia coli	$\sim 10^{-6}$ (3)	—
Uterus	$\sim 10^{-6}$ (7)	3–4 (4)

* In the presence of 5 mM-ATP, 20 mM histidine buffer, pH 7, 20° C. (1) Weber *et al.* 1964; (2) Filo *et al.* 1965; (3) Schädler, 1967; (4) Hasselbach & Ledermair, 1958; (5) Jewell & Rüegg, 1966; (6) Körnig, unpublished; (7) Christomanos, unpublished.

linking actin and myosin. Thus, activation by calcium ions is obviously produced by increasing actin–myosin interaction, i.e. by increasing the number of reactive cross-links by the recruitment of cross-bridges. Activated links probably produce a fixed amount of tension, while splitting a fixed amount of ATP per unit time. On this assumption tension and ATPase activity should be proportional to the number of activated bridges and also proportional to each other. In fact the ratio of tension-dependent energy turnover (ATPase activity) to tension production has been found to be a constant at quite different calcium concentrations and its reciprocal is a measure of the tension-holding economy when related to unit length of the preparation (Schädler, 1967). A similar linear relation between energy turnover and tension production has been found in vertebrate (Bülbring, 1953) and invertebrate smooth muscle (Bozler, 1930; Baguet & Aubert, 1965). Of course the economy of tension maintenance is quite different in the contractile structures of different types of muscle, though in all cases tension is probably produced by the same fundamental mechanism namely the cross-linking of actin and myosin filaments by cross-bridges which split ATP in a sliding filament system.

4. HOLDING ECONOMY AND SPEED OF CONTRACTION IN RELATION TO FILAMENT LENGTH

The ability of smooth muscles to maintain tension or 'muscle tone' much more economically than striated muscle has been correlated with and related to their slowness of relaxation (Bozler, 1930; Ritchie, 1928); it allows tension to be maintained with only infrequent stimulation. It is not quite obvious, however, why there should be such a correlation, since in a tetanus the muscle fibres are always *continuously* activated, regardless of whether the stimulation is frequent or infrequent or whether it is a slow (economical) tetanus or a fast tetanus. The tetanized muscle is continuously in the active state (i.e. able to redevelop tension after a quick release) and it is likely that throughout the tetanus the intracellular calcium concentration is high (cf. Hasselbach, 1964) and thus activating the actomyosin ATPase. However, the economy is not only related to relaxation speed but also to the speed of shortening, especially to the velocity constant b. The latter is in fact about 150 times smaller in ABRM than in frog sartorius, which on the other hand maintains a tension 250 times less economically than smooth muscle (Baguet & Gillis, 1967). This finding is not so surprising since it is known (Hill, 1938) that the speed of contraction (Hill's constant b) is related to the reciprocal of the economy, i.e. the heat of maintenance (the product of constants a and b), because both are determined by the rate at which energy is released during contraction (Hill, 1938).

It is tempting to speculate that the rate of energy release reflects simply the speed of cycling of actin–myosin cross-linkages or the turnover number of the enzymic ATPase sites at the cross-bridges, which in turn should be related to the speed of shortening (see Bárány's (1967) correlation of specific actomyosin ATPase activity with shortening speed). Consequently the suggestion was made (Baguet & Gillis, 1967) that the slowness of contraction as well as the slowness of the energy release and the high economy may result from the slow cycling of actin–myosin cross-links. It is important to realize, however, that a slow rate of energy release may not necessarily be due to the 'slowness' of cycling bridges but may simply result from the fact that in slow economical muscles fewer cross-bridges are cycling than in fast muscle, and that, for structural reasons, more of them are acting in parallel. The main structural factor determining both the rate of shortening and the economy of tension maintenance is the length of myofilaments. [Consider the example shown in Fig. 2.]

With a given cycling rate of actin–myosin cross-linkages, i.e. with a given rate of sliding, the two short sarcomeres will shorten twice as fast as the one long sarcomere with double-length filaments. On the other hand, the two sarcomeres with short myofilaments develop only half as much tension with the same number of cross-bridges as the sarcomere with the long myofilaments. This is because there are only half as many cross-bridges acting in parallel in the short sarcomeres. In other words, a muscle fibre may maintain tension more economically and with fewer active cross-links, if it is made up of long myofilaments instead of short ones, but the greater economy is paid for by a correspondingly lower shortening velocity. This is illustrated in Table 3 which relates tension, number of filaments in a cross-sectional area, the holding economy and the speed of shortening to the length of thick filaments in various types of smooth and striated muscles.

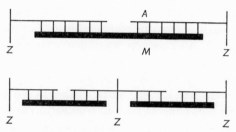

Fig. 2. Diagram illustrating the influence of filament length or sarcomere length on the tension production and shortening speed obtained with a given number of cross-bridges and with a given rate of sliding. Muscles with long filaments have more cross-bridges acting in parallel than short-filament muscles, but any gain in holding economy is offset by a loss of speed. (*A*, Actin; *M*, myosin; *Z*, Z-line.)

Table 3. *Structure and function relationships in various muscles*

Muscle	Length of thick filaments (μ)	Speed of shortening (lengths/sec.)	Force (kg./cm.²)	No. of actin filaments/μ^2	Economy (sec.)
Frog sartorius	1·6	6–10	2·3	1335	1
Oyster yellow adductor	5–8	1·5	5	750	—
ABRM	30	0·25	14	300	200–400*

* During tetanic stimulation.

Structural data: Page & Huxley, 1963; Hanson & Lowy, 1961; Lowy & Hanson, 1962; Lowy, Millman & Hanson, 1964. Mechanical measurements: Hill, 1938; Jewell, 1959; Lowy & Millman, 1963. Energetics: Hill & Woledge, 1962; Baguet, 1965; Baguet & Gillis, 1967.

Compare the yellow adductor muscle of the oyster and the byssus retractor of *Mytilus* (ABRM) with frog sartorius muscle. Per cross-sectional area the oyster muscle has only half as many actin filaments and the ABRM only a quarter. This means, presumably, that 1 g. of oyster adductor contains only half as many cross-bridges and 1 g. of ABRM only a quarter (since the ratio of actin to myosin is about the same in all of these muscles). And yet the oyster muscle produces twice as much tension and the ABRM even 5–6 times as much. In other words a given quantity of cross-bridges/g. muscle produces 4 times more tension in the oyster muscle and even 20 times more in the ABRM. Assuming a constant force per cross-bridge, this would be possible only if the oyster adductor had 4 times as many cross-bridges acting in parallel and the ABRM 20 times as many. If the distance between cross-bridges is similar in all types of muscle, the thick filaments ought to be 4 times longer in oyster muscle and about 20 times longer in ABRM in order to accommodate all the cross-bridges acting in parallel. Consequently the maximal speed of shortening should be 4 times slower in the oyster adductor and 20 times slower in ABRM than it is in the sartorius. The rate of sliding or the cycling rate of actin–myosin cross-bridges may be comparable in the three types of muscle. In fact, the actomyosin ATPase activity of actomyosins prepared from frog sartorius (Bárány, 1967) and of the translucent and opaque smooth adductor of *Pecten* (similar to the yellow oyster adductor and the ABRM) are found to be not very different (see Rüegg, 1961 a). Since in ABRM about 20 times fewer cross-bridges are required than in frog sartorius to maintain a given tension, the smooth muscle is about 30 times more economical as judged by Abbot & Lowy (1958a) and at least 200 times as calculated by Baguet & Gillis (1967).

5. EVIDENCE FOR A FUSION OF MYOFILAMENTS IN 'CATCH'

In the state of prolonged contraction (the catch) of certain molluscan smooth muscles, tension may be maintained about 10 times more economically than during a tetanus (Baguet, 1965) or even without any energy expenditure at all (Minihan-Nauss & Davies, 1966; see table 4). In the following, some evidence will be reported suggesting that thick filaments aggregate in the catch state so that the effective filament length may be much longer than in relaxed or tetanically contracted muscles.

Mechanical experiments on ABRM suggested in 1959 to Jewell that during prolonged contraction catch muscles were not in the active state but in a 'fused state'. The ABRM remains contracted after cessation of 'tonic' stimulation and behaves as a rigid and highly cross-linked body as if the sliding myofilaments were locked or fused in the contracted state. In the 'fused state' the stretch-resistance is unusually high (up to 50–100 kg./cm.² compared with 10 kg./cm.² during death rigor of skeletal muscle), though the signs characteristic of contractile activity are missing (Jewell, 1959;

see also Lowy & Millman, 1959; Johnson, 1958; Twarog, 1967b). For instance, the ABRM is unable to shorten or to redevelop tension when it has been quickly released during contraction. The latter is not associated with electrical activity of the membrane (Twarog, 1960) so that it is obviously quite distinct from the less economical tetanus observed during 'phasic' stimulation. The 'fused state' is unlocked when the ABRM is stimulated by inhibitory nerves (reaching the ABRM from the pedal ganglion) or by serotonin, the possible neurotransmitter of these nerves (Twarog, 1954). This drug does not alter the membrane potential nor does it impair the contractile response after stimulation (Twarog, 1954). However, serotonin does reduce membrane resistance (Hedaka, Osa & Twarog, 1967; Twarog, 1967a) and it increases the consumption of oxygen (Baguet, 1965) and of arginine phosphate (Minihan-Nauss & Davies, 1966).

Table 4. *The different economy of ABRM in tetanic contraction and catch (fused state)*

	$1/T^*$	Energy† (20° C.)		Method
During tetanic stimulation...	0·03	55–75	(1)	Heat production
		70	(2)	O_2 consumption
During 'catch'...	10^{-3}	10–25	(1)	Heat production
		11	(1)	O_2 consumption
		Nil	(3)	Argininephosphate consumption

* T is the time for half-relaxation in seconds.
† Energy for the maintenance of 1 kg./cm.² during 1 sec. in 1 g. (μcal). In frog sartorius this value is 1900 at 0° C. (see Hill & Woledge, 1962). (1) Baguet, 1965, (2) Baguet & Gillis, 1967, (3) Minihan-Nauss & Davies, 1966.

As yet, the molecular basis of the fused state is still a matter of controversy (compare Lowy *et al.* 1964, with Rüegg, 1964b). On the one hand, the tension as well as the high stretch resistance in the fused state have been attributed to linkages between actin and myosin which are either locked in the attached state (Minihan-Nauss & Davies, 1966) or break slowly under tension (Lowy & Millman, 1963); they would have to break and reform at once during and after a large muscle extension (cf. Rüegg, 1965). The nature of these supposed linkages is not well understood but at least it seems clear that the rigor-like stiffness is not caused by a cross-linking of actin and myosin of the type occurring in skeletal muscle fibres after ATP depletion. For the levels of ATP (Rüegg & Strassner, 1962), arginine phosphate and inorganic phosphate (Minihan-Nauss & Davies, 1966) are nearly identical in the catch state and in the relaxed state. As an alternative to the actomyosin linkage hypothesis of the catch, it has therefore been suggested that the catch may be due to cross-links between interacting paramyosin (thick) filaments (Rüegg, 1961 b, 1964 b) rather than to linkages between actin and myosin.

Functional evidence for a fusion of thick (paramyosin) filaments in glycerinated ABRM muscle fibres has been obtained recently (Rüegg, 1964 a, b). Contractile structures of different kinds of muscle reproduce the special functional performance of these muscles when they are isolated by glycerol extraction of the soluble cell components and suspended in ATP-salt solutions. For instance, glycerinated insect fibrillar muscle fibres oscillate like living fibrillar muscle during flight (Jewell & Rüegg, 1966) and glycerinated ABRM fibre bundles show catch-like phenomena (Rüegg, 1961 b; Rüegg & Weber, 1963).

In the ABRM the 'catch' *follows* the cessation of active (tonic) contraction (Jewell, 1959) and it has been shown that contraction of living muscle is terminated by a reduction of the intracellular level of free calcium (see the review of Hasselbach, 1964). When the calcium-induced ATP contraction of glycerinated ABRM is terminated by lowering the calcium concentration with EGTA or EDTA, the contractile structures remain partly contracted (Rüegg, 1964 a). Though they are not in the active state (tension does not recover after a quick release), the stretch resistance is comparable to that in the catch state (Rüegg & Weber, 1963) which follows the cessation of stimulation *after* a tonic contraction (Jewell, 1959) or the reduction of the free calcium concentration in living ABRM (Leenders, 1967).

Like living ABRM in the fused state, extracted fibres treated with EDTA or EGTA maintain passive tension without any energy expenditure (without actomyosin-ATPase), or at least much more economically than during actively maintained contraction. This is illustrated in Figs. 3 and 4, which show the tension and the energy consumption during the contraction of living muscle (Fig. 3, cf. Baguet, 1965) and of glycerinated ABRM fibres (Sawaya & Rüegg; Fig. 4). In the latter a strong contraction remains after a calcium-induced ATP contraction when the free calcium concentration is lowered to about 10^{-7} M. This calcium concentration is unable to induce contraction when applied before contraction, though the actomyosin ATPase activity is identical and very slightly elevated in both cases. It follows that, as in living muscle, tension maintenance following a contraction is more economical than active contraction and that less free calcium is required to maintain tension passively than to produce it actively (cf. Leenders, 1967). Since calcium activation is probably produced by recruitment of cross-bridges, it follows further that many fewer cross-bridges are required to maintain passive tension than active tension. This is par-

ticularly obvious when a strong contraction remains even after complete inhibition of the actomyosin ATPase with EDTA (Leenders, 1966) or EGTA
(Figs. 4, 5) or after dissociation of actomyosin with thiourea (Rüegg, 1964b).

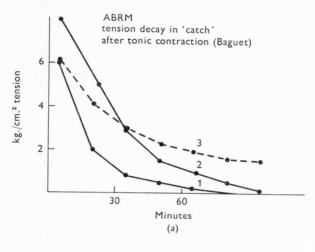

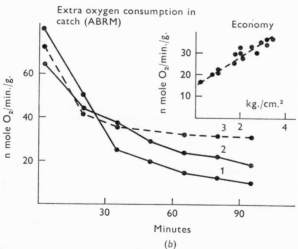

Fig. 3. Decline of tension (graph a) and extra-oxygen consumption (graph b) of ABRM in
the 'fused state' (catch) *after* a tonic contraction induced by acetylcholine. Inset: plot
of oxygen consumption in relation to maintained tension in similar experiments. Reciprocal of the slope measures economy. (Replotted from results by Baguet, 1965.)

Lowy *et al.* (1964) concluded that, 'if genuine contraction remainders in
extracted fibres can be firmly established, a specialized contractile system
based on two types of cross-linkages would have to be seriously taken into
account'. Indeed the maintenance of high tension and the high stretch

resistance of glycerinated fibres poisoned with inhibitors of actin–myosin interaction still have to be accounted for. Rüegg (1959, 1961, 1964) and Johnson, Kahn & Szent-Györgyi (1959) have suggested that the thick paramyosin filaments (containing predominantly tropomyosin A or paramyosin) constitute a holding apparatus (the tropomyosin–paramyosin system) which is operating functionally in parallel to the actomyosin contractile system. Since the paramyosin filaments are sliding and discontinuous (Lowy *et al.* 1964; Heumann, 1967), a functional continuity of the

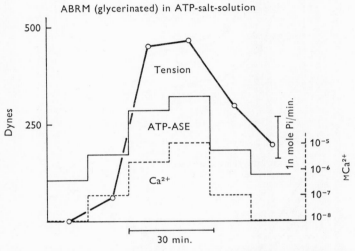

Fig. 4. Tension and ATPase activity in 0·5 cm. long ABRM fibre bundles after glycerol extraction, in ATP-salt solutions at various Ca^{2+} concentrations (buffered with Ca-EGTA according to Jewell & Rüegg, 1966). The temperature was about 20° C. and the pH 6·5. Note the contraction remainder.

paramyosin system is only possible if these filaments are able to interact with each other as suggested by Rüegg (1961 *b*, 1964 *a*, *b*). Indeed, extracted ABRM fibre bundles, contracted isotonically under load, fail to relax after inhibiting the actomyosin-ATPase and actin–myosin interaction with 4 mM EGTA at slightly acid pH (6·4), but they do relax at pH 7·8, i.e. under conditions which are known to plasticize artificial tropomyosin threads (paramyosin threads) (Fig. 5). In fact ABRM fibre bundles inhibited with EDTA or EGTA are plasticized under all those conditions which are also known to plasticize artificial tropomyosin A threads (see Rüegg, 1961 *b*; Rüegg & Weber, 1963). It is therefore concluded that the catch-like contractions of extracted fibres are supported by paramyosin filaments which fuse at slightly acid pH and dissociate at slightly alkaline pH. It is obvious that even a slight interaction of paramyosin filaments during contraction

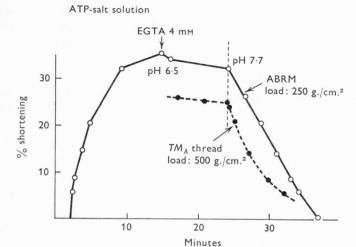

Fig. 5. Isotonic shortening and relaxation of glycerinated ABRM fibre bundle suspended in ATP-salt solution. A contraction is induced by 10^{-5} M Ca^{2+} and terminated by immersing the preparation into the relaxing solution (5 mM Mg-ATP, 4 mM EGTA, pH 6·5). Though the Ca-activated Mg-actomyosin ATPase is completely inhibited (cf. Fig. 4 and Schädler, 1967) the preparation does not relax until the pH rises to 7·8, i.e. to conditions which plasticize the loaded tropomyosin A thread (TM_A thread, see broken line).

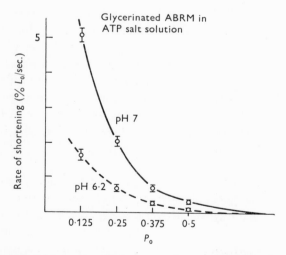

Fig. 6. After isometric tension development, glycerinated ABRM fibre bundles were isotonically released to either 0·125, 0·25, 0·375 or 0·5 times the isometric tension at L_0 under the conditions of Fig. 5. The shortening speed (ordinate) is greatly reduced at acid pH.

would greatly affect the shortening. It has in fact been found that the degree of maximal shortening (Johnson *et al.* 1959) and the speed of shortening (Fig. 6) are greatly reduced at slightly acid pH though the ATPase activity and the isometric tension are similar under these conditions and at neutral pH (see Schädler, 1967).

Structural studies (see Lowy *et al.* 1964) seem, however, not to be in agreement with the concept of a fusion of paramyosin, since thick filaments have always been found separated by thin filaments and unable to interact or to fuse with each other. Separated thick filaments are indeed predominant in relaxed ABRM (Tina Gori, quoted by Twarog, 1967*b*; Heumann, 1967; Heumann & Zebe, 1968), but in tonically contracted preparations only a few single paramyosin filaments can be seen. The majority of these thick filaments are laterally aggregated to form bundles of fused thick filaments (see Plate 1 and Heumann, 1967), even in a catch-like contraction following a strictly isometric contraction (Heumann & Rüegg, 1968). The thin filaments are not then surrounding the thick filaments; instead most of them are found to be located separately, especially at the outside of the muscle fibre. It would appear therefore that in tonically contracted ABRM the thick filaments fuse and are not separated from each other by thin filaments as presumed by Lowy *et al.* (1964). It is likely (see Rüegg, 1964*b*) that the fusion occurs because of the interaction of tropomyosin A (paramyosin), which is so abundant in these thick filaments (see the functional experiments, quoted above). The fused filaments probably form a coherent paramyosin network with a holding capacity capable of supporting tension in the 'fused state' of surviving ABRM or in extracted fibres even after inhibiting actin myosin interaction. Evidence for a fusion of thick filaments in living ABRM has been recently obtained in our laboratory by Schurmacher (unpublished), who found that stretch-resistance by ABRM fibres greatly increased *after* contraction when they went into the fused state, an effect which could be reversed by serotonine.

The physiological consequences of filament interaction may be variable, since sometimes thick paramyosin filaments fuse probably only to a small extent so that a coherent paramyosin network is not formed during the catch; tension cannot, then, be supported without the participation of actin–myosin linkages and without some energy turnover (see Baguet, 1965). In this case, nevertheless, the tension maintenance ought to be more economical than during a tetanus because the aggregated filaments are functionally longer than disaggregated filaments and they are able to link more cross-bridges of actin and myosin in parallel (see Fig. 7). Even a very weak interaction between thick paramyosin filaments would give rise to frictional forces between thick filaments sliding relative to each other during shortening or extension. Therefore a resistance of a viscous type (muscle viscosity, viscous tone of Winton, 1937) would be met with when molluscan smooth muscles are slowly stretched (see also Jordan's (1938) studies on the creep behaviour of smooth muscles).

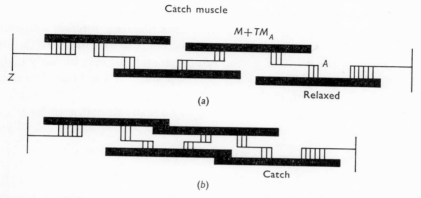

Fig. 7. Diagram illustrating the effect of a partial fusion of thick filaments on the number of cross-bridges acting in parallel in ABRM. For the functional consequences see Fig. 2. (a) Relaxed state in serotonine; (b) fused state (catch). Thick filaments containing tropomyosin A (TM_A) or paramyosin and myosin (M) are probably also linked to actin filaments (A).

The plasticity of vertebrate smooth muscles (plastic tone) has been studied extensively (see for instance Greven, 1950), and Bozler (1953) pointed out that tonic properties as well as the slowness of relaxation could best be attributed to frictional forces resulting from weak protein interaction, which perhaps acted between sliding filaments as Schatzmann (1964) remarked. Interaction may be caused by tropomyosin located in thin filaments (Tsao *et al.* 1965; Ivanov, Mirovich, Zhakhova & Tuchakinsky, 1962) and may cause catch-like phenomena of the type observed by Winton (1930), Rüegg (1962) and Somlyo (1967).

6. CONCLUSIONS

Purified actin and myosin of smooth-muscle actin and myosin are 'basically' similar to the contractile proteins of striated muscle (sometimes called 'tonoactomyosin') and are apparently much more soluble than actomyosin from striated muscle. None the less there does not seem to be any difference in the fundamental contractile mechanism of the two types of muscle since both involve essentially an actin–myosin interaction in the presence of Mg-ATP which is reflected in the superprecipitation (super-contraction) of actomyosin gels. Contraction is probably associated with a sliding of actin and myosin filaments but in smooth muscles additional mechanisms are probably involved. In invertebrate smooth muscles, for instance, thick filaments also contain tropomyosin A; they are not kept in register, so that they slide also relative to other thick filaments during shortening or extension. This is possible since in the smooth muscle fibre Z-disks are replaced by dense bodies. Consequently excessive muscle shortening may occur, but if the sliding thick filaments interact with each other, a resistance of a viscous type (viscous tone, catch) is met with during re-extension of the fibres or during relaxation and this may be fairly high, since the interacting filaments are 30–$100\,\mu$ long. It has been shown in § 4 that the great length of the filament may be one of the decisive reasons for the slowness and the great economy of so many smooth muscles.

REFERENCES

ABBOT, B. C. & LOWY, J. (1958a). *J. Physiol., Lond.* **141**, 385.
ABBOT, B. C. & LOWY, J. (1958b). *J. Physiol., Lond.* **141**, 398.
ASTBURY, W. T. (1947). *Proc. R. Soc.* B **134**, 303.
BAGUET, F. (1965). Etude de l'énergétique d'un muscle lisse de lamellibranche en contractions phasique et tonique. Ph.D. thesis, University of Louvain.
BAGUET, F. & AUBERT, X. (1965). *Archs int. Physiol.* **73** (2), 389.
BAGUET, F. & GILLIS, J. M. (1967). *J. Physiol., Lond.* **188**, 67.
BAILEY, K. (1956). *Pubbl. Staz. zool. Napoli* **29**, 96.
BAILEY, K. (1957). *Biochim. biophys. Acta* **38**, 239.
BANDMANN, H. J. & REICHEL, H. (1954). *H. Z. Biol.* **107**, 68.
BÁRÁNY, M. (1967). *J. gen. Physiol.* **50**, 197.
BEAR, R. S. (1945). *J. Am. chem. Soc.* **67**, 1625.
BOZLER, E. (1930). *J. Physiol., Lond.* **69**, 443.
BOZLER, E. (1953). *Experientia* **9**, 1.
BÜLBRING, E. (1953). *J. Physiol., Lond.* **122**, 111.
CARSTEN, M. E. (1965). *Biochem., Washington* **4**, 1049.
CHOI, J. K. (1962). *5th Int. Congr. Electron Microsc.*, Philadelphia, vol. II, p. M9.
CSAPO, A. (1955). In *Modern Trends in Obstetrics and Gynaecology*, 2nd series, p. 20. London: Butterworth Co.
EBASHI, S., EBASHI, F. & MARUYAMA, K. (1964). *Nature, Lond.* **203**, 645.
ELLIOTT, G. F. (1964). *Proc. R. Soc.* B **160**, 467.
ELLIOTT, G. F. (1967). *J. gen. Physiol.* **50**, 171.
FILO, R. S., BOHR, D. F. & RÜEGG, J. C. (1963). *Am. J. Physiol.* **205**, 1247.
FILO, R. S., BOHR, D. F. & RÜEGG, J. C. (1965). *Science, N.Y.* **147**, 1581.
FISCHER, E. (1944). *J. cell. comp. Physiol.* **23**, 113.
GORDON, A. M., HUXLEY, A. R. & JULIAN, F. J. (1964). *J. Physiol., Lond.* **171**, 28P.
GREVEN, K. (1950). *Z. Biol.* **103**, 139.
GREVEN, K. & SIEGLITZ, G. (1951). *Z. Biol.* **104**, 100.
HAMOIR, G. & GASPARD-GODFROID, A. (1964). *Angiologica* **1**, 317.
HAMOIR, G. & LASZT, L. (1962a). *Nature, Lond.* **193**, 622.

HAMOIR, G. & LASZT, L. (1962b). Biochim. biophys. Acta 59, 365.
HANSON, J. & LOWY, J. (1959). Nature, Lond. 184, 286.
HANSON, J. & LOWY, J. (1961). Proc. R. Soc. B 154, 173.
HANSON, J. & LOWY, J. (1964a). Proc. R. Soc. B 160, 449.
HANSON, J. & LOWY, J. (1964b). Proc. R. Soc. B 160, 523.
HANSON, J. & LOWY, J. (1964c). In Biochemistry of Muscle Contraction, p. 400. Boston: Little, Brown and Co.
HANSON, J., LOWY, J., HUXLEY, H. E., BAILEY, K., KAY, C. M. & RÜEGG, J. C. (1957). Nature, Lond. 180, 1134.
HARTSHORNE, D. J., PERRY, S. V. & SCHAUB, M. C. (1967). Biochem. J. 104, 907.
HASSELBACH, W. (1964). Progr. Biophys. 14, 167.
HASSELBACH, W. & LEDERMAIR, O. (1958). Pflügers Arch. ges. Physiol. 267, 532.
HEDAKA, T., OSA, T. & TWAROG, B. M. (1967). J. Physiol., Lond. 192, 877.
HEUMANN, H. G. (1967). Vergleichende Untersuchungen über Feinbau und Funktionsweise von Muskeln wirbelloser Tiere. Ph.D. thesis, Heidelberg University.
HEUMANN, H. G. & RÜEGG, J. C. (1968). Pflügers Arch. ges. Physiol. (in the Press).
HEUMANN, H. G. & ZEBE, E. (1967). Z. Zellforsch mikrosk. Anat. 78, 131.
HEUMANN, H. G. & ZEBE, E. (1968). Z. Zellforsch. mikrosk. Anat. 85, 539.
HILL, A. V. (1938). Proc. R. Soc. B 126, 136.
HILL, A. V. & WOLEDGE, R. C. (1962). J. Physiol., Lond. 162, 311.
HURIAUX, F., PÉCHÈRE, J. F. & HAMOIR, G. (1965). Angiologica 2, 15.
HUXLEY, H. E. (1963). J. molec. Biol. 7, 281.
IVANOV, I. I., MIROVICH, N. J., ZHAKHOVA, Z. N. & TUCHAKINSKY, S. E. (1962). Biokhimiia (USSR) 27, 76.
JAISLE, F. (1960). Arch. Gynaek. 194, 277.
JAISLE, F. (1962). Gynaecologia (Basle), 153, 19.
JEWELL, B. R. (1959). J. Physiol., Lond. 149, 154.
JEWELL, B. R. & RÜEGG, J. C. (1966). Proc. R. Soc. B 164, 428.
JOHNSON, W. H. (1958). J. cell. comp. Physiol. 52, 190.
JOHNSON, W. H., KAHN, J. S. & SZENT GYÖRGYI, A. G. (1959). Science, N.Y. 130, 160.
JORDAN, H. (1938). Ergebn. Physiol. 40, 437.
KAHN, J. S. & JOHNSON, W. H. (1960). Archs Biochem. Biophys. 86, 138.
KAMINER, B. (1967). Fedn Proc. 26, 728.
LANE, B. P. (1965). J. Cell Biol. 27, 199.
LASZT, L. & HAMOIR, G. (1961). Biochim. biophys. Acta 50, 430.
LEENDERS, H. J. (1966). Naturwissenschaften 53, 617.
LEENDERS, H. J. (1967). J. Physiol., Lond. 192, 681.
LOWY, J. & HANSON, J. (1962). Physiol. Rev. 42 (Suppl. 5), 34.
LOWY, J. & MILLMAN, B. M. (1959). J. Physiol., Lond. 146, 32P.
LOWY, J. & MILLMAN, B. M. (1963). Phil. Trans. R. Soc. B 246, 105.
LOWY, J., MILLMAN, B. M. & HANSON, J. V. (1964). Proc. R. Soc. B 160, 525.
MILLMAN, B. M. & ELLIOTT, G. F. (1965). Nature, Lond. 206, 1357.
MINIHAN-NAUSS & DAVIES, R. E. (1966). Biochem. Z. 345, 173.
NEEDHAM, D. M. & CAWKWELL, J. (1956). Biochem. J. 63, 337.
NEEDHAM, D. M. & SHOENBERG, C. F. (1964). Proc. R. Soc. B 148, 517.
NEEDHAM, D. M. & WILLIAMS, J. M. (1959). Biochem. J. 73, 171.
NEEDHAM, D. M. & WILLIAMS, J. M. (1963a). Biochem. J. 89, 534.
NEEDHAM, D. M. & WILLIAMS, J. M. (1963b). Biochem. J. 89, 552.
NORMAN, A., RONDELL, P. A. & BOHR, D. F. (1959). Am. J. clin. Path. 32, 465.
OSBORNE, M. P. (1967). J. Insect Physiol. 13, 1471.
PAGE, S. & HUXLEY, H. E. (1963). J. Cell Biol. 19, 369.

PANNER, P. J. & HONIG, C. R. (1967). *J. Cell Biol.* **35**, 303.

PETERSON, R. P. (1963). *J. Cell Biol.* **18**, 213.

RITCHIE, A. D. (1928). *The Comparative Physiology of Muscular Tissue*. Cambridge University Press.

RÜEGG, J. C. (1959). *Biochim. biophys. Acta* **35**, 278.

RÜEGG, J. C. (1961*a*). *Proc. R. Soc.* B **154**, 209.

RÜEGG, J. C. (1961*b*). *Proc. R. Soc.* B **154**, 224.

RÜEGG, J. C. (1962). *Pflügers Arch. ges. Physiol.* **278**, 18.

RÜEGG, J. C. (1964*a*). In *Biochemistry of Muscle Contraction*, p. 412. Ed. J. Gergely. Boston: Little, Brown and Co.

RÜEGG, J. C. (1964*b*). *Proc. R. Soc.* B **160**, 536.

RÜEGG, J. C. (1965). *Helv. physiol. pharmac. Acta* (Suppl.) **16**, 1.

RÜEGG, J. C. & STRASSNER, E. (1962). *Z. Naturf.* **18***b*, 133.

RÜEGG, J. C., STRASSNER, E. & SCHIRMER, R. H. (1965). *Biochem. Z.* **343**, 70.

RÜEGG, J. C. & WEBER, H. H. (1963). In *Perspectives in Biology*, p. 301. Ed. C. F. Cori, V. G. Foglia, L. F. Leloir and S. Ochoa. Amsterdam: Elsevier Publishing company.

SAWAYA, T. & RÜEGG, J. C. (In preparation.)

SCHÄDLER, M. (1967). *Pflügers Arch. ges. Physiol.* **296**, 70.

SCHATZMANN, H. J. (1964). *Ergebn. Physiol.* **55**, 27.

SEIDEL, D. & WEBER, H. H. (1967). *Pflügers Arch. ges. Physiol.* **297**, 1.

SELBY, C. C. & BEAR, R. S. (1956). *J. Biochem. biophys. Cytol.* **2**, 71.

SCHIRMER, R. H. (1965). *Biochem. Z.* **343**, 269.

SCHUMACHER, T. (In preparation.)

SHOENBERG, C. F. (1958). *J. Biophys. biochem. Cytol.* **4**, 609.

SHOENBERG, C. F. (1962). *5th Int. Congr. Electron Microsc.*, Philadelphia, vol. II, p. M8.

SHOENBERG, C. F. (1968). *Tissue and Cell* (in the Press).

SHOENBERG, C. F., RÜEGG, J. C., NEEDHAM, D. M., SCHIRMER, R. H. & NEMETCHEK-GANSLER, H. (1966). *Biochem. Z.* **345**, 255.

SOMLYO, A. P. (1967). *J. gen. Physiol.* **50**, 168.

TSAO, T. C., TAN, P. H. & PENG, C. M. (1956). *Scientia. Sin.* **5**, 91.

TWAROG, B. M. (1954). *J. cell. comp. Physiol.* **44**, 141.

TWAROG, B. M. (1960). *J. Physiol, Lond.* **152**, 220.

TWAROG, B. M. (1967*a*). *J. gen. Physiol.* **50**, 157.

TWAROG, B. M. (1967*b*). *J. Physiol., Lond.* **192**, 847.

WEBER, A., HERTZ, R. & REISS, J. (1964). *Proc. R. Soc.* B **160**, 489.

WEBER, H. H. & RÜEGG, J. C. (1966). *MCV Quarterly* **2** (2), 72.

WINTON, F. R. (1926). *J. Physiol., Lond.* **61**, 368.

WINTON, F. R. (1930). *J. Physiol., Lond.* **69**, 393.

WINTON, F. R. (1937). *J. Physiol., Lond.* **88**, 492.

PLATE I

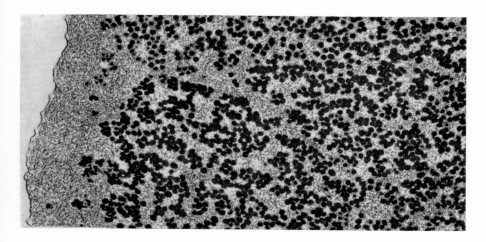

Cross-section of an ABRM fibre in 'catch'. Explanation see text. Magnification 25,000 times. (From Heumann, 1967.)

(*facing p.* 66)

MECHANO-CHEMICAL TRANSFORMATION IN STRIATED MUSCLE

By J. W. S. PRINGLE

Department of Zoology, Oxford

INTRODUCTION

In the field of cell motility, research on muscular contraction holds a special place. Muscles not only contain the most successful of the various types of cellular mechanism for the generation of mechanical energy, but they have also provided the material upon which most of our knowledge of the process is based. It has even been said (Mazia, 1967) that students of muscle contraction now know almost everything about the system except how it actually works.

This review summarizes some of the evidence obtained from work on striated muscles about the nature of the mechano-chemical transformation process at the macromolecular level, for it is at this level of organization that similarities are most likely to be found with other motile systems. The evidence is necessarily indirect, since no technique has yet been found that provides direct information about the form of the molecular events during activity. The volume of indirect evidence is impressive and the discussion will be selective; in particular, no attempt will be made to assess fully the evidence from X-ray diffraction studies, which is considered in detail by Huxley & Brown (1967).

THE CYCLIC NATURE OF MOLECULAR EVENTS DURING ACTIVE CONTRACTION

In the immediately post-war phase of thinking about muscular contraction, much attention was devoted to apparent similarities in behaviour between muscle fibres and various types of natural and synthetic fibres (Pryor, 1950). The pioneering X-ray diffraction studies of Astbury (1947) led naturally to a model of contractility in organic fibres which involved a change from a more-ordered to a less-ordered molecular configuration, the energy for shortening against a load being derived directly from entropy changes in the material. The properties of these models are readily formulated in thermodynamic terms and it appears, at first sight, attractive to compare them with the results of studies of viscoelasticity and thermoelasticity in living muscle (Mandelkern, 1967). Unfortunately for such speculations, there are now a large number of experimental observations which indicate that the development of tension and shortening in striated muscles and in isolated bundles of myofibrils does not involve a change in length of the protein filaments nor a change in the molecular configuration of those parts of the myosin or actin molecules that form the longitudinal elements of the filamentous structure (Huxley, 1963). It is also clear that chemical energy from the hydrolysis of ATP is not converted into mechanical energy by a mechanism that involves a progressive increase in the entropy of longitudinally oriented structures as shortening proceeds, but is achieved through repetitive cycles of configurational change in highly localized parts of the myofibrils. The most important observations on frog and rabbit muscles that have led to general acceptance of this changed viewpoint are as follows:

(1) Interference microscopy and electron microscopy of extended and shortened muscles show that there is no difference in the length of either the thick or thin filaments of the myofibril. This was the original evidence for the sliding filament hypothesis of H. E. Huxley & Hanson (1954) and A. F. Huxley & Niedergercke (1954).

(2) X-ray diffraction measurements of the longitudinal spacing of subunits in the myosin and actin filaments show no change between the extended and shortened states. During isometric contraction in which high tensions are developed there is again no large change in any of the main spacings (Elliott, Lowy & Millman, 1965; Huxley, Brown & Holmes, 1965).

(3) The active isometric tension developed on excitation is not monotonically related to the length of the fibres, as would be expected from an entropic model, but declines above a certain length and becomes zero when the sarcomeres are extended to the point where there is no overlap between the thick and thin filaments. Furthermore, active tension is linearly proportional to the extent of overlap over a considerable range of lengths (Gordon, Huxley & Julian, 1966).

(4) It was thought for a long time that measurements of heat production indicated an additional evolution of energy proportional to the distance shortened (Hill, 1938) and that this indicated a difference in state between the extended and shortened condition. In a reinvestigation of the heat production by frog muscle, Carlson, Hardy & Wilkie (1963) were unable to demonstrate any 'heat of shortening'; they found that the total energy production by a contracting muscle could be described by a constant term (the energy of activation) plus a term proportional to the work done. The apparent dependence of heat production on the extent of shortening arose from failure to extend the heat measurements over a sufficiently long period of time.

(5) Finally, Cain, Infante & Davies (1962) and Davies (1965) showed that the amount of creatine phosphate hydrolysed by frog rectus abdominis muscles was linearly proportional to the work done, when the extent of shortening was constant and the load was varied; and, conversely, that the same amount of creatine phosphate was hydrolysed for the same work done, even though the extent of shortening varied. Literally, this means that there is no difference in the free energy of the macromolecular system between the extended and the shortened states and that mechanical energy must be generated by a cyclic process which is repeated many times over during the course of a single shortening.

It is now widely accepted that contractility in vertebrate striated muscle involves the relative movement of nearly rigid filaments produced by cycles of mechano-chemical transformation in the cross-bridges between them; these bridges are formed from projecting heads of myosin molecules and include the parts of the protein structure conferring both ATPase and actin-combining activity; the complex within which the mechano-chemical transformation process takes place must be considered to include the actin molecules, since myosin by itself does not couple ATP-hydrolysis with the generation of mechanical energy.

Much less attention has been given to other types of striated muscle, but the following further evidence from other tissues is worthy of note:

(6) Unlike frog and rabbit muscles, which are plastic in the relaxed state and can be extended by 50% or more without the development of appreciable tension, many vertebrate and most arthropod muscles show considerable resting elasticity; this is particularly true of insect fibrillar muscles in which tension, comparable in magnitude to the active tension, is developed by extension of the resting muscle by a few per cent. Some continuous viscoelastic element is evidently present in these tissues and White (1967) and Pringle (1967a) have discussed the evidence that this material is located between the myosin filaments and the Z-line, as first suggested from electron-microscopical evidence by Auber & Couteaux (1962). It was shown by Weis-Fogh (1956) that good structural evidence for relative sliding of the filaments can nevertheless be obtained from locust flight muscle and that its different mechanical properties can be considered to be due to passive elastic elements in parallel with the contractile elements. In fibrillar muscle also, the resting viscoelasticity is, to a considerable extent, in parallel with the active mechanism and a first approximation to the properties of the contractile system can be obtained by subtracting the measurements on resting muscle from those on active muscle (Machin & Pringle, 1960; Abbott, 1968); but in this tissue the two elements interact to give rise to the peculiar oscillatory activity (Thorson & White, 1968).

(7) The essentially cyclic nature of the contractile mechanism is directly manifested in the oscillation of insect fibrillar muscle. Here the imposition of length changes tends to synchronize the cycles of mechano-chemical activity throughout the fibres, so that they generate mechanical work intermittently but can function at a high frequency. The mechanism by which this is achieved is discussed by Pringle (1967a, b) and will not be considered in this review. A model giving good quantitative agreement with observations can be devised by supposing that, in insect fibrillar muscle, the probability of initiation of a cycle of mechano-chemical activity is directly influenced by the local mechanical state of the filaments (Thorson & White, 1968). The success of this formulation in explaining the peculiar properties of this tissue gives further support to the view that a relative sliding of myosin and actin filaments under the influence of the cross-bridges is a general feature of the contractile mechanism of striated muscles.

TURNOVER FREQUENCY OF THE
MECHANO-CHEMICAL PROCESS

If the mechanical energy is generated cyclically it should be possible to estimate the frequency of operation of the mechano-chemical process in different muscles and correlate chemical activity with mechanical phenomena. Gergely et al. (1965) first showed that it is the myosin and not the actin component that is different in muscles with different speeds of mechanical and chemical activity. These authors compared the biochemical properties of proteins extracted from rabbit red and white muscles and found a significantly higher Ca^{2+}-activated Mg-ATPase activity in myofibrils and actomyosin from white muscle. When they studied actomyosin reconstituted from purified actin and myosin they found that that made with myosin from white muscles always had the higher activity; it made no significant difference which actin was used in the complex.

Extending earlier work of a similar nature to this, Bárány (1967) prepared myosin from a wide variety of muscles and showed for different cat muscles, for striated muscles from various vertebrates and for a few muscles from invertebrates that there is an approximate proportionality between the actin-activated ATPase activity of the myosin and the maximum velocity of shortening. Both chemical and mechanical activities covered about a 200-fold range. In most cases, actin from rabbit skeletal muscle was used as the activator, but variation of the source of F-actin had no effect on either the extent of actomyosin formation or the activation of myosin ATPase. There was also no great difference in the actin-binding ability of the different myosins, only in their ATPase activity. This important investigation shows clearly that it is the myosin which is chemically different in different muscles and that the speed of contraction is related to the ATPase activity.

In any enzyme preparation, the total catalytic activity is given by the product of the number of active centres and the average turnover frequency. If it can be assumed that all the enzyme is active, then comparative figures for enzyme activity show the relative turnover frequency of the different biochemical species. Bárány (1967) indicated that, if his data were to be expressed in terms of moles of ATP per 500,000 g. myosin per second, the turnover would vary from 0·1 to 20. This is a very slow rate compared with figures which have been quoted for globular enzymes such as carbonic anhydrase (10^6/sec) or myokinase (3,000/sec) (Long, 1961), and it indicates that the formation of the active complex during the ATPase activity of actomyosin involves some relatively improbable events. The analysis of ATPase activity into its two components becomes particularly important when considering the mechanism of generation of mechanical energy by the cross-bridges in striated muscle, since the series-parallel arrangement of these structures in the myofibril suggests that active tension should be related to the fraction of bridges that are simultaneously in the attached phase of their cycle of activity, while the velocity of shortening should be related to the frequency of cyclic activity (A. F. Huxley, 1965). The two components of the mechanical energy output are easily separable by experiment and it is significant that the maximum tensions that can be generated by different vertebrate striated muscles per unit cross-sectional area are rather similar, 0·5–4·0 kg. cm.$^{-2}$ (Wilkie, 1954); this range might be reduced still further if account were taken of differences in the density of filaments in the cross-sections of the different muscles. The range of maximum velocities, however, is much greater. It thus seems that the fraction of bridges which is simultaneously active may be relatively constant and that differences in ATPase activity represent differences in turnover frequency in different muscles.

In the oscillatory contraction of insect fibrillar muscle, the maximum efficiency of conversion of chemical energy into oscillatory mechanical work should occur when there is complete synchronization of the cycles of operation. Any lack of synchronization must lead to the injection of mechanical energy into the cycles of length change at a phase that is not optimal for the performance of mechanical work. For any particular type of fibrillar muscle there is an optimum frequency for the performance of oscillatory work. There should therefore be a relationship between this optimum oscillation frequency for the efficient performance of maximum oscillatory work and the turnover frequency of the ATPase of the actomyosin complex.

Pringle (1967b) calculated from the data of Rüegg & Tregear (1966) that the maximum ATPase activity of stretched glycerinated fibres from water-bug flight muscle corresponds to a turnover of 4 moles ATP per mole myosin per sec., if all the myosin is enzymically active. The data of Maruyama, Pringle & Tregear (1968) for actomyosin from the same species give the similar figure of 3 moles ATP per mole myosin per sec. This is approximately the optimum frequency for oscillatory work at the same temperature. Measurements by Rüegg (1967) of the ATPase activity during maximal oscillatory work have also indicated the hydrolysis of approximately 1 molecule of ATP per molecule of myosin per cycle of oscillation at the optimum frequency and a proportionality between oscillatory work done and ATP hydrolysed, with an efficiency of up to 3,000 cal./mole of ATP. None of these series of experiments can yet claim an accuracy sufficient to do more than indicate the order of magnitude of the relationship, and recent experiments by Mannherz & Tregear (unpublished) suggest that a hydrolysis of more than 1 mole ATP per mole myosin per cycle of oscillation can sometimes be obtained. It does, however, appear to be established that a considerable degree of synchronization of the cycles of mechano-chemical transformation is achieved in insect fibrillar muscle and that therefore the optimum frequency provides a direct indication of the approximate frequency of operation of the molecular generator (Tregear, 1968).

In summary up to this point, there is evidence from work on striated muscles of a cyclic mechano-chemical transformation process operating at a turnover frequency of a few tens of cycles/sec., which is correlated in isotonic contractions with the maximum velocity of shortening and in oscillatory contractions with the optimum oscillation frequency. How the chemical reaction generates mechanical energy cannot be discovered from biochemical studies alone and for further progress it is necessary to consider the evidence from studies of fine structure.

THE ACTIN FILAMENT AND THE
STRUCTURE OF ACTOMYOSIN

The most constant element in the fine structure of muscles is the F-actin filament. Hanson & Lowy, in a series of papers (1960, 1963, 1964a), have shown that thin filaments differing only in length can be isolated from all muscles studied and that they have the same structure as filaments prepared by polymerization of purified G-actin. With negative staining, the filament is seen to be formed from a double string of globular actin monomers, 55 Å. in diameter, twisted into a regular helix.

The actin monomers in the two strings of the double helix have the same polarity. This was first demonstrated by Huxley (1963), who showed that actin filaments take up heavy meromyosin (HMM) strongly and then have a characteristic arrow-headed appearance, probably due to a double helix of HMM molecules attached around the outside of the actin helix (Huxley, 1964). A similar appearance is given by vertebrate or insect actomyosin suspensions dried down from 0·6 M-KCl, under which conditions the myosin is depolymerized (Plate 1). It is evidently a general feature of the actomyosin complex that the myosin attaches to the actin filament at an acute angle.

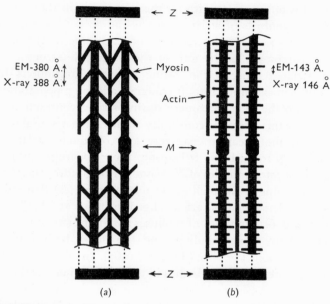

Fig. 1. Characteristic cross-bridge positions and dominant axial periodicities of glycerinated water-bug flight muscle in (a) rigor and (b) relaxation. (Reedy, Holmes & Tregear, 1965.)

The arrow-head appearance of vertebrate actomyosin disappears if ATP is added to the suspension, leaving clean actin filaments (Huxley, 1964). Reedy, Holmes & Tregear (1965) showed by combined X-ray diffraction and electron-microscope studies that this is also true in the intact myofibrils of insect fibrillar muscle. Cross-bridges on the myosin filaments were detached from the actin and orientated mainly at right angles to the filaments in glycerinated fibres relaxed by ATP and EGTA, but were angled and attached when ATP was absent (Fig. 1). Since these observations were not made on actively contracting muscle, they do not provide evidence about the structural change that occurs during activity, but the difference in angle of the cross-bridges in relaxation and rigor is highly suggestive, since tension is developed on going into rigor and is maintained in the absence of ATP (White, 1967).

The structure of Z-lines

If the relative sliding of actin and myosin filaments in each half-sarcomere is to produce tension and shortening in the whole myofibril, it is necessary that actin filaments of opposite polarity be joined together to form a continuous mechanical element. Continuity in the myosin filaments is ensured by the pattern of spontaneous aggregation of myosin monomers (Huxley, 1963) but actin polymerizes with all the monomers in the same polarity. In the intact myofibrils of striated muscle the polarity of the bundles of actin filaments is nevertheless reversed on each side of the Z-line, thus defining the sarcomere as the unit of the contractile structure. In some crustacean striated muscles the Z-line is not a continuous transverse element, but can separate into fragments, allowing penetration of the A-filaments into the next sarcomere during strong contraction (Hoyle & McAlear, 1963); this lateral discontinuity of the Z-line material is even more pronounced in molluscan transversely and obliquely striated muscles (Hanson & Lowy, 1961; Lowy & Hanson, 1962; Twarog, 1967) and in the very obliquely striated muscles of Nematoda (Rosenbluth, 1967), where the angle of the banding is so small (4° in relaxed muscles) that it is difficult to see that the 'dense bodies' are arranged in bands at all. Finally, in the unstriated paramyosin muscles of molluscs and in the smooth-muscle fibres of mammals there is no banding, and the dense bodies are arranged irregularly throughout the fibre (Twarog, 1967). In all cases, however, the actin filaments enter the dense bodies in the same manner as they enter the Z-line of striated muscles. Although there is as yet no direct evidence except for striated muscle, it seems likely that a reversal of polarity of the actin filaments always takes place at the dense bodies and that polarized actin filaments are a general feature of the structure of all muscles. It thus becomes important to consider how actin filaments of opposite polarity are joined together to complete the necessary continuous mechanical element. Some recent information about the structure of the Z-line of insect muscles (Ashhurst, 1967) makes it possible to suggest a generalized picture of the way in which this is achieved.

The Z-line of the fibrillar flight muscles of giant water-bugs, which is a thick structure 1,000–1,400 Å. in longitudinal dimension as compared with the 330–660 Å. in vertebrate muscles (Franzini-Armstrong & Porter, 1964), is formed by the overlapping of the ends of the actin filaments of adjacent sarcomeres. The actin filaments do not divide as suggested for vertebrate muscle by Knappeis & Carlsen (1962); the higher density of the Z-line compared with the rest of the sarcomere is formed by additional material linking the filaments together in this region. Because of the peculiar lattice found in insect flight muscles (actin/myosin ratio 3:1), interdigitation of the actin filaments gives rise to a pattern of small hexagons (Fig. 2), which was described (as circles) by Auber & Couteaux (1963). No lateral

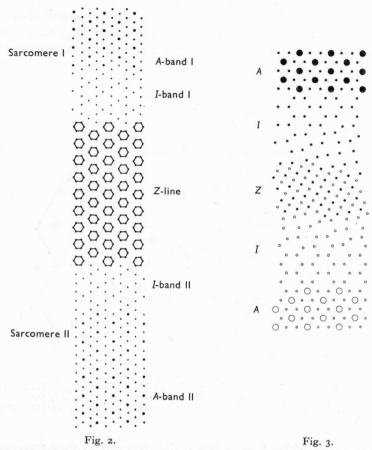

Fig. 2.   Fig. 3.

Fig. 2. Diagram, based on the appearance of a slightly oblique transverse electron-micrograph of water-bug flight muscle, showing how interposition of the I-filament lattices of adjacent sarcomeres produces the hexagonal lattice of the Z-lines. (Ashhurst, 1967.)

Fig. 3. Diagram of the filament lattice of vertebrate striated muscle, showing how a transformation similar to that of Fig. 2 can produce a rhomboidal lattice in the Z-line.

displacement of the actin filaments from their normal positions in the lattice is required in order to generate this pattern; its relationship to the lattice of the myosin filaments is therefore clearly seen in slightly oblique transverse sections in which, owing to the extreme structural regularity of these tissues, one can follow actin filaments all the way from the overlap region to their termination at the opposite side of the Z-region. The Z-line pattern arises if the myosin-filament lattice of one sarcomere is displaced relative to that of the next so that each myosin filament is in the trigonal position of the other lattice; that is, to the position occupied by the actin filaments in the overlap-region lattice of vertebrate muscle.

The Z-line lattice of vertebrate muscle has usually been described as square and, since the actin filaments are arranged in a hexagonal pattern in the overlap region (actin/myosin ratio 2:1), it is not possible for them to form

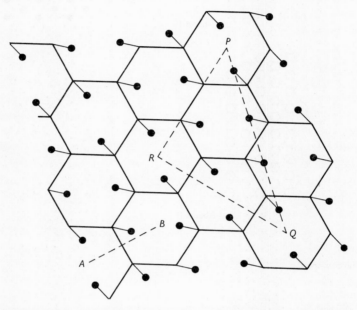

Fig. 4. Transformation of a hexagonal into a rhomboidal lattice by equal displacement of elements. If the distance between the centres of the hexagons $AB = 1$, then $PQ = \sqrt{7}$ and $QR = 2$. Thus the acute rhomboidal angle $PQA = 2 \times PQR = 2 \times \cos.^{-1}(2/\sqrt{7}) = 81° 47'$.

a square lattice without some lateral displacement as they traverse the I-band. This was first pointed out by Knappeis & Carlsen (1962), but the particular form of displacement suggested by them does not generate a square lattice over a large area of the section if each actin filament is displaced by the same distance. Model experiments show that equal lateral displacement of actin filaments produces the most symmetrical twofold pattern if the displacements are as shown in Figs. 3 and 4 and the pattern is not square but rhomboidal with an angle of 81° 47'. As in the original suggestion of Knappeis & Carlsen (1962), each actin filament from one sarcomere lies at the centre of the regular pattern formed by the actin filaments of the other sarcomere, but together they generate a rectangular lattice with sides in the ratio $(\sqrt{3}/2)$. This Z-line pattern arises if the myosin filaments of one sarcomere are displaced so that they would lie at the mid-point of the line joining two myosin filaments of the other sarcomere, in the position occupied by actin filaments in the overlap lattice of insect flight muscle. The situation is thus exactly the inverse of that found in insect flight muscles. If the myosin filament spacing is 400Å., the required lateral displacement of the actin filaments as they traverse the I-band is 104Å. This appears to be the only way in which the myosin filaments of one sarcomere can be displaced relative to those of the next so that over-lapping actin filaments will generate a regular lattice with twofold symmetry in the Z-line when they are all displaced by a similar distance.

Many published electron-micrographs of transverse sections through the Z-lines of vertebrate muscles show a rhomboidal and not an exactly square lattice, but this pattern would, of course, be produced if a truly square lattice was sectioned at an angle that was not exactly transverse. Similarly, an exactly square pattern could be produced by slightly oblique sectioning of a rhomboidal lattice. It does not seem possible from published evidence to decide which is the true relationship. A naturally rhomboidal lattice could distort into a truly square lattice if the section of the whole myofibril became elliptical rather than circular.

The model studies thus suggest that it is possible to explain the Z-line lattice of vertebrate striated muscle in the same manner as for insect flight muscle and that there is no need to postulate a splitting of the double helix of the actin filaments at their ends. The continuous mechanical element is formed by the filamentous material which joins the ends together and forms the sides of the rectangles seen in transverse sections. This material seems to be a different protein from actin; Briskey, Seraydarian & Mommaerts (1967) have suggested that it may be α-actinin. Whatever its chemical nature, the zig-zag appearance of longitudinal sections cut in certain planes shows that it attaches to the actin filaments at an acute angle similar to that at which myosin monomers attach in the absence of ATP. Reedy's (1964) transverse sections of the Z-line show that it also attaches tangentially rather than radially, again similar to the way in which the cross-bridges attach to the actin filaments in rigor in insect flight muscle (Reedy, 1967a). It seems possible that the sites of attachment of the Z-line protein and of myosin to the actin filaments may be the same.

The thickness of the Z-line in the longitudinal direction differs in different vertebrate muscles (Franzini-Armstrong & Porter, 1964). There is no difficulty in accounting for this if the actin filaments overlap by different amounts in different muscles and are joined by Z-line protein throughout the overlap region. In the thin Z-line of tadpole caudal muscles described by Franzini-Armstrong & Porter (1964), only a small number of the actin monomers at the ends of the filaments are linked by Z-line protein and no actual overlap of actin filaments occurs; the pyramidal peaks of the corrugated Z-line membrane that they describe are interpreted as the surface of helical cones of individual filamentous elements at the pitch of the double actin helix.

It remains to explain the appearance similar to the 'square' lattice seen by Huxley (1963, 1964) in certain 'tropomyosin' crystals. If the interpretation of Z-line structure given here is correct, these must, in fact, have been double crystalline formations of actin and α-actinin. Recent studies with antibodies (Pepe, 1966) suggest that tropomyosin is not located in the Z-line but is dispersed throughout the sarcomere. The identification since 1964 of the minor protein constituents of the myofibril suggests that it may be necessary to re-examine the properties and structure of 'tropomyosin' preparations.

Myosin filaments

In contrast to actin, myosin is not found in the same type of organized structure in different muscles. In some mammalian smooth muscles, there is no agreement as to whether myosin filaments are present at all (Needham & Shoenberg, 1964; Shoenberg, 1965; Shoenberg et al. 1966), though short artificial filaments can be prepared from the extracted protein (Hanson & Lowy, 1964b). In other muscles both the length and thickness of the myosin-containing filaments vary over a wide range. Only in the case of the thick filaments of vertebrate striated muscles is there information about the internal molecular structure of the filaments; here electron-microscopical and X-ray diffraction studies by Huxley (1963) and antibody studies by Pepe (1967) have revealed the molecular structure of the filaments.

The thick filaments of vertebrate striated muscle form by lateral association of myosin molecules, joining with tail-to-tail orientation in the centre of the sarcomere and head-to-tail in more distal portions of the filaments (Huxley, 1963). In the centre of the sarcomere—the M-line—the filaments are roughly triangular in cross-section and are joined to each other by fine filaments of M-line material, which Pepe (1966) has shown to be antigenically distinct from the other myofibrillar proteins. Pepe (1967) suggests that the triangular section arises from close-packing of 12 myosin molecules, associated tail-to-tail, with the M-line protein attaching at the tail-to-tail junctions (Fig. 5). To these myosin molecules others attach with a head-to-tail orientation, overlapping the heavy-meromyosin portions of the first group of molecules. On each side of the M-line the filament thus consists of an inner core composed of light-meromyosin (LMM) segments, outside which lie the helical parts of the HMM segments and the projections which form the cross-bridges. Because the length of the helical part of the HMM segment is about half that of the LMM segment, the filament consists of 18 subunits for most of its length; it tapers at the ends as the number of constituent molecules is progressively reduced.

Staining with anti-myosin antibody shows up seven bands at a periodicity of about 430 Å. in the middle region of each half-filament. Pepe (1967) suggests that the antibody is also absorbed elsewhere but that visible banding occurs only where the molecules are in accurate register. In the middle of the filaments register is upset by the fact that the longitudinal spacing of the tail-to-tail association is not exactly the same as that of the head-to-tail association; at the ends of the filaments register is inexact owing to the taper.

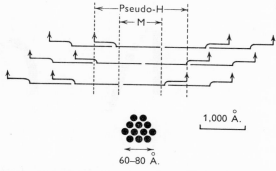

Fig. 5. Representation of the longitudinal arrangement of myosin molecules in vertebrate striated muscle, producing the M-line, pseudo-H zone and the triangular section of the thick filaments. (Pepe, 1967.)

The antigenic activity of different segments of the myosin molecule was explored by first absorbing the anti-myosin antibody with one of the meromyosins after various periods of tryptic digestion. In this way it was possible to demonstrate three antigenically distinct regions, corresponding to the LMM and HMM segments and the segment between these that is sensitive to tryptic digestion (Fig. 6). The accessibility of these three antigenic sites to antibody in the intact myofibril is as follows: (a) the HMM sites are accessible only where there is no overlap between the thick and thin filaments; (β) the trypsin-sensitive sites are accessible only in the middle one-third of each half of the thick filaments; (γ) the LMM sites are accessible only at the ends of the thick filaments.

The banding seen with untreated myosin antibody is due to staining of the trypsin-sensitive region of the molecules, since it is not observed if the antibody is first absorbed with LMM prepared by short tryptic digestion but only if the LMM has been digested for a longer period which removes the whole of the trypsin-sensitive region. The HMM sites are evidently accessible only when these are not obscured by combination with actin; these sites must be close to the actin-combining sites at the ends of the cross-bridges. The LMM antigens are able to combine with antibody only when the packing of the myosin molecules is loosened and Pepe suggests that this occurs towards the ends of the filaments where the internal

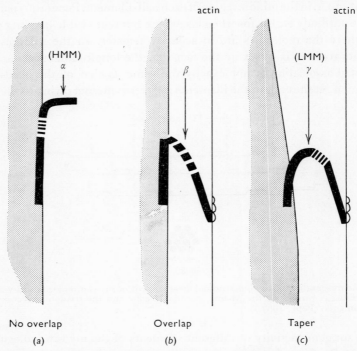

Fig. 6. Representation of actin–myosin interaction at different places along the thick filament, showing the availability for antibody staining of the three parts of the myosin molecule (α, β, γ). (a) Region of no overlap; (b) region of overlap where the myosin molecules are precisely packed into the thick filament; (c) near the tapered end of the thick filament. (Pepe, 1967.)

structure is disturbed by the bending out of bridges attached to the actin filaments; LMM staining is more intense at shorter sarcomere lengths when the inter-filament distance in the lattice is greater and there is there-fore more distortion of the myosin packing by strained bridges. To explain the more intense staining of trypsin-sensitive sites in the middle of each half-sarcomere he suggests that this region of the myosin molecule is flexible and that where the packing of the LMM segments is more regular and therefore tighter the strain of attached bridges is borne by the trypsin-sensitive segments, thus exposing their antigenic sites more completely (Fig. 6, β); this staining is also more intense at shorter sarcomere lengths.

Pepe (1967) described his model for the myosin filament in terms of a central core of 12 molecules (Fig. 5), which implies that there is one myosin per cross-bridge. He points out, however, that on this assumption the over-all diameter of the filament would be smaller than that observed by Huxley (1963) using negative staining, and that biochemical determinations of the absolute amount of myosin in vertebrate muscle indicate a greater amount than can be accounted for by the number of bridges (Huxley, 1960). An alternative model for the mode of packing can be constructed with 24 myosin molecules in the M-region and 36 in the overlap region; this actually has a more obviously triangular section. It is interesting that the most sym-metrical packing in a model with three myosins per cross-bridge generates a smoother outline to the section. There are three myosins per cross-bridge in water-bug flight muscle (Chaplain & Tregear, 1966) and the thick fila-ments are elliptical in cross-section in the M-region (Ashhurst, 1967); in some insect flight muscles the outline is a figure-of-eight (Reger & Cooper, 1967). There is also evidence from electron-microscope and X-ray diffraction studies (Reedy, 1967b; Miller & Tregear, unpublished) that the structure of the thick filaments of insect flight muscle is different from that of vertebrate striated muscle.

THE GENERATION OF MECHANICAL ENERGY

These studies of the structure and antibody-combining elements of the myofibril make it possible to formulate a rather precise model of the mode of generation of mechanical energy. This model is largely implicit in the discussion in Pepe (1967) but is here stated explicitly. It is evident that a bond can form between the ends of the cross-bridges and the actin filaments that is strong enough to disturb the packing of the myosin molecules and even to distort the shape of the flexible trypsin-sensitive region. In rigor, this bond is at an acute angle to the axis of the filaments. Under activating con-ditions the cyclic activity at the bridges may involve the following steps:

(1) Binding of ATP to the active enzyme site of the myosin, which is located near the end of the bridges.

(2) Attachment of the bridge to the actin filament.

(3) Hydrolysis of the terminal phosphate of ATP, leading to a change in the angle of attachment to the actin filaments and the appearance of mechanical force in the form of a bending moment in the bridge and thus of tension between the two ends of the sarcomere proportional to the number of bridges in each half-sarcomere that are simultaneously attached.

(4) If shortening and sliding can occur, the release of this mechanical potential energy as work.

(5) Exchange between the bound ADP and free nucleotides in the sarco-

6

plasm. If ATP replaces the bound ADP, the bridge detaches and the cycle is repeated.

In this cycle of events, mechanical energy is generated at the point of attachment of the bridges to the actin filaments and not at the base of the bridge. The bridge itself and that part of the HMM segment which tends to pack into the backbone of the filament is more rigid than the trypsin-sensitive region, and the stress in angled bridges can only be released by relative sliding of the filaments, with bending at the flexible point of the myosin molecule and a pulling away from the backbone of the rigid basal part of the HMM segment. When the bridge detaches after rebinding of ATP, the tendency of this region to align itself to the filament axis restores the projecting bridge to its approximately rectangular orientation. Elliott (1967) has argued that variation of the interfilament spacing from 50 Å. to 130 Å. at different sarcomere lengths argues against a model involving a direct bond between the ends of the cross-bridges and the actin filaments. This objection is overcome if the flexible region of the myosin molecule is located in the part forming the backbone rather than at the base of the bridge, for random movement of the whole HMM segment when ATP is bound will then have a pronounced lateral component as well as some freedom in the longitudinal and azimuthal directions. The low turn-over rate of the ATPase enzyme is consistent with there being a low probability of attachment to the actin filament. It is not easy to predict from first principles whether this probability should be greater or smaller when there is a larger separation between the filaments, since this will also depend on the accuracy required longitudinally and in azimuth.

A mathematical formulation of a model of this general type has recently been worked out by Thorson & White (1968), the significant feature being that there is a finite probability of attachment of detached bridges and of detachment of attached bridges, each attached bridge generating a longitudinal force between the filaments. By allowing these probabilities to be affected by the local mechanical conditions, it is shown that such a model can describe accurately the peculiar contractile properties of insect fibrillar muscle for small length changes. When appreciable sliding occurs, it is necessary to introduce further features into the model defining the rigidity of the bridges and the relationship between detachment probability and stress in the bridge. It is probably also necessary to specify the effect of exchange between bound and free ADP. There is evidence from studies of glycerinated water-bug fibres that the concentration of ADP in the solution does affect the contractile mechanism (Chaplain, 1966; Maruyama & Pringle, 1967), but these effects have not yet been studied in sufficient detail to permit them to be incorporated in a precise way into the model.

Applicability to other contractile tissues

The essential difference between this model and others that have been suggested for the mechanism of mechano-chemical transformation is that mechanical energy is generated by an active change of angle between the myosin and actin molecules at their site of interaction. Other models that have located the mechanical energy generator in the bridges have supposed either that the force is generated at the base of the bridge (A. F. Huxley, 1957) or that the bridges shorten (Davies, 1963). Davies's model is rendered less probable by the demonstration that the angled attachment of myosin to actin in the actomyosin complex, and of bridges to thin filaments in myofibrils in rigor, is in the wrong sense to permit tension to be generated by bridge shortening. Any hypothesis involving movement of bridges of fixed projecting length is vulnerable to the objections of Elliott (1967).

Similarities in the properties of contractile proteins prepared from different muscles make it desirable that any hypothesis about the generation of mechanical energy in striated muscles should be applicable also to other contractile tissues. We have seen that polarized actin filaments are the elements most consistently present and the model is therefore applicable to other muscles. It is the polarity of the actin that determines the direction of sliding and it is not an essential feature of the model that there should be polarized myosin filaments in which all the molecules have the same polarity throughout the overlap region. If the flexible portion of the myosin molecule has rotational as well as lateral freedom of movement, the correct orientation of the actin-combining sites at the ends of the bridges could be achieved whatever the orientation of the LMM segments in the backbone. The probability of attachment would presumably be greatly reduced, but would still be finite.

The thick filaments of the striated heart muscles and obliquely striated adductor muscles of Mollusca do not show any 'pseudo-H' region bare of cross-bridges in the middle of the filament, nor any other sign that the myosin molecules in the two halves are arranged with opposite polarity (Twarog, 1967). In the very thick paramyosin filaments of molluscan unstriated muscles there is also no sign of a different arrangement of the constituent molecules in different parts of the filament structure. In these filaments the myosin molecules may be associated laterally without preferred orientation; sliding in a particular direction will still occur by the mechanism proposed, the polarized actin filaments attaching preferentially to those myosins which have the correct orientation.

On this view, striation is seen primarily as a way of organizing the polarity of the myosin molecules so as to increase the probability of attach-

ment in the overlap regions. In paramyosin muscles with long thick filaments, the total distance over which sliding can occur will be greater,
though the velocity of movement will be less. In striated muscles with full
polarization of the myosins, sliding will be faster since all the myosins can
combine with actin in the overlap regions. If there is also a perfect hexagonal
array and corresponding azimuthal symmetry within the thick filaments
another degree of freedom is removed and the bridges can be restricted to
movement in a single plane. An interesting possibility is that association of
more than one myosin monomer in the formation of the cross-bridges in
insect muscles may be related to this final restriction of the freedom of
bridge movement.

Striation has evolved independently many times in the animal kingdom,
but the similarity between different striated muscles is not surprising if its
main functional advantage is the greater velocity of shortening made
possible by polarization of the myosin filaments. Its chief disadvantage is
that it limits the range of lengths over which the muscle can develop
tension. It also limits the total amount of possible shortening unless the
myosin filaments as well as the actin filaments can overlap in neighbouring
half-sarcomeres. Separation of the Z-line material into dense bodies permits this in some crustacean muscle, in which the numerous actin filaments
are associated in bundles at the ends of the sarcomeres (Hoyle & McAlear,
1963). Such a feature would be difficult in vertebrate striated muscles,
where the Z-line pattern allows maximal mutual association between actin
filaments from the two sarcomeres.

The model also offers a possible explanation of the mechanism of
mechano-chemical transformation in less highly organized tissues. Provided that polarized actin filaments are present and have some mechanical
connexion with the tissues surrounding the cell, the minimum further
requirement for an over-all change of shape by the cell is a myosin dimer,
so that a relative force can develop between actin filaments with opposite
polarity. With lateral association between the helical tails of the myosin
molecules, such a dimer would be of too small a size to be identifiable in
electron-micrographs, particularly if the tail of such primitive 'myosins'
was shorter than in the myosin of striated muscles. It may therefore not be
surprising that only actin filaments have been observed in some types of
vertebrate smooth muscle. At an even lower level of organization, a protein
resembling heavy meromyosin might exist without even the ability to
associate into a dimer. An active change in the angle of attachment of such
a molecule to the actin filaments when ATP is hydrolysed could produce
protoplasmic streaming past the filaments due to mobilization of the associate water molecules. Such a mechanism is therefore worth considering as

the general basis of cell motility. It provides a way of bringing the problem of motility into its logical relationship with that of enzyme activity in general, where there is beginning to be evidence for changes in protein configuration during the formation of the active complex with the substrate (Blake *et al.* 1967).

SUMMARY

1. A summary is given of some of the evidence for cyclic activity in the cross-bridges during the active contraction of striated muscles.

2. The molecular turnover frequency of the cyclic mechano-chemical process is low compared with that of most other enzymes and is related to the speed of shortening in normal muscles and to the optimum frequency of oscillation in insect fibrillar muscles.

3. A summary is given of the molecular structure of the filaments of striated muscles, with a new interpretation of the structure of the vertebrate Z-line.

4. A model is proposed for the mechanism of generation of mechanical energy, based on an active change of the angle of attachment of the end of the myosin molecule to the polarized actin filament.

5. It is suggested that this model provides a common basis for the mechanism of cell motility at the molecular level.

REFERENCES

ABBOTT, R. H. (1968). D.Phil. thesis, Oxford University.
ASHHURST, D. E. (1967). *J. molec. Biol.* **27**, 385.
ASTBURY, W. T. (1947). *Proc. R. Soc.* B **134**, 303.
AUBER, J. & COUTEAUX, R. (1962). *C. r. Acad. Sci. Paris*, **254**, 3425.
AUBER, J. & COUTEAUX, R. (1963). *J. Microsc.* **2**, 309.
BÁRÁNY, M. (1967). *J. gen. Physiol.* **50**, 197.
BLAKE, C. C. F., JOHNSON, L. N., MAIR, G. A., NORTH, A. C. T., PHILLIPS, D. C. & SARMA, V. R. (1967). *Proc. R. Soc.* B **167**, 378.
BRISKEY, E. J., SERAYDARIAN, K. & MOMMAERTS, W. F. H. M. (1967). *Biochim. biophys. Acta* **133**, 424.
CAIN, D. F., INFANTE, A. A. & DAVIES, R. E. (1962). *Nature, Lond.* **196**, 214.
CARLSON, F. D., HARDY, DONNA J. & WILKIE, D. R. (1963). *J. gen. Physiol.* **46**, 851.
CHAPLAIN, R. A. (1966). *Archs Biochem. Biophys.* **115**, 450.
CHAPLAIN, R. A. & TREGEAR, R. T. (1966). *J. molec. Biol.* **21**, 275.
DAVIES, R. E. (1963). *Nature, Lond.* **199**, 1068–74.
DAVIES, R. E. (1965). In *Muscle*, p. 49. Ed. W. M. Paul *et al.* Oxford: Pergamon Press.
ELLIOTT, G. F. (1967). *J. gen. Physiol.* **50**, 171.
ELLIOTT, G. F., LOWY, J. & MILLMAN, B. M. (1965). *Nature, Lond.* **206**, 1357.
FRANZINI-ARMSTRONG, CLARA & PORTER, K. R. (1964). *Z. Zellforsch. mikrosk. Anat.* **61**, 661.
GERGELY, J., PRAGAY, D., SCHOLZ, A. F., SEIDEL, J. C., SRETER, F. A. & THOMPSON, M. M. (1965). In *Molecular Biology of Muscular Contraction*, p. 149. Ed. S. Ebashi, F. Oosawa, T. Sekine and Y. Tonomura. Amsterdam: Elsevier.

GORDON, A. M., HUXLEY, A. F. & JULIAN, F. J. (1966). *J. Physiol., Lond.* **184**, 170.

HANSON, J. & LOWY, J. (1960). In *Structure and Function of Muscle*, vol. I, p. 265. G. H. Bourne. New York: Academic Press.

HANSON, J. & LOWY, J. (1961). *Proc. R. Soc.* B **154**, 173.

HANSON, J. & LOWY, J. (1963). *J. molec. Biol.* **6**, 46.

HANSON, J. & LOWY, J. (1964a). *Proc. R. Soc.* B **160**, 449.

HANSON, J. & LOWY, J. (1964b). *Proc. R. Soc.* B **160**, 523.

HILL, A. V. (1938). *Proc. R. Soc.* B **126**, 136.

HOYLE, G. & MCALEAR, J. H. (1963). *Science, N.Y.* **141**, 712.

HUXLEY, A. F. (1957). *Progr. Biophys.* **7**, 255.

HUXLEY, A. F. (1965). *Abstracts XXIIIrd Int. Congr. Physiol. Tokyo*, p. 36.

HUXLEY, A. F. & NIEDERGERCKE, R. (1954). *Nature, Lond.* **173**, 971.

HUXLEY, H. E. (1960). In *The Cell*, vol. IV, p. 365. Ed. J. Brachet and A. E. Mirsky.

HUXLEY, H. E. (1963). *J. molec. Biol.* **7**, 281.

HUXLEY, H. E. (1964). *Proc. R. Soc.* B **160**, 442.

HUXLEY, H. E. & BROWN, W. (1967). *J. molec. Biol.* **30**, 383.

HUXLEY, H. E., BROWN, W. & HOLMES, K. C. (1965). *Nature, Lond.*, **206**, 1358.

HUXLEY, H. E. & HANSON, J. (1954). *Nature, Lond.* **173**, 973.

KNAPPEIS, G. G. & CARLSEN, F. (1962). *J. cell Biol.* **13**, 323.

LONG, C. (editor) (1961). *The Biochemist's Handbook.* London: E. and F. N. Spon, Ltd.

LOWY, J. & HANSON, J. (1962). *Physiol. Rev.* **42** (Suppl. 5), 34.

MACHIN, K. E. & PRINGLE, J. W. S. (1960). *Proc. R. Soc.* B **152**, 311.

MANDELKERN, L. (1967). *J. gen. Physiol.* **50**, 29.

MARUYAMA, K. & PRINGLE, J. W. S. (1967). *Archs Biochem. Biophys.* **120**, 225.

MARUYAMA, K., PRINGLE, J. W. S. & TREGEAR, R. T. (1968). *Proc. R. Soc.* B **169**, 229.

MAZIA, D. (1967). *J. gen. Physiol.* **50**, 221.

NEEDHAM, D. M. & SHOENBERG, K. (1964). *Proc. R. Soc.* B **160**, 517.

PEPE, F. A. (1966). *J. Cell Biol.* **28**, 505.

PEPE, F. A. (1967). *J. molec. Biol.* **27**, 203, 227.

PRINGLE, J. W. S. (1967a). *Progr. Biophys. molec. Biol.* **17**, 1.

PRINGLE, J. W. S. (1967b). *J. gen. Physiol.* **50**, 139.

PRYOR, M. G. M. (1950). *Progr. Biophys.* **1**, 216.

REEDY, M. K. (1964). Fine structure of the Z band. *Proc. R. Soc.* B **160**, 458.

REEDY, M. K. (1967a). *J. molec. Biol.* **31**, 155.

REEDY, M. K. (1967b). *Am. Zoologist* **7**, 465.

REEDY, M. K., HOLMES, K. C. & TREGEAR, R. T. (1965). *Nature, Lond.* **207**, 1276.

REGER, J. F. & COOPER, D. P. (1967). *J. Cell. Biol.* **33**, 531.

ROSENBLUTH, J. (1967). *J. Cell Biol.* **34**, 15.

RÜEGG, J. C. (1967). *Am. Zoologist* **7**, 457.

RÜEGG, J. C. & TREGEAR, R. T. (1966). *Proc. R. Soc.* B **165**, 497.

SHOENBERG, C. F. (1965). *Nature, Lond.* **206**, 526.

SHOENBERG, C. F., RÜEGG, J. C., NEEDHAM, D. M., SCHIRMER, R. H. & NEMETCHEK-GENSLER, H. (1966). *Biochem. Z.* **345**, 255.

THORSON, J. & WHITE, D. C. S. (1968). *Proc. R. Soc.* B (in the Press).

TREGEAR, R. T. (1968). *Bioenergetics* **2**, 269.

TWAROG, BETTY M. (1967). *J. gen. Physiol.* **50**, 157.

WEIS-FOGH, T. (1956). *J. exp. Biol.* **33**, 668.

WHITE, D. C. S. (1967). D.Phil. thesis, Oxford University.

WILKIE, D. R. (1954). *Progr. Biophys. biophys. Chem.* **4**, 288.

PLATE I

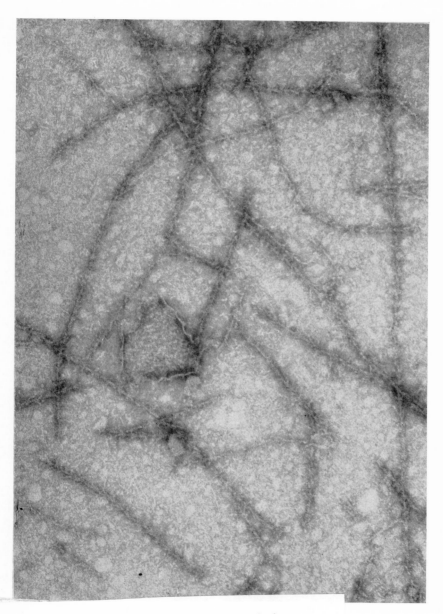

The caption for the plate facing page 86 is missing.
It should read:

Actomyosin from water-bug flight muscle, showing pola-
rized arrow-head appearance; from a preparation in 0·6M
KCl, negatively stained with uranyl acetate, x 91,000
(Maruyama and Ashhurst, unpublished).

MEMBRANE SYSTEMS IN MUSCLE CELLS

By R. J. PODOLSKY

National Institute of Arthritis and Metabolic Diseases,
National Institutes of Health, Bethesda, Maryland 20014

In muscle cells the myofilaments are enclosed in a complex system of membranes that plays an important role in controlling contraction. The outer surface of the cell is formed by an electrically polarized membrane with properties similar to those of unmyelinated nerve cells. In frog fast muscle fibres, which were used in all the experiments I shall discuss here, the volume within the cell is divided into two spaces: (1) that containing the myofilaments (MF) and (2) that enclosed by the membranes of the sarcoplasmic reticulum (SR) (Plate 1). To a certain extent, the SR is divided into segments which bear a 1:1 relation to the striation pattern, but longitudinal connexions between segments also occur quite frequently, and it is possible that the entire SR forms a single network (Peachey, 1965). The terminal sacs of the SR segments are in close contact with transverse tubules that are continuous with the outer membrane (Huxley, 1964) and which conduct the influence of depolarization to the inner parts of the cell (Huxley & Taylor, 1958). As there are relatively few mitochondria, and since the area of the internal membranes is several hundred times greater than that of the outer membrane (Peachey, 1965), elements of the internal membrane system clearly make up the bulk of the membranous components of the cell.

SKINNED MUSCLE FIBRES

Many lines of experimentation show that the activity cycle depends on movements of calcium ions between the SR and MF spaces. It will not be possible to discuss methods using either autoradiography of muscle fibres fixed in various states of contraction (Winegrad, 1965a) or spectrophotometry of cells loaded with a calcium indicator (Jöbsis & O'Connor, 1966), but processes involved in these intracellular translocations can be conveniently examined in muscle fibre segments from which the surface membrane has been dissected away, and I would like to describe some of these studies in detail. The main advantage of using such 'skinned fibre' preparations is that solutions can be applied directly to the MF space and to the surfaces of the internal membranes which border on that space.

The preparation, which is due to Natori (1954), is shown in Fig. 1. A bundle of fibres is cut out of a frog muscle in Ringer solution (Fig. 1a).

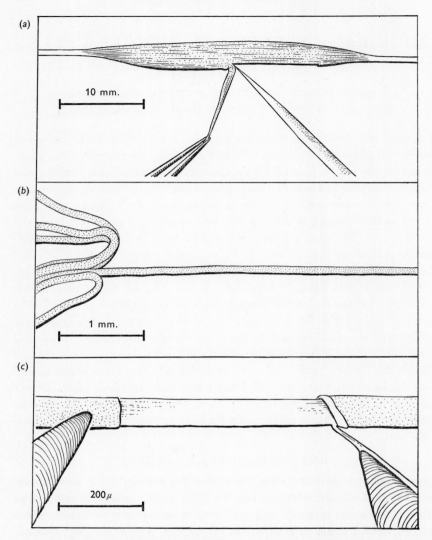

Fig. 1. Technique for preparing 'skinned' muscle fibres. (*a*) Dissection of fibre bundle from muscle; (*b*) isolation of single fibre in oil; (*c*) removal of surface membrane and some superficial myofibrils.

The bundle is blotted, laid on a glass slide, covered with paraffin oil, and one of the fibres is isolated along several millimetres of its length (Fig. 1*b*). Then the outer membrane and possibly some superficial myofibrils are teased off with a sharpened steel needle (Fig. 1*c*). The entire procedure takes only a few minutes.

Electron microscopy shows that the dissection does not affect the morphology of either the myofibrils or the internal membrane system (Plate 2). The triads described by Porter & Palade (1957), consisting of a transverse tubule flanked by two terminal sacs of the SR, are well preserved. The longitudinally orientated SR elements that connect the terminal sacs at opposite ends of the sarcomere are also essentially the same as in intact fibres. In sections that include the periphery of the preparation the internal membranes are often vesiculated near the surface, and it seems likely that some of the broken ends of the transverse tubules may seal themselves off after the outer membrane is dissected away.

ACTIVATION

The calcium for normal activation is stored within the SR. This can be visualized in the electron microscope by perfusing skinned fibres with oxalate, which forms an electron-dense precipitate with calcium. The section shown in Plate 3 was not stained (since this procedure dissolves the oxalate deposits) but sufficient contrast is present to make out the main structural features. The deposits are found only in the SR and appear to be restricted to the terminal sacs (Costantin, Franzini-Armstrong & Podolsky, 1965). Although such local precipitation techniques are rich with possibilities for artifact, the result appears to have been confirmed by the autoradiographic studies of Winegrad (1965 b), which showed that the ^{45}Ca picked up by intact fibres from a labelled Ringer solution is also localized in areas that correspond to the terminal sacs of the SR.

During normal activation, calcium associated with the SR is made available to the myofilaments. The first step in this process is depolarization of the outer membrane. The proximity of the terminal sacs of the SR to the tubules that conduct this depolarization inward suggests that an electrical stimulus might trigger the release of calcium from the SR. Although their experiments were interpreted along different lines, reports by Csapo (1959) and by Natori & Isojima (1962) that local contractions can be elicited in skinned fibres by longitudinal electric currents appear to provide evidence for this idea, and therefore it seemed worth while to examine these electrical effects more closely. However, before turning to that, I would like to describe briefly the response of skinned fibres to added calcium ions, since this is important for an understanding of other activating stimuli.

Calcium response

The contractile mechanism is directly activated by calcium ions (Heilbrunn & Wiercinski, 1947; Niedergerke, 1955; Podolsky & Hubert, 1961). By applying calcium with a micropipette, any part of a fibre can be activated. Provided the added calcium makes contact with the myofilaments, it makes no difference whether the fibre is skinned or unskinned. The response is always maximal at the site of application, is completely reversible, and can be repeated many times. When a calcium droplet is applied to the surface of a skinned fibre, contraction is limited to the region near the droplet (Plate 4). Its time course and extent indicate that relaxation is due to removal of calcium by an intracellular sink rather than by diffusion into the bulk of the fibre (Podolsky & Costantin, 1964).

Electrical response

Turning now to the response of skinned fibres to current flow, this differs from the calcium response primarily in being very patchy and usually much less repeatable. The study by L. L. Costantin and myself (Costantin & Podolsky, 1967) was made by passing current pulses between silver wire electrodes in contact with the two ends of the preparation. To avoid artifacts due to the electrodes *per se*, the wires were placed at least 1 mm away from the skinned region. A typical response is shown on the left in Plate 5. Although the current is presumably uniformly distributed along the cross-section of the fibre, contraction in these experiments occurs only at one or two regions in several millimetres of skinned fibre, and over just a few sarcomeres in each region. Larger currents increase the number of contracting sarcomeres at a given responsive region, and often activate additional regions, but contraction over the entire skinned region was never seen even with currents 100 times greater than the threshold value.

These local responses to current flow appear to be initiated by depolarization of the internal membrane system. They do not occur in unskinned fibre segments, where the internal membranes would be expected to be already depolarized. Presumably removal of the surface membrane makes it possible for the internal membranes to develop a membrane potential, perhaps because broken ends of the transverse tubules seal off, isolating certain parts of the internal membrane system with respect to ion flow. This idea was tested further by preparing skinned fibres from muscles that had been treated with strophanthidin at concentration levels known to block the active Na/K exchange process; such preparations should not be able to develop potentials across their internal membranes after skinning. It was found that the response to current flow was indeed absent in these preparations, and that responsiveness could be restored by washing away the strophanthidin. It seems fair to conclude, then, that polarization of the internal membranes is a prerequisite for the local response to current flow, and therefore that the response itself is probably due to a change in this potential.

Ionic response

Another conventional method for changing membrane potential is to change the ionic distribution across the membrane. This technique can be used to examine the internal membranes of muscle fibres since ionic concentrations on the side that borders the MF space can easily be altered by applying *relatively large* droplets of appropriate solutions to the surface of a skinned fibre in oil. The main result of a systematic study of the effects of various monovalent ions is that appropriate solutions can activate the contractile mechanism through an indirect rather than a direct mechanism, and that this indirect mechanism is probably the same as that underlying the electrical response (Costantin & Podolsky, 1967). Thus, like the electrical effect but unlike the calcium effect, only certain regions are responsive. These often turn out to be the same regions that are activated by electric current, and in some preparations the actual distribution of the contraction through the volume of the fibre is strikingly similar in the two cases (Plate 5) (Costantin & Podolsky, 1965). Again in contrast to the action of added calcium ions, the ionic response can spread away from the applied droplet, and can do so asymmetrically (Plate 6) as well as symmetrically, showing that responsiveness is not uniformly distributed throughout the preparation.

The specificity of the ionic response—KCl and Tris propionate are both effective, but K propionate is not—indicates that the effective ions act by changing the membrane potential across the internal membrane system. The argument is shown diagrammatically in Fig. 2. In Fig. 2a, the shaded region is the MF space; the unshaded region represents the lumen of the responsive element. Figures 2b–d show the changes that take place when a relatively large droplet of isotonic salt solution is added. The normal ionic composition of the MF space should be close to that of the intact fibre; that is, high in K^+ and low in Cl^-. When the added droplet contains KCl, the K^+ concentration in the MF space will be essentially unchanged but the Cl^- concentration will increase; if the membrane of the responsive element is permeable to Cl^-, the change in Cl^- concentration will increase the potential of the MF space relative to the lumen of the responsive element (Fig. 2b). The same polarity will develop when a droplet of Tris propionate is added if the membrane is also permeable to K^+, since diffusion of K^+ into the added volume will lower the K^+ concentration in the MF space. Lowering the Cl^- concentration should have relatively little effect on the membrane potential, as the Cl^- concentration is already low (Fig. 2c). For the same reasons, addition of K propionate should have no effect on the membrane potential (Fig. 2d). The potential change produced by the KCl and Tris propionate will lower the existing potential, and presumably release calcium, if the MF space were normally negative with respect to the lumen, as would be the case if an active transport mechanism cleared K+ ions from the lumen.

Although these experiments do not identify the responsive element, they strongly suggest that calcium release from the SR is controlled by internal

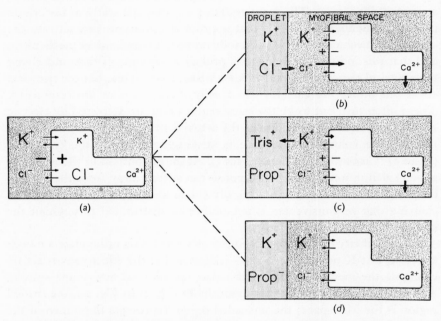

Fig. 2. Interpretation of response of skinned fibre in oil to application of relatively large droplets of isotonic salt solutions. (*a*) Relative concentrations of K+, Cl−, and Ca²⁺ in the myofibril space (shaded) and internal membrane bounded space (unshaded). (*b–d*) Ionic movements due to applied droplets and the resulting potential changes across the internal membranes. Calcium permeability of the internal membrane system appears to be correlated with a decrease in the internal membrane potential (*b* and *c*).

membrane potentials. Since the electrical and ionic effects are similar in many respects, the responsive element is more likely to be the SR than the transverse tubules because the dimensions of the tubules appear to be too small for uniform longitudinal currents to produce much of a voltage change (Costantin & Podolsky, 1967).

Several important questions remain unsettled. One is how, during normal activation, the potential change conducted inward along the transverse tubules is coupled to the SR. A possibility suggested by morphological considerations is that the triadic junction may function as a 'tight junction' (Fahrenbach, 1965), in which case the two potentials would be electrically coupled, but no functional evidence for this view has been put forward as yet.

Another puzzling question is why the electrical and ionic responses are so patchy. This might be a subtle matter of experimental technique, since Natori (1965) has demonstrated that, in skinned fibre preparations from the Japanese toad, electrically activated contractions occasionally propagate as a 'bead' along the entire skinned region, moving from the anode to the cathode. Further studies along these lines would certainly be of interest. However, it is worth pointing out that the patchiness in our experiments turned out to be a very useful property, since it enabled us to establish a relation between the electrical and ionic responses, and to distinguish both of these from the direct action of calcium on the myofibrils.

RELAXATION

Turning now to the relaxation process, it is clear that in order for muscles to contract many times, calcium released from the SR must ultimately be replaced. Since isolated membranes form vesicles that can accumulate Ca^{2+} (Hasselbach & Makinose, 1961; Ebashi & Lipmann, 1962) and reduce the calcium concentration in the medium to very low levels, it is generally supposed that the SR re-accumulates Ca^{2+} released into the MF space, allowing relaxation to take place. The possibility that relaxation is modulated by a soluble factor in the MF space has also been considered, but the evidence on this point is not very substantial.

The capacity of the fibre to sequester calcium (in addition to the amount normally present) can be estimated by means of the technique shown in Plate 7. The preparation in this case is a short, isolated segment of skinned fibre. Such segments remain relaxed for about 30 min., after which time they spontaneously shorten down to average sarcomere lengths of about 0.6μ. Before this time, however, it is possible to titrate the segments with droplets of calcium-containing solutions. The amount of calcium in each droplet is estimated from the composition of the applied solution and droplet volume, which is generally substantially less than the segment volume. Initially, the segment relaxes after the contraction elicited by each droplet (Plate 7). As the applied calcium accumulates, a point is reached where relaxation either becomes very incomplete or the fibre segment collapses. Using this as an end-point, the data shown in Fig. 3 were obtained. The wide range of results can be accounted for in part by the fact that each run gives only a lower limit to the amount of additional calcium that can be inactivated by the fibre, as the preparations contract spontaneously after some time. The maximum value of about $1 \mu M$

calcium/ml. fibre is probably the best estimate of the excess capacity, which is greater than the amount of calcium required to saturate the actomyosin (Weber, Herz & Reiss, 1963) by about a factor of 5 to 10.

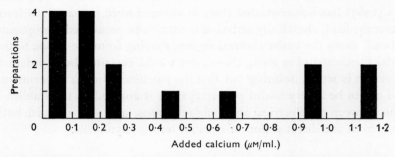

Fig. 3. Capacity of skinned fibre segments for calcium. Abscissa is total amount of calcium added to preparation by means of the technique shown in Plate 7 before the ability to relax was substantially reduced; the upper limit is close to 1 μM/ml. fibre.

PERFUSED SKINNED FIBRES

In the experiments I have described so far, the preparations were in all cases immersed in oil and activation was monitored by the contraction it produced. Since local movements are rather difficult to measure quantitatively, it seemed worth while devising a system in which force rather than displacement could be recorded, which would require that test solutions be applied by perfusion rather than locally as droplets. Until recently this approach was not feasible, since the contractile mechanism is activated by concentrations of calcium ions smaller than the trace levels introduced by the other reagents in the perfusion solution. However, the technique could be worked out when it became possible to control the calcium ion concentration in the perfusion solution with EGTA (ethyleneglycol bis (amino ethyl ether) tetra-acetic acid), a chelating agent with a much higher affinity for Ca^{2+} than the other important ions in the muscle system.

A second technical problem was to make the perfusion uniform over the length of the preparation. This, of course, is one of the main functions of the SR in the intact cell. With an isolated fibre segment the perfusion will be sufficiently uniform if the length of the preparation is restricted to about 1 mm and the solution changes are made very quickly.

The apparatus developed by D. C. Hellam and myself is shown diagrammatically in Fig. 4. The preparation G is held by two fine forceps, F and J. One of these, F, is suspended by leaf springs, A and A', which bend towards the preparation when force is developed, moving vane B across light beam C. The change in light intensity, which is monitored by a photodiode, is proportional to the contractile force. Perfusion solutions are contained in wells milled in plastic block *I* (only one, *H*, is shown). The wells are all covered by a common layer of oil *E*. Test solutions are changed by lowering the block until the preparation leaves the perfusion solution and enters the oil layer, moving a well containing another perfusion solution under the preparation, and then raising the block again. The actual solution change takes place in the final step of this manœuvre, which can be done very quickly.

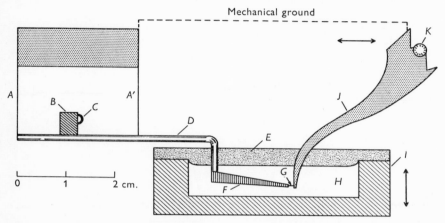

Fig. 4. Apparatus for measuring isometric force developed by skinned muscle fibre *G* perfused with solution *H*. See text for details.

When fibre segments are perfused with physiological solutions (120–140 mM-KCl, 1 mM-MgCl$_2$, 5 mM ATP, pH 7·0) they produce forces in the normal range (*c.* 2·5 kg./cm.^{2}) when the calcium concentration exceeds 1 μM; half-maximal force is developed at a concentration of about 0·1 μM (Hellam & Podolsky, 1966). The dependence of force upon *p*-Ca in this system is close to that found by Weber & Herz (1963) for calcium binding to isolated myofibrils. The segments can be relaxed by reducing the calcium concentration, and can be carried through several contraction cycles.

EGTA KINETICS

When the perfusion technique worked well enough for us to begin analysing the kinetics of force development, we were at first puzzled by the fact that minutes rather than seconds were often required for steady forces to develop. Such delays seemed much too long to be attributable to diffusion effects, particularly since there is no reason to believe that either Ca-EGTA or EGTA, the two main species in the calcium buffer system, interacts with either the myofilaments or the internal membranes. It soon became apparent, however, that the Ca^{2+} concentration established by the Ca-EGTA system within the fibre is probably substantially lower than that in the perfusion solution, and that this difference is associated with calcium transport by the SR. This would be the case, for example, if the buffer system equilibrated slowly compared with the rate of calcium uptake by the SR.

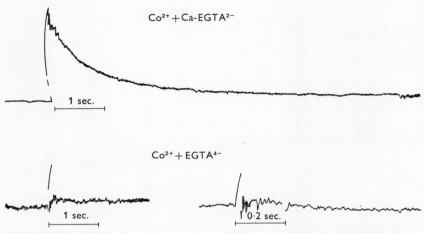

Fig. 5. Kinetics of calcium displacement from the Ca-EGTA complex by cobalt. Reaction followed by absorption change at 600 mμ. Initial conditions: (top) 10 mM Ca-EGTA, 12·5 mM-Co(acetate)$_2$, 200 mM-K cacodylate; (bottom) 10 mM EGTA, 12·5 mM-Co-(acetate)$_2$, 200 mM-K cacodylate; all runs made at pH 7·0 and 25° C.

When calcium is being removed from solution, the rate-limiting step in buffer equilibration is the dissociation of the Ca-EGTA complex. To confirm the suspicion that dissociation is relatively slow, R. L. Berger and I measured the displacement rate of the calcium ion in the EGTA complex by cobalt, which has a greater stability constant. Since rates of complex formation are generally very fast, and since one of the mechanisms for the displacement reaction is dissociation of the calcium complex followed by formation of the cobalt complex, the displacement rate clearly sets an upper limit for the rate we are interested in. The actual dissociation rate may be much slower than this if other reaction mechanisms figure prominently in the displacement process.

Figure 5 shows some data collected with these ideas in mind. The traces show light absorption at 600 mμ following quick mixing of cobalt ions with either Ca-EGTA or EGTA. The absorption change is due to the spectral shift of the cobalt ion associated with complex formation.

The lower traces show that the binding of the cobalt ion to EGTA alone is indeed rapid. The upper trace shows that the half-time for the over-all displacement reaction is about 0·5 sec. Dissociation of the Ca-EGTA complex is at least as slow as this process; it could be considerably slower if, for instance, the direct attack of cobalt on the calcium complex contributed appreciably to the over-all reaction. In any event, it is clear that the Ca-EGTA system may not be able to maintain a constant level of calcium ions in the face of rapid calcium uptake.

KINETICS OF FORCE DEVELOPMENT IN SKINNED FIBRES

Returning now to the perfused skinned fibre systems, in many runs the time course of force development was unusual in the sense that the force remained close to zero for many seconds and then rose rather suddenly to a steady value. Such force patterns indicate that the Ca-EGTA buffer system is not at equilibrium within the fibre, for if it were the force should have reached a steady value in the inward diffusion time (about 0·2 sec. in a 70 μ diameter preparation). The data suggest that the intracellular Ca^{2+} remains below the contraction threshold as long as the SR accumulates calcium faster than it can be supplied through dissociation of the Ca-EGTA complex, and that force develops when this process can no longer keep the free calcium concentration below the level necessary for contraction.

This interpretation is supported by the time course of calcium uptake by the fibre from a ^{45}Ca-labelled solution buffered with EGTA to a calcium concentration well above the contraction threshold. C. Parsons and I found that the major part of this uptake takes place during the delay phase (Fig. 6). The appearance of force is associated with a marked decrease in the accumulation rate, at which time the calcium concentration within the fibre would be expected to approach that of the perfusion solution. The preferential uptake of calcium by the internal membranes shows directly that their affinity for calcium is greater than that of the myofilaments. This, of course, is consistent with the demonstration by Weber and her associates (Weber et al. 1963) that reticular fragments have a higher affinity for calcium than isolated myofibrils.

Another indication that the production of force in these preparations is delayed until the SR is practically saturated is the observation by L. E. Ford and myself that the delay becomes longer when, at a given p-Ca, the total EGTA concentration is reduced. This would be expected to decrease the rate at which calcium ions are supplied by dissociation of the Ca-EGTA

7

complex and therefore to prolong the time required to fill the SR. In the same way, the delay is increased when, at a given total EGTA concentration, the p-Ca is increased.

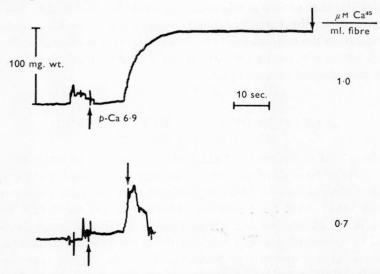

Fig. 6. Force developed by perfused skinned muscle fibre. Runs made with segments from the same fibre. Segment transferred from relaxing solution (p-Ca = 9) to ^{45}Ca-labelled contracting solution (p-Ca = 6·9) at time marked by upward arrow, and removed from this solution at time marked by downward arrow. Segment in upper record kept in contracting solution for 60 sec; force appeared after a delay of about 10 sec. Segment in lower record removed from contracting solution at the end of the delay phase. ^{45}Ca uptake per millimetre of fibre segment (μM/ml. fibre) assayed after a several-second rinse in relaxing solution followed by dehydration in alcohol. Perfusion solution: 120 mM-KCl, 1 mM-MgCl$_2$, 5 mM ATP, 4 mM (Ca-EGTA+EGTA), 10 mM imidazole, pH 7·0, 20° C. Fibre diameter (approximate), 70 μ.

The final uptake level of ^{45}Ca corresponds to about 1 μm calcium/ml. fibre, which is essentially the same as the maximum amount of calcium that could be added to skinned fibre segments in oil before they collapsed. This agreement is informative since a soluble relaxing factor would have been lost in the perfused system but retained in preparations kept in oil, enhancing their ability to inactivate added calcium. As no substantial enhancement was seen in the latter series, relaxation appears to be due primarily to calcium uptake by the SR.

SUMMARY

In the resting cell, calcium appears to be stored in the terminal sacs of the SR, close to the transverse tubules that carry the influence of depolarization of the outer membrane to the cell interior. Since muscle fibres from which the outer membrane has been removed can be activated by depolarizing stimuli, movement of this calcium into the MF space is probably controlled by the potential across the SR membrane. This raises the possibility that the membrane potential of the SR may be directly coupled to that of the surface membrane, but there is no clear evidence on this point.

Calcium in the MF space can bind to the myofilaments only transiently, since the affinity of the internal membrane system for calcium exceeds that of the myofilaments. Calcium can be taken up by the SR until the average concentration in the fibre is about 1 mM. No evidence was found for a soluble calcium complexing factor.

These observations are all in accord with the thesis that activation of muscle fibres is due to movement of calcium ions from the SR into the MF space, and that relaxation is due to calcium movement in the reverse direction.

REFERENCES

COSTANTIN, L. L., FRANZINI-ARMSTRONG, C. & PODOLSKY, R. J. (1965). *Science, Washington,* **147**, 158.

COSTANTIN, L. L. & PODOLSKY, R. J. (1965). *Fedn Proc.* **24**, 1141.

COSTANTIN, L. L. & PODOLSKY, R. J. (1967). *J. gen. Physiol.* **50**, 1101.

CSAPO, A. (1959). *Ann. N.Y. Acad. Sci.* **81**, 453.

EBASHI, S. & LIPMANN, F. (1962). *J. Cell Biol.* **14**, 389.

FAHRENBACH, W. H. (1965). *Science, Washington,* **147**, 1308.

HASSELBACH, W. & MAKINOSE, M. (1961). *Biochem. Z.* **333**, 518.

HEILBRUNN, L. V. & WIERCINSKI, F. J. (1947). *J. cell comp. Physiol.* **29**, 15.

HELLAM, D. C. & PODOLSKY, R. J. (1966). *Fedn Proc.* **25**, 466.

HUXLEY, A. F. & TAYLOR, R. E. (1958). *J. Physiol., Lond.* **144**, 426.

HUXLEY, H. E. (1964). *Nature, Lond.* **202**, 1067.

JÖBSIS, F. F. & O'CONNOR, M. J. (1966). *Biochem. biophys. Res. Commun.* **25**, 246.

NATORI, R. (1954). *Jikeikai med. J.* **1**, 119.

NATORI, R. (1965). *Jikeikai med. J.* **12**, 214.

NATORI, R. & ISOJIMA, C. (1962). *Jikeikai med. J.* **9**, 1.

NIEDERGERKE, R. (1955). *J. Physiol., Lond.* **128**, 12–13 P.

PEACHEY, L. D. (1965). *J. Cell Biol.* **25**, 209.

PODOLSKY, R. J. & COSTANTIN, L. L. (1964). *Fedn Proc.* **23**, 933.

PODOLSKY, R. J. & HUBERT, C. E. (1961). *Fedn Proc.* **20**, 301.

PORTER, K. R. & PALADE, G. E. (1957). *J. biophys. biochem. Cytol.* **3**, 269.

WEBER, A. & HERZ, R. (1963). *J. biol. Chem.* **238**, 599.

WEBER, A., HERZ, R. & REISS, I. (1963). *J. gen. Physiol.* **46**, 679.

WINEGRAD, S. (1965 a). *J. gen. Physiol.* **48**, 455.

WINEGRAD, S. (1965 b). *J. gen. Physiol.* **48**, 997.

PLATE I

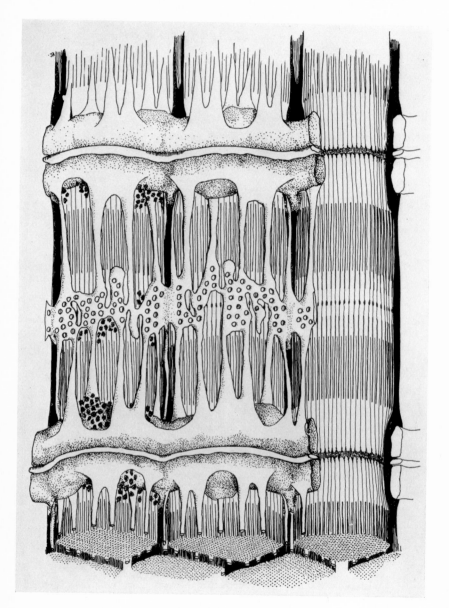

Three-dimensional reconstruction of the internal membranes associated with seacvel myofibrils in the frog fast muscle fibre. The major features are the segments of the sarcoplasmic reticulum and the transverse tubules. (Reprinted by permission of the Rockefeller University Press from *J. Cell Biol.* **25** (1963), 209.)

PLATE 2

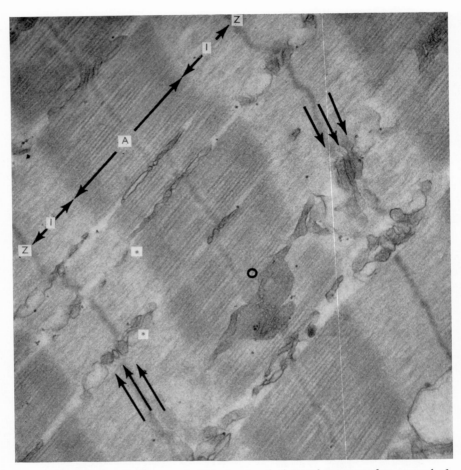

Longitudinal section of a frog muscle fibre showing the internal structure after removal of the sarcolemma. The A, I, and Z bands of the myofibrils are marked for reference. The interfibrillar space contains triads (three arrows) at the level of the Z lines; the central element of the triad is a section through the transverse tubular system and the lateral elements are formed by terminal sacs of the sarcoplasmic reticulum. Along the A band are longitudinally orientated elements of the sarcoplasmic reticulum (asterisks) which connect the terminal sacs at opposite ends of the sarcomere and fuse together to form a flattened cisterna in the middle of the sarcomere (○). × 34,000. (Costantin *et al.* 1965.)

PLATE 5

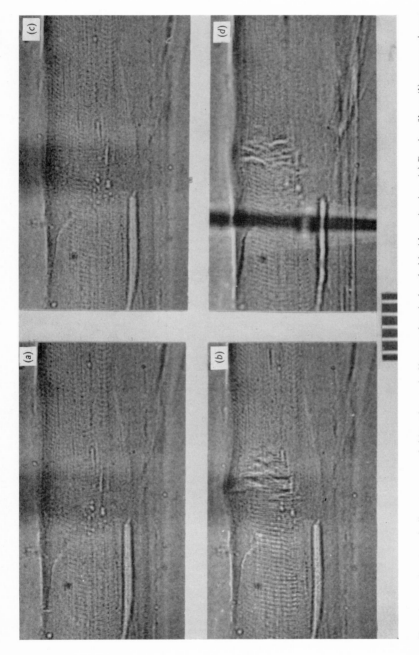

Experiment showing similar response of skinned muscle fibre to electrical and chloride activation. (a) Resting fibre; (b) same region at peak of contraction during 1 sec. pulse of 6·7 μA.; (c) same region following cessation of electric stimulation; (d) same region at the peak of contraction about 1 sec. following application of 1·2 mμl. of 140 mM-KCl to the preparation. Vertical shadow near centre of each field is out-of-focus image of micropipette containing KCl solution. Grid spacing, 10μ. (Costantin & Podolsky, 1965.)

PLATE 6

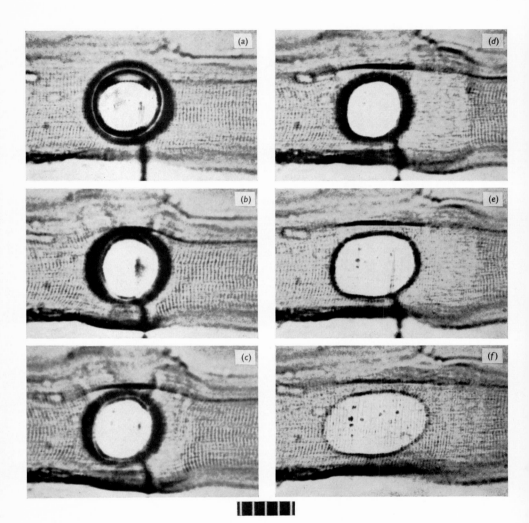

Response of skinned muscle fibre to a KCl droplet. (*a*) Initial contact of 0·3 mµl. droplet of 140 mM KCl with surface of skinned fibre; (*b–f*) 0·5, 1, 2, 3 and 4 sec. following droplet contact. Note asymmetrical distribution of contraction about region of droplet application. Grid spacing, 10 µ. (Costantin & Podolsky, 1967.)

PLATE 7

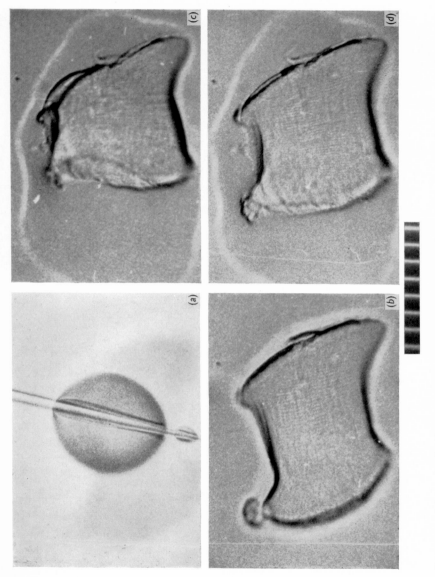

Response of frog muscle fibre segment in oil to calcium loading. (a) Droplet of $CaCl_2$ (1 mM)+NaCl (140 mM) formed at tip of micropipette in oil. (b–d) Skinned muscle fibre segment (b) before application of droplet; (c) about 5 sec. after contact of droplet, at peak of contraction; (d) at end of relaxation; relaxation was half complete in about 3 sec. Grid spacing, 10μ. (Podolsky & Costantin, 1964)

MECHANISMS OF SPERM MOVEMENT

By C. J. BROKAW

Division of Biology, California Institute of Technology
Pasadena, California

I would like to approach the problem of the mechanisms of flagellar motility by looking first at the morphology of flagellar movement, then discussing some recent studies on the biochemistry of flagellar movement, and finally discussing two very simple theoretical models which illustrate some of the problems involved in trying to reach an understanding of what we know about flagellar movement. Although this discussion will be largely based on observations on the movement of sea-urchin spermatozoa, which is relatively simple because the flagellum bends predominantly in one plane, I do not think they are unique. The objective is an understanding of the mechanisms of flagellar movement which can be applied to all eucellular flagella and cilia, and their diverse movements.

THE MORPHOLOGY OF MOVEMENT

Recent high-resolution photomicrographs of swimming spermatozoa from sea urchins and some other marine invertebrates (Brokaw, 1965) and of a protozoan flagellum (Brokaw & Wright, 1963) show that the undulations of the flagellum are not sinusoidal, as suggested in Sir James Gray's pioneering study (Gray, 1955). Instead, the flagellum shows bent regions of uniform curvature, forming circular arcs, separated by short regions which are not bent. Examples of this type of photograph are shown in Plate 1 a–c, and an interpretative diagram is shown in Fig. 1. Not all flagella show bending waves such as these, in which the radius of curvature of the bent regions remains constant as the waves pass along the flagellum. For example, in bull spermatozoa, the amplitude and curvature of the waves increase as they are propagated along the tail (Gray, 1958; Rikmenspoel, 1965). However, in those bending waves which do contain bent regions of constant curvature it is easy to see two significant characteristics of the movement:

(1) The constant curvature within a bent region indicates that the shape of a bent flagellum is not significantly influenced by the bending moment resulting from external viscous resistance as the flagellum moves through its supporting medium, since the magnitude and direction of this bending moment will vary along the length of the flagellum. In other words, the

bent flagellum is very stiff (Brokaw, 1965). A similarly high stiffness is also required for the straight portion of a cilium during its effective stroke (Brokaw, 1966b). Since the work which would be required to bend a flagellum or cilium with this high stiffness is large compared to the work which is done against the viscous resistance of the medium, this stiffness is probably not due to structures in parallel with the bending mechanism, but represents instead a property of the inactive state of the bending mechanism.

(2) The constant curvature within a bent region indicates that the amount of bending, indicated by the radius of curvature, at a particular point on the flagellum does not change between the time it becomes bent and the time that it unbends. The time sequence of events at any point on

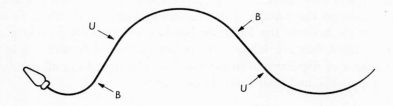

Fig. 1. Interpretative diagram showing the form of the flagellum of a swimming sea-urchin spermatozoon. The arrows mark the points of bending (B) and unbending (U) where there are rather abrupt transitions between bent and straight states of the flagellum, as the bends pass backwards along the flagellum.

the flagellum is thus a relatively simple alternation between bent and unbent states, and very little information is required to control the sequence. Propagated bending waves are generated as rather abrupt transitions between bent and unbent states and move from point to point along the flagellum.

These two conclusions rest on the elimination of a more trivial explanation for the constant curvature observed with a bent region—the possibility that the bending mechanism or the internal resistance to bending is simply non-linear, so that it becomes much more difficult for the flagellum to bend once it has bent to its normal radius of curvature. This explanation appears to be precluded by observations that sperm flagella can produce bends having a much greater curvature, particularly when swimming in more viscous solutions as shown in Plate 1d (Brokaw, 1965, 1966c). These observations require that the bending mechanism must be able to generate different degrees of bending at any particular point on the flagellum, and must therefore have a mechanism to control this capability, so that it is an oversimplification to think in terms of an alternation between only two possible states of the flagellum.

Thinking about flagellar bending waves in terms of propagated bending and unbending transitions has the advantage that it can easily be extended to ciliary beat patterns and to asymmetrical flagellar beat patterns, such as those illustrated in Plate 1 e and f. These asymmetrical patterns are often found with glycerinated spermatozoa at low ATP concentrations, but it is only rarely that a glycerinated spermatozoon is found moving without a head, so that the behaviour of the leading end of the flagellum can be clearly photographed. Although this movement is certainly abnormal, it is not so very different from the asymmetrical bending which a cilium might undergo (Sleigh, 1962), and there is no reason to expect it to occur by a mechanism other than the normal one for bend propagation. My interpretation of photographs such as these is that a bend on the flagellum is self-propagating, and is not dependent upon mechanical interaction with bending occurring on other parts of the flagellum such as the basal end. This type of propagated bending appears to be difficult to interpret in terms of mechanisms such as Machin's proposal for the propagation of symmetrical sinusoidally derived waves (Machin, 1958, 1963).

The mechanism for flagellar wave propagation developed by Machin emphasizes the mechanical interdependence of movement throughout the flagellum. The proposal that bending waves are generated by locally propagating bending and unbending transitions goes to the other extreme in emphasizing the independence of events at each transition point. I would like to explore the consequences of this proposal in depth in the present paper.

MECHANO-CHEMICAL COUPLING

Since bending waves pass along a sperm tail with little or no decrease in amplitude, most of the energy dissipated against the viscous resistance to movement through the surrounding medium must be generated locally along the length of the flagellum (Gray, 1955; Machin, 1958; Rikmenspoel, 1965). The reactivation of glycerinated flagella and cilia with adenosine triphosphate (ATP) as the only added source of chemical energy (Hoffmann-Berling, 1955) suggests that ATP serves as the energy donor for flagellar movement, as it does for muscular contraction and many other cellular processes. ATP dephosphorylating activity has been found in preparations of flagella by Nelson (1951, 1954) and many subsequent workers. More recently, Gibbons & Rowe (1965) have isolated the ATP dephosphorylating enzyme associated with the axonemal structures of *Tetrahymena* cilia, and named it dynein. Dynein is distributed regularly along the length of the cilium, at least in *Tetrahymena* (Gibbons, 1963, 1965). Calculation of the rate of diffusion of ATP through the aqueous phase within a flagellum or cilium suggests that this process is sufficient to account for energy transport along flagella (Brokaw, 1966b). All these observations point to the conclusion that the mechanical energy needed to propagate bending waves is generated locally all along the flagellum, by mechano-chemical processes coupled to the dephosphorylation of ATP by dynein.

Gibbons has pointed out that the dynein from *Tetrahymena* has an activity which when expressed in terms of moles of ATP dephosphorylated per sec. per dynein molecule is similar to ciliary beat frequencies (Gibbons, 1966). This observation suggests that each dynein molecule may use just one ATP molecule during each ciliary beat cycle. The dynein molecules of *Tetrahymena* cilia appear to extend along the cilium in longitudinal chains (Gibbons, 1965; Gibbons & Rowe, 1965). The propagated transitions between bent and straight states of the flagellum, which generate bending waves, may therefore be the external manifestations of conformational changes propagated along the chains of dynein molecules, involving the dephosphorylation of one ATP molecule by each dynein molecule in turn along the length of the chain.

Half of the dynein molecules may be arranged to cause bending in one direction, while the other half is arranged to cause bending in the opposite direction, in which case each dynein molecule would use one ATP molecule during a complete cycle of a planar bending wave. However, the con-formational changes involving each dynein molecule must form a complete cycle, representing unbending as well as bending, and the time in the cycle at which the ATP molecule is dephosphorylated is not indicated.

On the other hand, the time of ATP binding can be partially localized. Since the velocity of bend propagation along a sea-urchin sperm flagellum is about 900 μ/sec. (Brokaw, 1965), the dynein molecules in a chain with 170Å. spacing (see below) must act one after another at intervals of about 0·02 msec. Silvester & Holwill (1965) calculated on the basis of absolute reaction rate theory that the collision frequency for ATP molecules with an enzyme site would be of the order of 10–100/sec., and pointed out that this would therefore be too slow to allow ATP to react with a dynein molecule *after* arrival of a signal resulting from reaction of ATP with the preceding dynein in the chain. A reaction between ATP and dynein must take place during the period of inactivity before bending (or unbending) which establishes an activated state, so that the arrival of a signal from the pre-ceding dynein unit triggers a conformational change.

Gibbons' work on *Tetrahymena* cilia indicates that the dynein molecules form the two 'arms' projecting from each of the nine outer doublet micro-tubules in the ciliary cross-section (Gibbons, 1965). If each of these 'arms' is assumed to represent a single chain of dynein molecules, there will be

18 chains of dynein molecules extending along the cilium, with a periodicity of about 170Å. (Gibbons & Rowe, 1965; Grimstone & Klug, 1966). The assumption that there is just one dynein chain in each 'arm' is supported by Gibbons' measurements of the amount of dynein in the cilium. The structural protein of the microtubules appears to be globular, with a longitudinal periodicity equal to one-quarter that of the dynein molecules, and with 13 radially symmetrical units in a microtubular section, and about 23 units in a doublet microtubule (Ringo, 1967). A segment of outer fibre with a length of 170Å. will thus contain two dynein molecules of 600,000 molecular weight (Gibbons & Rowe, 1965) and 92 microtubular protein molecules of 40,000–60,000 molecular weight (Ringo, 1967; Stevens, Renaud & Gibbons, 1967), giving a weight ratio of about 1:4. This is very close to the ratio obtained by Gibbons for the ciliary fractions containing dynein and structural protein (Gibbons, 1963).

If these measurements can be extrapolated to a sea-urchin sperm flagellum 42 μ long, it will contain approximately $4 \cdot 5 \times 10^4$ dynein molecules, or $7 \cdot 5 \times 10^{-20}$ moles of dynein. If the maximum available energy from the dephosphorylation of ATP is about 10 kcal./mole, the use of $7 \cdot 5 \times 10^{-20}$ moles of ATP during each beat cycle by a sea-urchin spermatozoon beating normally at 30 beats/sec. will provide it with up to $9 \cdot 3 \times 10^{-7}$ ergs/sec. of available energy. This is adequately greater than the estimated amount of work done against viscous resistances under these conditions, which is about 3×10^{-7} ergs/sec. (Brokaw, 1965).

The preceding discussion predicts that it should be possible to measure a linear relationship between the beat frequency of a flagellum and the rate at which it dephosphorylates ATP, and that the use of ATP by a sperm flagellum should amount to about $7 \cdot 5 \times 10^{-20}$ moles/beat. Experiments to test these predictions have been attempted by using sea-urchin spermatozoa treated with 50% glycerol to make them permeable to ATP. When resuspended in solutions containing ATP, these spermatozoa are reactivated (Kinoshita, 1958) and show the same types of movement shown by normal spermatozoa (Brokaw, 1966c). ATP dephosphorylation by suspensions of glycerinated spermatozoa has been measured with a recording pH-stat (Brokaw, 1967) and beat frequencies of individual spermatozoa in samples taken from the ATP dephosphorylation assay suspensions have been measured using a stroboscopic illuminator. This type of experiment indicates that when the ATP concentration is varied, there is an approximately linear relationship between ATP dephosphorylation and beat frequency (Brokaw, 1967). The slope of this relationship corresponds to a use of $6 \cdot 5 \times 10^{-20}$ moles of ATP per beat per spermatozoon, which is very close to the estimated number of dynein molecules per spermatozoon.

However, only a fraction of the spermatozoa in these suspensions resumes normal movement after glycerination, so that this type of experiment does not indicate the amount of ATP used by a motile spermatozoon. In fact, when ATP concentration is the variable, the same linear relationship between ATP dephosphorylation and beat frequency is obtained with sperm suspensions in which almost none of the spermatozoa are motile. There is therefore no indication of any direct mechano-chemical coupling under these conditions.

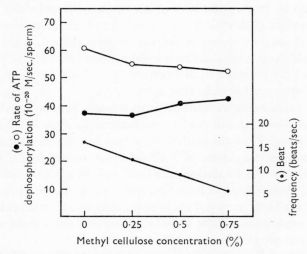

Fig. 2. Effect of methyl cellulose on ATP dephosphorylation and beat frequency of gly-cerinated spermatozoa from the sea urchin, *Strongylocentrotus purpuratus*. Each ATP dephosphorylation point is the average of four measurements with different sperm preparations; the upper curve (O) represents unbroken spermatozoa and the lower curve (●) represents broken spermatozoa. Each beat frequency point represents the average of 60 or more spermatozoa.

Several more recent experiments (Brokaw & Benedict, 1968) with glycerinated spermatozoa have provided clear evidence for mechano-chemical coupling. An example of this type of experiment is illustrated in Fig. 2. The upper curve represents the ATPase activity of suspensions of glycerinated spermatozoa containing motile spermatozoa. The beat frequencies of these spermatozoa have been measured and are indicated by the lowermost curve. The middle curve represents the ATPase activity of suspensions of glycerinated spermatozoa which have been mixed vigorously for 30 sec. in a Vortex mixer. This treatment breaks the tails off from most of the spermatozoa, and almost completely destroys their ability to move. The reduction in ATPase activity which accompanies this loss of motility may represent the ATP dephosphorylation which is directly coupled to flagellar motility.

The effect of adding methyl cellulose to the sperm suspensions, to increase their viscosity, was also examined in this experiment. The decrease in motility at increased viscosity is accompanied by a selective inhibition of the difference between the rates of ATP dephosphorylation by broken and unbroken spermatozoa, with no inhibition of dephosphorylation by broken spermatozoa. This result provides strong support for the conclusion that this component of the ATP dephosphorylation is directly coupled to sperm movement. The results also suggest that the rate of ATP dephosphorylation by this movement-coupled component is proportional to beat frequency as the viscosity is changed, but further experiments are required to exclude the possibility that the number of motile spermatozoa or the energy expenditure by the spermatozoa may be more significant variables than the beat frequency.

These measurements of the difference in ATPase activity between unbroken and broken suspensions of glycerinated spermatozoa could lead to an estimate of the ATP used per beat by a motile spermatozoon, if the number of motile spermatozoa in the suspension were known. However, this number is difficult to estimate, except to say that it probably lies somewhere between 10% and 50% of the total number of spermatozoa. With these limits, the extra ATP used per beat by a motile spermatozoon appears to lie between 3 and 15×10^{-20} moles per beat, indicating that the ratio between the number of ATP molecules used and the number of dynein molecules lies between 0·4 and 2.

There are several reasons for expecting that the use of ATP by flagella might not always correspond to the use of one ATP molecule per beat by each dynein molecule:

(1) The radial arrangement of dynein in the ciliary cross-section indicates that the dynein chains are not all in the same relationship to the plane of bending, and therefore might not be expected to participate equally in such bending. There is therefore no certainty that nine chains will use ATP for bending in one direction and the other nine chains for bending in the opposite direction.

(2) The calculated energy expenditure for *Chaetopterus* spermatozoa swimming in methyl cellulose solutions at high viscosities, with the type of movement shown in Plate 1 d, is about 6×10^{-7} ergs/sec. (Brokaw, 1966c), but the beat frequency is around 10/sec, so that the use of one ATP molecule per dynein molecule per beat under these conditions would appear to provide a maximum of only 3×10^{-7} ergs/sec. This problem is being studied further.

(3) In a planar ciliary beat cycle, most of the work is done during the effective stroke, which involves bending in only a relatively short region

near the base of the cilium. The energy requirement during the recovery stroke, during which the bend progresses along the remainder of the length of the cilium, will be much less. It would appear to be very inefficient to use ATP uniformly along the length of the cilium, and, in fact, a rough calculation of the energy requirement during the effective stroke, using data from Yoneda (1962), indicates that it may be greater than can be supplied by the use of one ATP molecule per dynein molecule as a bend transition moves up from the base of the cilium. Further consideration of this problem requires more complete information about ciliary beat patterns than is available at present.

These considerations suggest that some caution is needed in thinking about model mechanisms involving a conformational change obligatorily coupled to the dephosphorylation of one ATP molecule, and suggest that it is important to study further the stoichiometry of mechano-chemical coupling in flagella and cilia.

THE 'LOCAL CONTRACTION' MODEL

Any complete model of the internal mechanisms for generating bending patterns on flagella and cilia must explain not only the cycle of bending and unbending transitions at a point on the flagellum, but also the propagation of transitions from point to point along the flagellum, and their rhythmic initiation at one end of the flagellum.

The most widely considered model for flagellar bending assumes that the bending of a short length of the flagellum is the direct result of local configurational changes within that segment of the flagellum, such as the contraction of longitudinally orientated fibres at one side of the flagellum (Gray, 1955; Machin, 1958; Silvester & Holwill, 1965). This contraction would be converted into bending by the presence of an appropriate 'skeleton' which resists compression. A very simple version of this model is illustrated in Fig. 3a. To complete the model, the bending of one segment is assumed to cause a signal to be transmitted to the next segment, causing it to contract, and a similar signalling mechanism can be assumed to propagate unbending (Brokaw, 1966a). A special autonomously rhythmic region near the base of the flagellum is postulated to initiate the signals for propagated bending and unbending at the appropriate times.

This specification of the model does not indicate how varying degrees of contraction, and thus bending, are accomplished, particularly if the segments regularly use the same amount of ATP per beat. I want to pass over this question, which probably must be answered at the molecular level, and discuss the model in detail at the phenomenological level, in order to focus attention on some other questions which it leaves unanswered, even though it appears to be the best model which has been proposed.

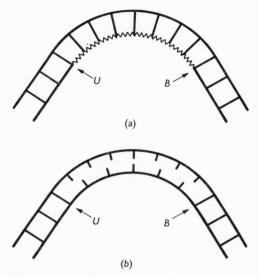

Fig. 3. Formation of a bent region according to two hypothetical models of flagellar bending, in which only two longitudinal fibrils are considered. (*a*) According to the local contraction model. (*b*) According to a 'sliding-filament' model. For clarity, the width of the flagellum and the distance between cross-connexions have been exaggerated relative to the length of the bent region. The actual width of the flagellum is less than one-twentieth the length of a bent region, and the actual distance between cross-connexions will probably be another order of magnitude smaller. The arrows indicate the bending transition points (*B*) and unbending transition points (*U*) for left-to-right propagation of the bent region.

Stiffness

The cross-connexions in the 'skeleton' of the local contraction model, as illustrated in Fig. 3*a*, do not need to be perfectly rigid (Brokaw, 1966*a*). If they are not, there will be a smoothing effect which will conceal variations in the amount of contraction in different segments. There will also be a smoothing effect at a boundary between a region with contracted segments and a relaxed region, which will cause some bending to spread ahead of a contracted region. This 'passively propagated' bending could serve as the signal for activating the contraction of adjacent relaxed regions, thus providing a very simple mechanism for bend propagation (Brokaw, 1966*a*). On the other hand, the cross-connexions must have sufficient rigidity to make longer regions of the flagellum, such as an entire bent region, effectively stiff, in order to enable it to maintain circular curvature when moving through a viscous medium (Brokaw, 1965, 1966*b*). This can be summarized by saying that the 'length constant' ($1/\alpha$ in Brokaw, 1966a) which relates bending to contraction is significantly greater than the length of one segment (170Å.?) and significantly less than the length of a bent region (3–8 μ). The length constant will be a function of the stiffness and dimensions of the cross-connexions.

The local contraction model, as specified here, fully agrees with the conclusion that the high stiffness observed within the bent region of a flagellum, or in the straight portion of a cilium during the effective stroke, cannot be in parallel with the mechanism of active bending, because the energy requirements for bending would be too great (Brokaw, 1965).

Interaction between bending and unbending

It would appear to be possible to construct a working model of a flagellum incorporating the features of the local contraction model. The local cycles of bending and unbending could be driven electrically by solenoids or a motor in each segment, controlled by on-or-off switches. The switch controlling each segment could be located in the preceding segment, so that it is turned on when the preceding segment has achieved a certain degree of bending, and turned off when the preceding segment unbends. A simple revolving timer could be used to initiate bending and unbending at the end of the series of segments. Such a system would appear to be capable of propagating bending or unbending in a realistic fashion.

However, this model has not been constructed, because it lacks one essential feature. There must be some mechanism or property of the system which ensures that the propagation velocities for bending and unbending transitions will be equal. To build this property into a working model, the possible rates of bending and unbending could be restricted to only one value, independent of conditions, or the self-propagation of unbending could be eliminated, with unbending automatically following bending after a set number of segments, or after a fixed time delay in each segment. However, none of these methods would realistically match the ability of flagella to carry out normal wave propagation at a wide range of propagation velocities, and to propagate waves of shorter wavelength when slowed down at increased viscosities (Brokaw, 1966c). I have not been able to think of a simple way of incorporating these features into the working model.

When sinusoidal bending waves are propagated along an elastic filament, unbending may be thought of as being driven by elastic energy stored in the bent filament. The propagation of unbending is determined by the balance between elastic and viscous bending moments acting on the filament at any point, and this balance will also, as a consequence, determine the wavelength of the propagated waves. The possibility that flagellar unbending might be driven and/or controlled in a similar manner is implicit in the formulation of sinusoidal flagellar wave propagation of Machin (1958) and has also been discussed with reference to waves composed of circular arcs (Brokaw, 1966c). In either case, the relationship between changes in the wavelength or related parameters of the waves, the beat frequency, and the viscosity of the medium can be predicted, if the elasticity of the flagellum is assumed to be constant. These predictions appear to be followed by flagella of *Strigomonas* (Holwill, 1965) and several species of spermatozoa (Brokaw, 1966c) when the viscosity is varied, but other variables such as temperature (Holwill & Silvester, 1965) or thiourea-inhibition (Brokaw, 1966c) cause changes in beat frequency which are not accompanied by the predicted changes in other wave parameters. Even at normal viscosities, very slow movements are possible without significant changes in wavelength, so that unless there are precisely correlated changes in the elasticity of the flagellum, some other mechanism must be regulating the propagation of unbending under these conditions.

The idea that the rate of propagated unbending is controlled by a balance between elastic and viscous bending moments also appears to be rather difficult to apply to very asymmetrical wave patterns, such as those shown in Plate 1e and f.

The above observations restate a difficulty with the idea of elastic re-covery during a bending–unbending cycle which was pointed out by James Gray in his book on ciliary movement (Gray, 1928). He noted that if the recovery stroke of a cilium were driven by elastic energy stored during the effective stroke, the velocity of the recovery stroke should be indepen-dent of the velocity of the effective stroke, but that actual observations show that the rate of the recovery stroke is proportional to the rate of the effective stroke, when the over-all cycle frequency is altered in various ways.

The maintenance of equal propagation velocities for bending and un-bending points therefore appears to require some internal interaction between bending and unbending which must be added to the specification of the local contraction model. The mechanism for this interaction is not apparent.

An additional indication that unbending and bending are not completely independent is supplied by the rarity of cases where bending occurs with-out being followed by unbending, causing the flagellum to curl into a com-plete circle. This does not occur even under conditions of very slow movement at normal viscosities, where viscous forces should be small. Attempts to create such situations experimentally have been carried out in our laboratory by Stuart Goldstein, by using a laser microbeam to break a flagellum between a bending point and an unbending point, without ever obtaining the result predicted by the local contraction model.

Bend initiation and termination

According to the local contraction model, bends will begin at, and propagate back from, the base of the flagellum without alteration in the waveform and, as a consequence, the base of the flagellum should oscillate from side to side through the full amplitude of the bending waves. This is contrary to observations. Even if the head is removed, the basal end of a sea-urchin sperm flagellum shows a restricted amount of side-to-side oscillation during the beat cycle (Plate 1*g* and Brokaw, 1965). Bends originating near the base have a relatively small radius of curvature initially, and then increase to normal size as they are propagated. This increase is suppressed under conditions such as increased viscosity, where propagated waves with a small radius of curvature are observed.

This appears to be a more complicated way of initiating bends than the model would require. An additional explanation is required for it, but this may be a relatively simple specification of different bending characteristics for the basal region of the flagellum. The necessity for this additional complication is not in this case a strong argument against the model, since there are conceivable advantages to restricting the side-to-side movement of the head which may justify the evolution of a more complicated mechanism for bend initiation.

A bend normally passes to the distal end of the flagellum and terminates without alteration in the parameters of the bend, in complete agreement with the local contraction model. However, if a piece of the distal end of the flagellum is broken off, bend termination becomes abnormal (Brokaw, 1965) in a manner which is not predicted by the local contraction model.

A 'SLIDING-FILAMENT' MODEL

The most serious deficiency of the local contraction model would appear to be the absence of a satisfactory explanation for the maintenance of equal propagation velocities for bending and unbending. In this model, the bending and unbending points are isolated, as far as internal mechanical interactions are concerned, by the stiffness of the cross-connexions shown in Fig. 3*a* (p. 109). Although these stiff cross-connexions appear to be necessary to explain the apparently high over-all stiffness of inactive regions of the flagellum, or a cilium, it may be instructive to consider the possibilities of a model which does not involve this assumption.

Figure 3*b* illustrates a model in which longitudinal fibres are linked by stiff cross-connexions within the straight region, but where there are no cross-connexions between the fibres within the bent region. Bending will be averaged over the entire bent region, so that there will be some direct interaction between the bending and unbending points. The bend results from the difference in length between the two longitudinal fibres within the bent region. However, once this difference is established, bend propagation does not require local contraction–elongation cycles, but can result simply from the breakage of cross-connexions at the bending point (*B*) and the formation of cross-connexions at the unbending point (*U*). A model involving this mechanism for bend propagation without contraction has some obvious similarities to 'sliding-filament' models of muscle contraction, since the fibrils themselves do not contract and the net result of the passage of a bend along the flagellum will be a shift of one filament longitudinally relative to the other.

If the cycle of breakage and formation of a cross-connexion uses one molecule of ATP, an interesting feature of this sliding filament model is that the flagellum can easily propagate bends with a different radius of curvature while using the same amount of ATP per beat. The radius of curvature will depend upon the length of the bent region and the total angle of bend of the bent region. This angle will be determined by the difference between the lengths of the two longitudinal fibrils (see Fig. 3*b*) within the bent region, which will not be expected to change as the bend propagates. The total angle of bend should therefore remain more constant than other parameters as the wave propagates. However, there are examples of situations where the angle of bend does not remain constant, as in Plate 1*d* and *h* and other photographs (Brokaw, 1965, 1966*c*).

Evidence has been presented elsewhere that there may be inextensible longitudinal fibrils in flagella (Brokaw, 1965) and electron-microscope observations on cilia (Satir, 1965; Horridge, 1965) have indicated that the outer doublet microtubules do not change their lengths during bending. Thus a sliding-filament type of model for flagellar movement is an attractive idea, and will be discussed with relation to the problems raised by the local contraction model. A sliding-filament mechanism for ciliary motility has recently been discussed by Satir (1967).

Interaction between bending and unbending

With the sliding-filament model an unbending point must follow a bending point at the same velocity in order to maintain a constant radius of curvature in the bent region. The formation of cross-connexions at the unbending point could be sensitive to the radius of curvature in such a

8

way that cross-connexions are formed at the rate required to maintain a constant radius of curvature. According to this interpretation, the velocity of bend propagation would be determined by conditions encountered at the bending point, while the radius of curvature would be determined by conditions encountered at the unbending point. There are some experimental observations which fit this interpretation:

The increased bending which occurs at high viscosities, as in Plate 1*d*, is accompanied by increases in the viscous bending moment which resists both bending and unbending (Brokaw, 1966*c*). A similar increase in bending is observed in the proximal portion of the tail of a spermatozoon which is attached to the microscope slide by its head (Plate 1*h*; and Brokaw, 1965). This increase may be the result of the propulsive thrust generated by the movement of the more distal regions of the flagellum, which will tend to compress the bends in the proximal region. This compressive force will assist bending and make unbending more difficult. The similarity between this situation and the effect of increased viscosity is at the unbending point, rather than at the bending point, suggesting that the radius of curvature is determined by the conditions at the unbending point, in particular by the resistance to unbending. This observation is difficult to explain by the local contraction model, where the radius of curvature must be determined at the bending point, the leading edge of the bend.

Bend initiation and termination

Bend initiation requires a different mechanism than that used for bend propagation by the sliding-filament model. Possibly some type of local contraction occurs in the basal region of the flagellum, to initiate a bend having the required total angle of bend, but a smaller length and radius of curvature. This is then propagated according to the sliding-filament model, and enlarges to the length and radius appropriate to a particular set of conditions. This is probably the weakest point in the specification of the sliding filament model, but it is consistent with the observation that there is a special mechanism for bend initiation.

When the bending point of a bent region reaches the broken end of a sperm flagellum, the bent region appears to straighten out rather suddenly (Brokaw, 1965). This type of abnormal bend termination is exactly as expected according to the sliding-filament model, if the fibres become disconnected as soon as a bending point reaches the broken end. However, the termination of bends at the normal end of the flagellum is difficult to explain by the sliding-filament model, and appears to require some special mechanism, as was the case for bend initiation.

A further serious difficulty with this sliding-filament model, which is related to the problems of bend initiation and termination, is the fact that there is a shift of one filament relative to the other after a bend has passed. If a symmetrical bending wave is propagated, the shift caused by bending in one direction will be reversed by bending in the opposite direction, but a series of unilateral propagated bends might be expected to be either impossible or seriously damaging. Such repeated unilateral bending does appear to occur, for instance, with cilia or with asymmetrical flagellar bending waves (Plate 1e and f), but in the latter case it is not clear whether the wave represents asymmetrical bending or symmetrical bending superimposed on a bent flagellum.

SUMMARY

The development of these two models has been an attempt to explore the consequences of the assumption that the bending patterns of cilia and flagella are generated by propagated transitions between bent and unbent states of the flagellum. The implication that each transition is independently self-propagating makes it difficult to explain the fact that the bending and unbending transitions normally propagate at the same velocity. There are other observations which suggest that each bend on the flagellum is propagated as an interrelated unit, with a bending transition at one end and an unbending transition at the other, and in which the radius of curvature throughout the bend is influenced by the viscous bending moment which must be overcome during unbending. These observations can be explained by a sliding-filament model, but are difficult to explain by a local contraction model. On the other hand, the sliding-filament model encounters difficulties at the ends of the flagellum, and does not provide an explanation of the apparently high stiffness of the flagellum within a bent region. Neither model appears to be a fully satisfactory working model of the internal events which accompany the bending patterns of cilia and flagella, suggesting that the original assumption about the generation of bending patterns by propagated transitions may be too gross an oversimplification. At the moment, our construction of such theoretical models appears to lag behind the accumulation of experimental evidence, thus making it difficult to choose the best direction for further experimental study of flagellar movement.

This work was supported in part by a grant from the N.I.H., U.S.P.H.S. (GM-14613).

REFERENCES

BROKAW, C. J. (1965). *J. exp. Biol.* **43**, 155.

BROKAW, C. J. (1966a). *Nature, Lond.* **209**, 161.

BROKAW, C. J. (1966b). *Amer. rev. Resp. Dis.* **93**, 32.

BROKAW, C. J. (1966c). *J. exp. Biol.* **45**, 113.

BROKAW, C. J. (1967). *Science, N.Y.* **156**, 76.

BROKAW, C. J. & BENEDICT, B. (1968). *Archs Biochem. Biophys.* (In press.)

BROKAW, C. J. & WRIGHT, L. (1963). *Science, N.Y.* **142**, 1169.

GIBBONS, I. R. (1963). *Proc. natn. Acad. Sci.* **50**, 1002.

GIBBONS, I. R. (1965). *Archs Biol. Paris,* **76**, 317.

GIBBONS, I. R. (1966). *J. Biol. Chem.* **241**, 5590.

GIBBONS, I. R. & ROWE, A. J. (1965). *Science, N.Y.* **149**, 424.

GRAY, J. (1928). *Ciliary Movement.* Cambridge University Press.

GRAY, J. (1955). *J. exp. Biol.* **32**, 775.

GRAY, J. (1958). *J. exp. Biol.* **35**, 96.

GRIMSTONE, A. V. & KLUG, A. (1966). *J. Cell Sci.* **1**, 351.

HOFFMANN-BERLING, H. (1955). *Biochim. Biophys. Acta* **16**, 146.

HOLWILL, M. E. J. (1965). *J. exp. Biol.* **52**, 125.

HOLWILL, M. E. J. & SILVESTER, N. R. (1965). *J. exp. Biol.* **42**, 537.

HORRIDGE, G. A. (1965). *Proc. R. Soc.* B **162**, 351.

KINOSHITA, S. (1958). *J. Fac. Sci. Tokyo Univ.* § 4, **8**, 219.

MACHIN, K. E. (1958). *J. exp. Biol.* **35**, 796.

MACHIN, K. E. (1963). *Proc. R. Soc.* B **158**, 88.

NELSON, L. (1951). *Nebraska Acad. Sci.* **61**, 12 (Abstr.).

NELSON, L. (1954). *Biochim. Biophys. Acta* **14**, 312.

RIKMENSPOEL, R. (1965). *Biophys. J.* **5**, 365.

RINGO, D. (1967). *J. Ultrastruct. Res.* **17**, 266.

SATIR, P. (1965). *J. Cell Biol.* **26**, 805.

SATIR, P. (1967). *J. gen. Physiol.* **50** (Suppl. 1), 241.

SILVESTER, N. R. & HOLWILL, M. E. J. (1965). *Nature, Lond.* **205**, 665.

SLEIGH, M. A. (1962). *The Biology of Cilia and Flagella.* Oxford: Pergamon Press.

STEVENS, R. W., RENAUD, F. L. & GIBBONS, I. R. (1967). *Science N.Y.* **156**, 1606.

YONEDA, M. (1962). *J. exp. Biol.* **39**, 307.

1:1 in different species (Table 1). All early workers considered the thin portion of the spermatozoon to be posterior and compared it with a 'flagellum'. Lowndes (1935) rightly noted that in a moving spermatozoon the thin part is carried in front and the undulations are produced in the thick part (Plate 3 c). The thin portion of the spermatozoon should there-fore be considered anterior and the thick portion posterior. The thin part is shaped like a corkscrew; this appearance is pronounced in species like *Candona* (Plates 1 b, 2 a, b) and *Cypricercus* (Plate 2 f) but is more difficult to detect with the light microscope in other species (e.g. Plates 1 a, n, 2 e). Running through the corkscrew portion is a more or less straight central shaft which continues posteriorly to form a spiral thread in the thick region of the cell (Plate 1 a, b, h, m). By following spermatogenesis with an electron microscope (Gupta, 1964) it can be shown that this spiral thread is the nucleus. There is a vesicular acrosome at the tip of the thin portion of the spermatozoon (Plates 1 n, 2 e). At the base of the acrosome the nucleus becomes invaginated to form what is comparable to the perfora-torium described by Colwin & Colwin (1964) in other animal spermatozoa. Thus the anterior straight part of the nucleus is in fact a nucleo-perfora-torial complex. It is birefringent (Forer & Gupta, 1967) but in the electron micrographs an organized structure could not be resolved in it (Plate 4 a, b). However, this apparently structureless material of the perforatorium in the mature spermatozoon arises from a bundle of microtubules (each about 250Å. thick) in the elongating spermatid. These microtubules disappear during the later stages of maturation and the cavity of the nucleo-perfora-torial tube becomes filled with a material of homogeneous electron-'staining' property. It is possible that there may be a preferentially orientated material in this region which is not resolved in the electron micrographs available. However, it is more likely that the birefringence of this nucleo-perforatorial shaft is due to a complex set of membranes which is present in this region (Plate 4 a, b). In any case, the anterior part of the spermatozoon does not appear to be intrinsically motile. The corkscrew shape of the anterior part is imparted by the forward extension of the chitinous sheath (Plate 4 a, b) that encloses the entire spermatozoon (Plates 1 f, g, r, s, 2 g, 6, 7 a). This chitinous sheath is not formed by the spermatid but is secreted by the cells of the vas deferens. The complex helical shape of the mature sperm is also attained in the vas deferens from a more or less cylindrical spermatid that leaves the testis (Müller, 1889; Gupta, 1964).

The posterior part of the spermatozoon has a complex helical shape with several component helices of different diameters (Fig. 1; Plate 2 c, d). All the component helices have been represented in the diagram by Retzius (Plate 1). They are formed by: (1) the chitinous sheath, (2) two bands, here called 'contractile bands' (see reasons below), arising from (3) a spiral nucleus, and (4) two mitochondria. Although the nucleus extends from one end of the spermatozoon to the other, the chromatin is confined to a segment only a few microns long. This segment of the nucleus is usually near the posterior end of the spermatozoon but in some species, such as *Candona*, it may lie in the middle of the thick portion. The region which contains chromatin can be identified by its positive reaction to the usual histochemical tests for DNA (Gupta, 1964) and by its strongly negative birefringence (Forer & Gupta, 1967).

In addition to the structures mentioned above, Müller (1889) noted a very fine 'axial thread' running through the middle of the thick helical part of the spermatozoon. Electron micrographs of spermatozoa from the seminal vesicles reveal that this axial thread is formed of aligned blocks of concentric myelin-like lamellae and is presumably composed of some lipoprotein material. It seems that this, together with a similar material filling in the spaces between the mitochondria and the contractile bands, provides the substrate for energy. In the spermathecae of older females the spermatozoa always appear in various stages of exhaustion when examined fresh; in electron micrographs of such spermatozoa the lipoprotein material appears in a variable state of dissolution (Plates 5, 6, 7a). When all the reserved food has been utilized, the cell body of the spermatozoon disintegrates but the empty chitinous sheath is left behind (Plate 2h). The spermathecae of older females usually have a very large number of such empty sheaths and only a few active spermatozoa. This fact led earlier workers to believe that either the spermatozoa of ostracods mature by moulting (Müller, 1889) or that most of them are not motile (Lowndes, 1935).

Two mitochondria form a spiral around the 'axial thread' (Plates 5, 6, 7a) and the nucleus is situated eccentrically between the two mitochondria. In cross-section the nucleus is not circular in most of the posterior region, and its shape varies in different species (cf. Plates 6, 7a). The nucleus is enclosed in an envelope of two membranes which in the mature sperm do not have any pores (Figs. 1, 2; Plate 7a, b). Two contractile bands with feather-like profiles arise from the outer membrane of the nucleus, encircle the rest of the cell body and end in a swollen 'rib' which fits into the concavities of a monorail-shaped ridge, formed by the invagination of the chitinous sheath. In three dimensions this ridge forms a spiral diametrically opposite to the nucleur spiral, and appears as a dark thread in sheaths examined with light microscopy (Plates 1r, 2h). The two contractile bands and the two mitochondria extend over the entire length of the posterior portion of the spermatozoon.

Fine structure of the contractile bands

Each contractile band is composed of a closed sac, the core-sac, both cyto-plasmic surfaces of which are almost completely covered by hollow cone-like processes (Plates 6, 7 a). The walls of the core-sac are approximately 200 Å. thick and are made up of two membranes, each about 80 Å. thick. The outer of the two membranes in each wall is continuous with the outer membrane of the nuclear envelope, while the inner membrane forms a closed sac (Figs. 1, 2; Plate 7 b). The core-sac of the contractile bands is thus a membrane-bound sac enclosed by an extension of the perinuclear space. During spermateleosis the core-sacs are formed by the cisternae of the endoplasmic reticulum which align in pairs at the two edges of a flattened nucleus and fuse with the outer membrane of the envelope. The enclosed lumen of the core-sac therefore was at one time the cytoplasm of the spermatid (Gupta, 1964).

The lumen enclosed by each core-sac is about 250 Å. wide. The luminal surface of each inner membrane of the walls is covered with a sheet of almost contiguous filaments (Fig. 2; Plate 7 a). Each filament in the sheet is about 100 Å. in diameter and in sections stained with either uranyl acetate, or lead citrate, or both, it generally appears hollow in cross-section (Plate 7 b). The filamentous sheets are separated from one another by a gap of about 50 Å. The long axis of the filaments is parallel to the long axis of the bands and therefore describes a helix around the long axis of the spermatozoon. Although it has not been possible to determine the length of these filaments by direct measurements on the electron micro-graphs, there is indirect evidence to suggest that the length of each filament may correspond to the length of each contractile band in one complete turn of the helix constituting the posterior thick portion of the sperma-tozoon (Gupta, 1964). It is also to be noted that in the mature spermatozoa the outer membrane of the core-sac and the nuclear envelope often does not reveal either a unit-membrane configuration or a uniform density. Instead, it appears to be made up of profiles which in three dimensions could be interpreted as 60 Å. thick rings arranged like closely fitted hoops on a barrel. If this arrangement is not an artifact of fixation then the original membrane in the spermatid undergoes a drastic change in con-figuration during the maturation of the spermatid. The inner membrane, however, remains unchanged.

Each of the conical processes covering the cytoplasmic surfaces of the contractile bands is about 100 mμ long. It is about 600 Å. wide at the base and tapers down to about 100 Å. near the tip. It is shaped more or less like a broad-based spine. The base of each conical process is slightly convex

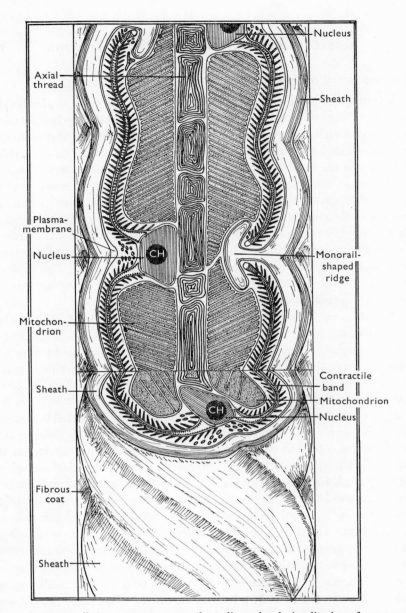

Fig. 1. A cut-out diagram to represent a three-dimensional visualization of one turn of the helix constituting the posterior thick part of the spermatozoon in freshwater ostracods. The reconstruction is primarily based on what is believed to be the fine structure of the spermatozoon from the seminal vesicle of *Notodromas monacha*. The structure is essentially similar in the spermatozoa of other ostracod species but varies specifically in the shape of the nucleus, in the shape and thickness of the chitinous sheath, and in the diameter and pitch of the helix. The complex helical structure is composed of several component helices of the same pitch but different diameters. The component helices are: (1) the outer sheath, (2) a monorail-shaped invagination of the sheath forming a helical ridge, (3) a single nuclear spiral, (4) two contractile bands, and (5) two mitochondria. The 'axial thread' of the complex helix is a lipoprotein material which is used as a substrate for energy by the spermatozoa in constant motion in the spermathecae of the females. Only the nucleus and the sheath extend into the thinner anterior region. Although the nucleus extends over the entire length of the spermatozoon (Plate 1), the Feulgen +ve, negatively birefringent chromatin (*CH*) occupies only a few microns of its length. The fibrous coat enclosing the spermatozoon in the seminal vesicles is not present in the spermatozoa from the spermathecae. It may therefore be one of the factors responsible for the lack of motility in the spermatozoa from the male specimens of ostracods.

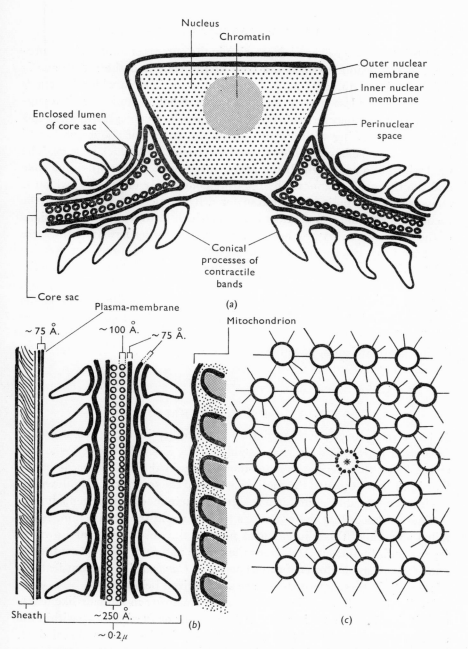

Fig. 2. Diagram showing the detailed structure of contractile bands. (a) The relationship of the nucleus and the contractile bands. (b) Details of a small portion of a contractile band as it is positioned between the plasma-membrane and one of the two mitochondria. The measured dimensions of the components are indicated in the diagram. (c) The arrangement of conical processes on the surface of the contractile bands as seen in high-resolution electron micrographs of fields where the section has cut the processes parallel to the surface of the band. The conical processes show a two-dimensional hexagonal packing and appear to be cross-linked by 30 Å. thick fibrils. The exact arrangement of the cross-linking fibrils is not clear from the micrographs available. In suitable cross-sections each conical process appears to be made up of 50 Å. units (asterisk).

and fits into a saucer-shaped depression in the outer membrane of the core-sac. No connexion between the base of the cone and the membrane is visible in electron micrographs. In tangential sections, in which the cones are cut more or less transversely, they appear hollow and there is a suggestion that they may be made up of 50Å. units. The conical processes show a hexagonal packing with a centre-to-centre spacing of about 400Å. and they appear to be laterally cross-linked by strands 30Å. thick (Fig. 2). The total width of a contractile band, as measured between the tip of one cone and the tip of the diametrically opposite cone, is about 200 mμ, which is above the lower limit of resolution for a light microscope. It should be mentioned that the two contractile bands which form wing-like extensions of the nucleus are very pronounced structures in early spermatids and were illustrated by Stühlmann (1886). In the mature spermatozoa Retzius (Plate 1 d', p, s) has provided the correct representation, but the contractile nature of these bands had not been detected by any of the earlier workers.

The salient features of the fine structure of the motile system in the spermatozoa of freshwater ostracods are represented in Figs. 1, 2. Further details of these structures, together with an account of their formation during spermateleosis, have been worked out (Gupta, 1964) and are to be published elsewhere.

MOTILITY OF THE SPERMATOZOA

It has already been mentioned that the motility in the spermatozoa of freshwater ostracods was firmly established by Lowndes (1935), who also showed that the spermatozoa are motile only in the spermathecae of the females. I have recorded the motile patterns of the spermatozoa both within the intact spermathecae and in a free condition in modified Ringer solution. A ciné-film recording these motions was shown at the symposium. A detailed analysis of this film confirms most of the observations of Lowndes (1935), and, further, it establishes the motile nature of the two contractile bands in the spermatozoa of three species of *Candona*. The salient features of motility in these spermatozoa are summarized below.

In discussing the motile patterns of spermatozoa in animals like ostracods it should be borne in mind that spermatozoa *in vivo* move within the spermathecae, and travel through a watch-spring-like spermathecal duct. The lumen of the duct is just wide enough to accommodate one spermatozoon (Plate 3 a, b). Spermatozoa therefore normally move through highly restricted spaces where they can neither stretch themselves fully nor produce any undulations detectable with the light microscope.

In a partially empty spermatheca, such as is shown in Plate 3 a, mounted in Ringer solution or under paraffin oil, one can follow the movement of one or two spermatozoa going round the central mass of degenerating sperm. Under such conditions their actual velocity varies considerably and probably depends on numerous factors such as the age of the sperm, pressure of the coverslip, heat, intensity of illumination, available oxygen, etc., but an average value in a number of species is about 40–50 μ/sec.

In completely intact spermathecae and while passing through the spermathecal duct, the spermatozoa seem to move even faster. In addition to the forward progression, the only other movement in such active spermatozoa is their rotation around their long axis. The frequency of this rotation or spin is proportional to the velocity of progression and for a velocity of 40 μ/sec. the rotation is about 4 cyc./sec. In spermatozoa swimming free in Ringer solution, the velocity is about 20 μ/sec. with a rotation of 1 cyc./ sec. These figures compare favourably with the data from flagellate spermatozoa like those of bull (e.g. Rikmenspöel, 1962). In the spermatozoa within a spermatheca, one cannot detect any undulatory waves in any part of the cells.

Undulatory waves

If a spermatheca is punctured in a drop of well-oxygenated Ringer solution covered with oil, the spermatozoa move out and swim freely. The movement in such cells persists for several hours, frequently overnight, and can be observed at very low magnifications, using dark-ground illumination, either under a stereomicroscope or an ordinary microscope, without the use of a coverslip. In such free-swimming spermatozoa from *Notodromas monacha*, from several species of *Cypria*, and from *Cyclocypris dentifera*, the maximum recorded velocity rarely exceeds 20 μ/sec. In addition to rotation, one can now see large-scale undulatory waves passing down the thick posterior part of the spermatozoon (Plate 3c, d). The undulations follow a helical path, but if a coverslip is placed on the preparation they become planar. Neither the frequency nor the amplitude of these waves seems to be constant even in the same spermatozoon. No undulations are present in the nucleo-perforatorial region.

Ripple waves

In both 'normal' and undulatory movements there are continuous series of very fine ripples passing in a helical course down the thick posterior part of the spermatozoon. The waves were first described by Lowndes, who believed that they were a unique feature among motile systems of cells. Using a stroboscope, Lowndes (1935) measured about 35–40 wave-crests/sec. at any one point on the surface of actively moving spermatozoon of *N. monacha*. However, the nature of these ripple waves can be much more easily analysed in the spermatozoa from the various species of *Candona*. In these species the spermatozoa are about 0·6 mm. long and 6 μ in diameter in the posterior part (Plate 2 *a–d*). Within the spermatheca the spermatozoa are as active as in other species. Outside the spermatheca the cells continue to rotate, though at a retarded rate, but do not show any forward progression. In such cells ripple waves are also very much slower and can be filmed at high magnifications under the phase-contrast or dark-ground illumination systems. Analysis of such ciné films show that the ripple waves are produced as fine undulations of the contractile bands working locally against the sheath. The actual mechanism as to how the bands work is not known at the moment. From the electron micrographs of single mature spermatozoa fixed presumably in an arrested state of motion, the contractile bands in any one section are not folded symmetrically (e.g. Plate 5 *a–c*), unlike the situation in inactive spermatozoa (Plate 7*a*). In such profiles one band appears to be more extended between the nucleus and the monorail-shaped ridge than the other. First, if this represents alternate contraction and relaxation of the bands at any one transverse plane of the spermatozoon, and if such waves of contraction pass down the length of the helical bands, they could form the ripple waves observed in live spermatozoa. Since the bands are attached to the spiral nucleus along one edge, the activity of the bands as postulated above will produce an oscillatory rotation of the nucleus about its longitudinal axis. Such an oscillation may be responsible for the rotation of the spermatozoon. Secondly, the oscillation of the nucleus and geometrical distortion of the sheath resulting from the activity of the bands would be expected to produce a cyclic change in the total length of the centre (i.e. the sheath, bands and the nucleus) with respect to the non-motile axial complex (mitochondria). Such a cyclic change in length is visible in the micro-ciné films of the spermatozoa in *Candona*.

On the basis of the present evidence it would seem that the primary cause of movement in the spermatozoa of freshwater ostracods is the 'fine helical undulatory waves' (ripple waves of Lowndes) generated by the contractile bands. Any further speculations on the mechanism of contraction in the bands is best left until more information is available on the nature of components.

The work reported here was done during the author's tenure as a Commonwealth Scholar from 1961 to 1964 and formed a part of his thesis for the Ph.D degree of Cambridge University. The author expresses his sincere gratitude to Dr L. E. R. Picken for his inspiring supervision and to the Commonwealth Scholarship Commission in U.K. for the award of a Scholarship. Thanks are also due to Dr A. Forer for his helpful criticism of the manuscript. Live specimens of *Cyclocypris dentifera* were very kindly sent by Professor W. T. Edmondson, from Washington University, Seattle, U.S.A.

REFERENCES

BISHOP, D. W. (1962). Sperm motility. *Physiol. Rev.* **42**, 1.

COLWIN, A. L. & COLWIN, L. H. (1964). In *Cellular Membranes in Development*, ed. M. Locke. New York: Academic Press.

FORER, A. & GUPTA, B. L. (1967). Observations to be published.

FRANZEN, A. (1956). *Zool. Bidr. Upps.* **31**, 355.

GUPTA, B. L. (1964). Cytological studies of the germ-cells in some freshwater ostracods and copepods. Ph.D. thesis, University of Cambridge.

HUGHES-SCHRADER, S. (1946). *J. Morph.* **78**, 43.

LOWNDES, A. G. (1935). *Proc. zool. Soc. Lond.* **1**, 35.

MAKIELSKI, S. K. (1966). *J. Morph.* **118**, 11.

MOSES, M. J. & COLEMAN, J. R. (1964). In *Role of Chromosomes in Development*, ed. M. Locke. New York: Academic Press.

MÜLLER, G. W. (1889). *Zool. Jb.* **3**, 677.

NATH, V. (1956). *Int. Rev. Cytol.* **5**, 395.

NATH, V. (1964). *Animal Gametes (Male).* London: Asia Publishing House.

PHILLIPS, D. M. (1966). *J. Cell Biol.* **30**, 499.

REGER, J. F. (1962). *J. Ultrastruct. Res.* **7**, 550.

RETZIUS, G. (1909). *Biol. Unters.* **14**.

RIKMENSPÖEL, R. (1962). In *Spermatozoan Motility*, ed. D. W. Bishop. Washington, D.C. (A.A.A.S.).

ROBINSON, W. G. (1966). *J. Cell Biol.* **29**, 251.

ROTHSCHILD, LORD (1961). *Q. Jl microsc. Sci.* **102**, 239.

SARS, G. O. (1889). *Christ. Vidensk. Forh.* **8**, 1.

SCHMÄLZ, J. (1912). *Arch. Zell-forsch.* **7**, 407.

STÜHLMANN, F. (1886). *Z. wiss. Zool.* **44**, 534.

WILSON, E. B. (1928). *The Cell in Development and Heredity*. New York: Macmillan.

ZENKER, W. (1854). *Arch. Naturgesch.* **20**, 1.

EXPLANATION OF PLATES

PLATE 1

Photographic reproduction of parts of two plates published by Retzius (1909), showing the light-microscopic structure of spermatozoa in two species of freshwater ostracods. The identification of various structures is based on the work reported here and is quite different from that given by Retzius. Figs. *a* and *i–s* are from *Notodromas monacha* and *b–h* from *Candona* sp.

a–h. a, b, Entire spermatozoon. *c, e, f,* Details of the posterior end (Retzius and many other earlier workers considered this end as the anterior); *d,* details from one turn of the helix constituting the posterior region; *d′,* a portion of the posterior part with the sheath removed, showing two mitochondria (here drawn parallel) and nuclear spiral with two ribbon-shaped contractile bands; *g,* a portion of an empty sheath; *h,* a part of a spermatozoon showing the transition from the posterior thick to the anterior thin parts.

i–s, Details from the spermatozoa of *Notodromas monacha. i,* Posterior end of a spermatozoon from the seminal vesicle; *j,* a small portion of the posterior region from a desheathed cell; *k,* junction of the posterior and anterior parts, showing the termination of the mitochondria and contractile bands (arrow); *l,* posterior end of a partly degenerated cell from the spermatheca; *m,* junction of the posterior and anterior parts, showing the continuity of the nuclear spiral and the outer sheath; *n,* acrosomal 'knob' at the anterior tip; *o, p,* partly unravelled portions from a desheathed spermatozoon, clearly showing the contractile bands as helical wing-like extensions of the nuclear spiral (specially in *p*); *q,* posterior tip of an elongated spermatid before spiralization; *r, s,* posterior region from a crushed spermatozoon, showing the chitinous sheath (*r*) separated from the cell body (*s*).

PLATE 2

a–h, Photomicrographs of fresh spermatozoa from the spermathecae of three different species, taken either with phase-contrast or dark-ground illumination.

a–d, From *Candona* sp.; *a,* the entire spermatozoon, which is 0·6 mm. in length; *b,* details of a portion 6 μ long near the anterior tip, showing a pronounced corkscrew appearance. Arrow points to the acrosomal vesicle. *c,* Junction of the anterior and posterior regions; *d,* portion of the posterior region, showing the complex helical organization (Fig. *a,* × 200; *b–d,* × 1,600).

e, Portion of the anterior part from *N. monacha*; arrow indicates the acrosomal vesicle (× 1,600).

f, Anterior cork-screw region of the spermatozoon from *Cypricercus dentifera.* In this species the spermatozoon is 4 mm. long. Arrow indicates the acrosomal vesicle (× 1,000).

g, A portion from *f,* under dark-ground illumination, showing that the corkscrew shape is imparted by the outer sheath on a straight nucleo-perforatorial shaft (× 2,000).

h, A portion of an empty sheath from *N. monacha*; the dark spiral is the monorail-shaped ridge (× 1,600).

PLATE 3

a–d, Photomicrographs under dark-ground illumination from *N. monacha* (× 100).

a, Both the spermathecae from one female. The spermatheca marked with an asterisk has been punctured and a number of active spermatozoa have moved out of it. *b,* A crushed spermatheca showing a mass of disintegrating spermatozoa, now mostly composed of empty sheaths. Note a portion of the spermathecal duct which *in vivo* is coiled like a watch-spring. The lumen of the duct can accommodate only one spermatozoon at a time.

c, d, Multiple flash exposures of single spermatozoa in motion; the duration of the electronic flash was 1/1000th sec. The interval between flashes was 15 sec. in *c,* and 5 sec. in *d.* Note that the thin anterior part of the spermatozoon is carried straight while the thick posterior part shows irregular undulations.

PLATE I

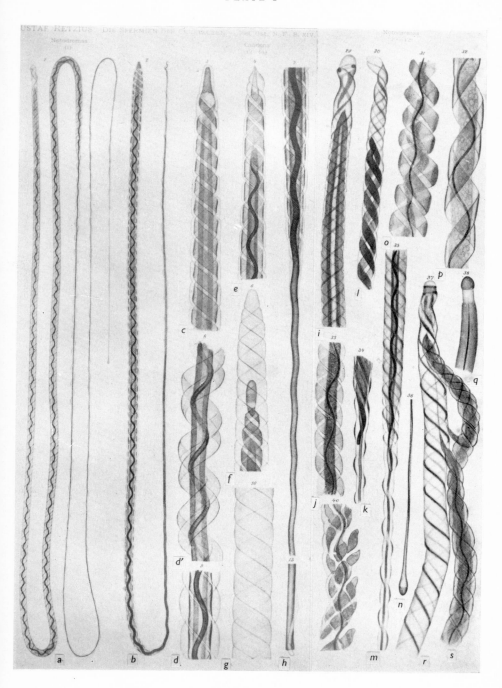

For explanation to Plates 1–7 see pp. 128–9

PLATE 2

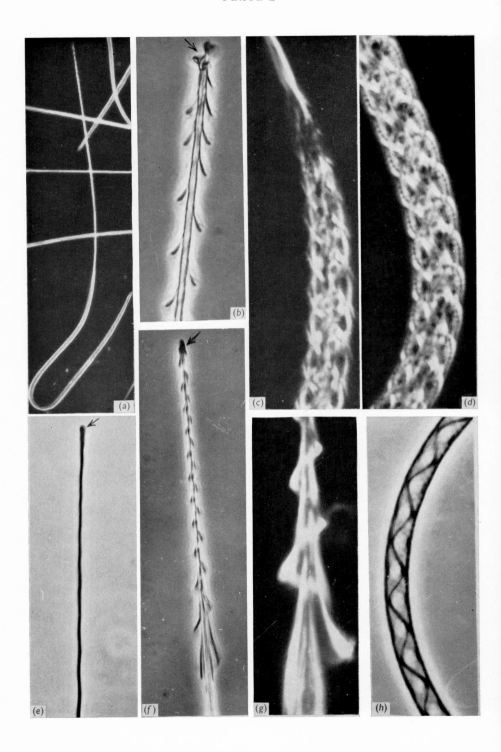

PLATE 3

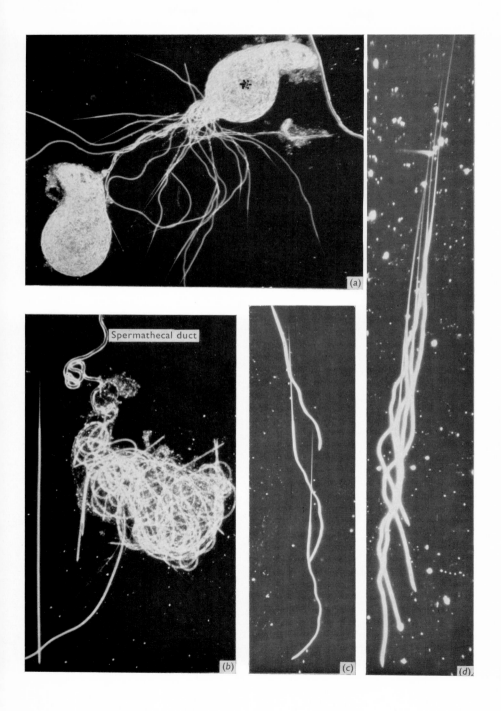

(a)

Spermathecal duct

(b)

(c)

(d)

PLATE 4

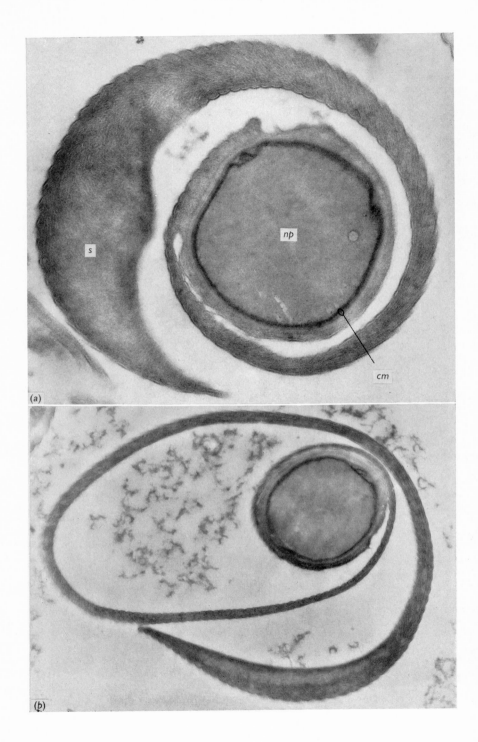

(a)

(b)

PLATE 5

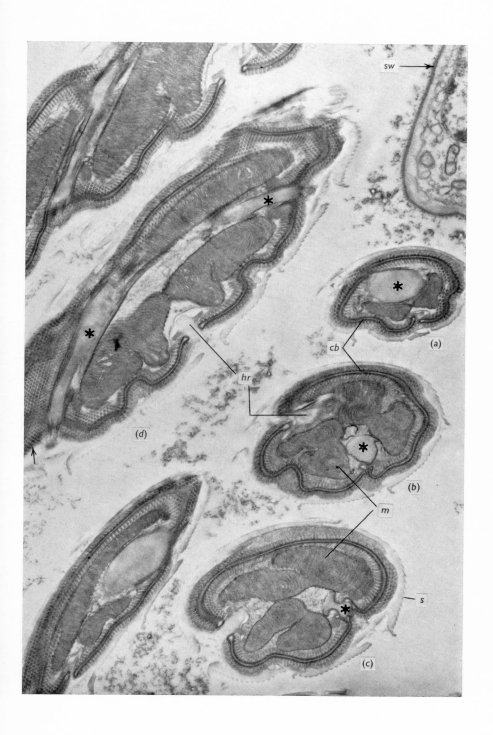

PLATE 6

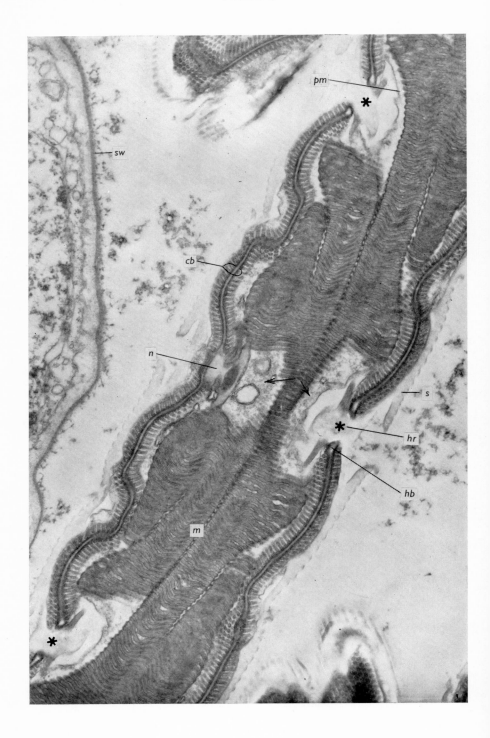

PLATE 7

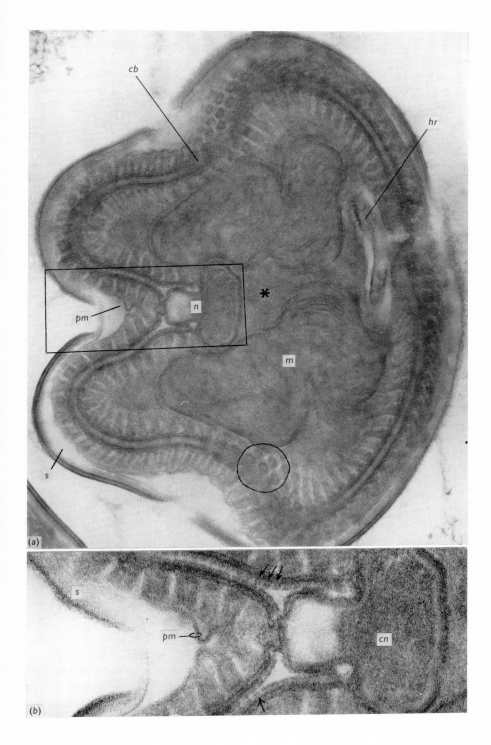

PLATES 4–7

Electron micrographs of material fixed in buffered 2% osmium tetroxide, embedded in Araldite, and sections stained in ethanolic uranyl acetate.

PLATE 4

a, b, Electron micrographs of transverse sections cut at two different levels of the anterior region of the spermatozoon from *Cypricercus dentifera* (cf. Plate 2 *f, g*), showing the nucleo-perforatorial shaft (*np*) enclosed in a spiral sheath (*s*). Note the fibrous substructure of the sheath. The complex membrane (*cm*) surrounding the nucleo-perforatorium arises from two nuclear envelopes of an invaginated nucleus and the plasma-membrane (Gupta, 1964) (*a,* ×80,000; *b,* ×50,000).

PLATE 5

A small field from a section of a spermatheca from *Cypricercus dentifera. a–c,* Near-transverse sections of the posterior region of three spermatozoa cut at different levels. Note the change in shape of the nucleus (asterisks) as it approaches the junction between the posterior and anterior regions (*a,* cf. Plate 1 *k*). Also note that two contractile bands in each profile are not symmetrically folded (cf. Plate 7 *a*). This asymmetry is interpreted here as indicating the activity of bands in moving spermatozoa 'arrested' at the time of fixation. *d,* A tangential section showing the helical nature of the nucleus (asterisks) and other components. Arrow points to an area where a two-dimentional hexagonal packing of the conical processes on the contractile bands is visible (cf. Fig. 2 *c*). (×20,000). *cb,* Contractile bands; *hr,* helical ridge; *m,* mitochondria; *s,* sheath; *sw,* spermathecal wall.

PLATE 6

One turn of the complex helix constituting the posterior part of a spermatozoon from *Cypricercus dentifera,* cut parallel to the long axis and showing the arrangement of various component structures (cf. Fig. 1). Note a tight packing of plate-like cristae in the mitochondria (*m*) and the origin of the contractile bands (*cb*) from the nucleus (*n*) and their termination in a 'rib' that fits into a groove of a helical ridge (*hr,* asterisks) formed by the invaginated sheath. The sheath (*s*) has a sculptured surface and is outside the plasma-membrane (*pm*). Arrows indicate the areas which, in the spermatozoa from seminal vesicles are occupied by a myelin-like lipoprotein material (×24,000).

PLATE 7

a, Transverse section through the posterior region of a stationary (at the time of fixation) spermatozoon from *Notodromas monacha.* The section has passed through the chromatin region of the nucleus. Note that the contractile bands (*cb*) are symmetrically folded (cf. Plate 5 *c*). Asterisk marks broken-down material from the 'axial thread' (see Fig. 1), while the circle encloses a few profiles of transversely cut conical processes indicating a substructure (×65,000).

b, The 'boxed' area from *a,* shown at a higher magnification. Note the unit-membrane structure of the plasma-membrane (*pm*) and hollow profiles (arrows) of transversely cut filaments lining the lumen of the core-sac of the contractile bands (*cb*). (×120,000.) *cn,* Chromatin; *hr,* helical ridge; *m,* mitochondrion; *n,* nucleus; *pm,* plasma membrane; *s,* sheath.

PATTERNS OF CILIARY BEATING

By M. A. SLEIGH

Department of Zoology, The University, Bristol

INTRODUCTION

In comparison with the relatively complete descriptions of the form of beat attained in recent studies of flagellar and sperm tail movement (reviewed by Holwill, 1966), the descriptions of the movement of cilia that have been published are quite inadequate. There are probably two main reasons for this—first, that most cilia are not readily accessible for study since they occur in tracts in which individual cilia cannot easily be seen, and, secondly, that the beat of cilia appears to be so variable that a comprehensive description of the movement is very difficult. In this study an attempt has been made to give a more adequate quantitative description of ciliary beating than has been published heretofore, and to compare the patterns of beating of different cilia examined under similar conditions and described in the same terms.

As a result of the inaccessibility of cilia, the best studies made to date, those of Gray (1930), of Kinosita & Kamada (1939) and of Yoneda (1960, 1962), have all been made on the same type of solitary cilium, the large abfrontal cilium of *Mytilus* gill. The beat of this cilium has some unusual features which make it unsuitable for use as an example to illustrate the generalized characteristics of ciliary movement, although the information it provides is still valuable.

It is my opinion that the prototype of the $9+2$ organelle was a flagellum along which a planar undulation was propagated. During evolution this has been adaptively modified in the flagellar form by the addition of such structures as mastigonemes and by the propagation of helical waves. The original organelle has also been modified in the direction of the cilium with a unilateral beat in which the mechanism of the $9+2$ structure must be used in a slightly different way.

The planar flagellar beat results from a regular alternation of bending of the basal region of the flagellar axis to one side and then to the other, and the propagation of these bends along the flagellum. The symmetry of the beat permits a quantitative description of the flagellar movement in terms of the beat frequency, the rate of propagation of the bending wave along the flagellum, the amplitude of the waves and the length of the flagellum. The ciliary beat is necessarily more complex because of its unilaterality. In a cycle of ciliary beating (see examples in Figs. 1–4), the movement begins from a resting position (at the left) with a flexure at the base which produces a swing of the ciliary axis called the effective stroke (towards the right). This is followed by a sharp movement back to the other side at the base, while the distal part of the cilium continues to swing in the effective direction. The bend in the cilium produced by these two angular swings at the base is then propagated up to the tip of the cilium during the recovery stroke. This beat can be described in terms of the change with time of the angular position of the basal region of the ciliary shaft and of the position of the bend along the ciliary axis (e.g. Fig. 1). A graphical representation of this type shows most of the interesting features of the ciliary beat, although it does not give information on the position of the cilium distal to the bend or the time at which maximum flexure occurs.

OBSERVATIONS

The movement of each cilium is described in a diagram showing a series of profiles of the cilium at stated time intervals during its beat, and graphical records of the time-change of the angular inclination of the basal region (which means in effect the proximal one-tenth of the ciliary length) and of the position of the bend along the axis of the same cilium as shown in the profiles. The measurements were made on prints or tracings obtained from ciné films of the cilia taken at 60 or 300–400 frames/sec. The detailed timing of the beat of a cilium is often not constant from one cycle to the next, and minor variations in timing can produce noticeable differences in the form of beat; the records given are examples typical of the cilium in question, since it is not possible to average out the individual differences between beats.

The comb plates of the ctenophore *Pleurobrachia* may beat slowly with a clear break between beats, and even in the faster beat shown in Fig. 1 the large compound cilium has a short interkinetic period between the time when the bend reaches the tip of the cilium at the end of the recovery phase and the time when the angular swing of the effective stroke begins. The beginning of the effective stroke is the usual rest position of cilia. From its position of rest (inclined at about 40° to the body surface) the shaft of the cilium swings more or less stiffly through nearly 100° around a bending region near the base of the shaft, and a slight further forward swing of the distal region of the cilium occurs while the extreme basal region of the shaft undergoes a quick backward movement which increases the flexure of the shaft. The angular velocity of the return movement at the base is about twice that of the forward movement. The flexure of the ciliary shaft then moves up the cilium at about 16 mm./sec.; there was no evidence in these films of any change of rate along the ciliary axis. In this very long cilium the basal region is in its resting position (40°) for about 75 % of the cycle time.

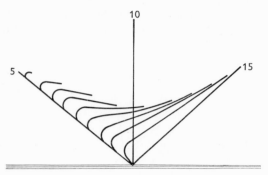

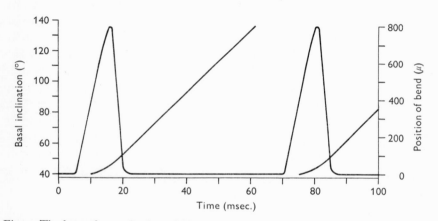

Fig. 1. The beat of a comb plate of *Pleurobrachia pileus* analysed from ciné film taken at 60 frames/sec. at 17° C.; the phase difference between adjacent comb plates of the row seen in the film was 6·5 msec. The ciliary profiles are drawn at 5 msec. intervals, and the times indicated correspond with those on the graph below. The graph shows the change in basal inclination of the comb plate (the angle between the body surface on the left-hand side and the ciliary axis), starting from its rest position at 40° and passing through an effective stroke and a basal recovery swing to return the basal region to the resting inclination at 20 msec., and remaining there until the next effective stroke at 70 msec. The propagation of the flexure of this first beat up the comb plate between 10 msec. and 61 msec. is also shown.

The membranelles of the ciliate protozoon *Stentor* have a more limited amplitude of the effective stroke (Fig. 2). A flexure is still present at the tip of the compound cilium after the effective stroke has begun—the recovery phase of one beat overlaps the effective stroke of the next beat. The cilium probably only stops when it is actively inhibited, and then the stationary position is approximately at the beginning of the effective stroke. The record of angular inclination is very much like that of *Pleurobrachia*, although the time spent by the basal region of the cilium in its 'rest position' is only about half of the cycle time.

The velar locomotor cilia of the veliger larva of the nudibranch mollusc *Jorunna* are longer and more flexible than the last type, and have a slow

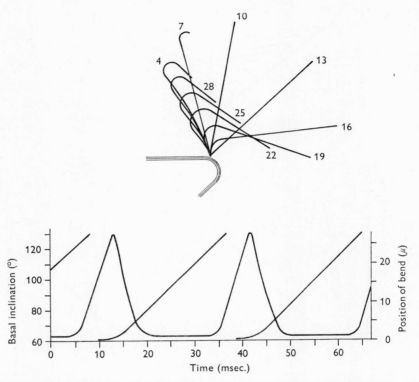

Fig. 2. The beat of a membranelle of *Stentor polymorphus*, filmed at 400 frames/sec. at 22° C. The times indicated on the profiles above correspond with times on the graph below.

beat of large amplitude (Fig. 3). However, the angular inclination record is much the same, and there is little or no overlap of successive beats; the cilia rest at the beginning of the effective stroke. The rate of propagation of the bend up the cilium shows a clear increase towards the tip, which is a common feature.

Compound cilia occur in transverse rows on the conical dorsal gills of the body segments of the polychaete worm *Sabellaria*. These usually show an extensive overlap of the recovery phase of one beat with the effective stroke of the next, and a rather limited swing during the effective stroke

(Fig. 4). Even near the end of the effective stroke there may be a flexure at the tip of the cilium from the previous beat as well as the basal bend. There are two implications of the overlap of adjacent beats which are of interest here: (i) the cilia rest at the beginning of the effective stroke, and, since the

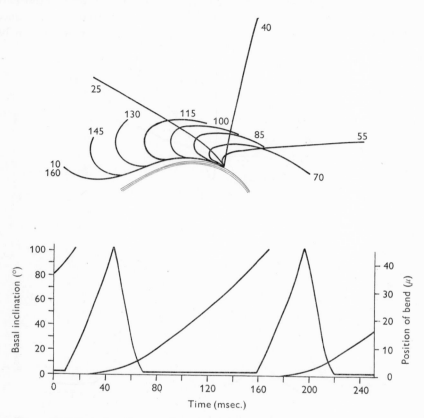

Fig. 3. The beat of a cilium on the velum of a veliger larva of *Jorunna tomentosa*, filmed at 340 frames/sec. at 22° C.

flexure is only part of the way up the cilium at this time, the cilia rest in the bent position shown by the profile at the extreme left in Fig. 4; (ii) since the effective length of the cilium increases during the effective stroke, the resistance offered to movement of the cilium by the water increases and the angular velocity of the effective stroke decreases, giving a modified shape to the record of angular inclination of the cilium.

The abfrontal cilia of the gills of *Mytilus*, mentioned earlier, rest in the bent position with the ciliary shaft more or less parallel to the gill surface (Fig. 5). From here there is a quick backward movement of the base which

starts the recovery phase (or preparatory phase as it is sometimes appro-
priately called in this case). The cilium starts to move forwards in the effective stroke long before the flexure of the previous recovery stroke reaches
the tip, but the forward swing of the effective stroke is far from constant in
its angular movement—the first part of the movement is always rapid and
brings the cilium to a fully extended position at about 90° to the cell surface,
in which attitude it may almost or completely stop before it moves slowly

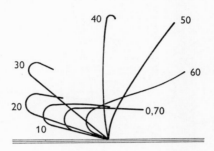

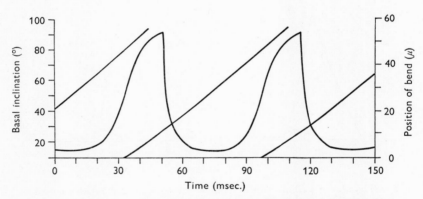

Fig. 4. The beat of a cilium from a dorsal gill of *Sabellaria alveolata*, filmed at
400 frames/sec. at 20° C.

onwards with some acceleration to the resting position. If the beat is
immediately followed by another the extent of the effective stroke may be
reduced, since the next recovery phase may begin before the cilium reaches
the gill surface; the cilium will only lie flat along the gill surface during an
interkinetic pause. The propagation of the bend up the cilium shows a
marked acceleration, associated particularly with the beginning of the
effective stroke, which carries the flexure to the ciliary tip by the time the
cilium reaches the perpendicular position.

Hypotrich ciliate protozoa characteristically possess conical compound cilia called cirri. Such cirri occur on the ventral surface and margins of *Stylonychia* and exhibit a variety of forms of beat—many cirri can beat in several different directions, and not all cirri are alike. For example, the anal

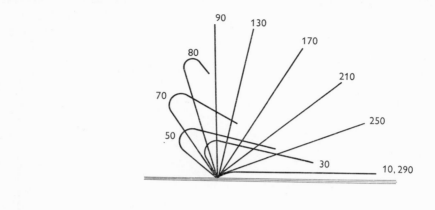

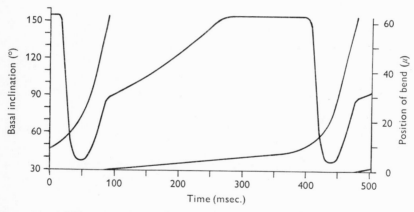

Fig. 5. The beat of an abfrontal cilium from a gill filament of *Mytilus edulis*, filmed at 300 frames/sec. at 20° C.

cirri show a more or less planar beat, the caudal cirri may show a helical beat, and the frontal cirri may show a beat in which the effective stroke occurs in one plane but the cirrus moves to one side in the recovery phase. A beat of this last type was described for the frontal cirrus of *Euplotes* by Gliddon (1965); here the tip of the cirrus was seen to follow the outline of a D, in which the planar movement of the effective stroke is followed by a sideways swing in which the cirrus moves anticlockwise (as seen from the tip) to return to the starting position. The most common movement of such a frontal cirrus is one in which the effective stroke is directed more or less straight back along the body; only this movement has so far been followed in detail in this study. These frontal cirri may beat rhythmically anywhere within a wide frequency range, but they are not continually active and may rest frequently in the position indicated in Fig. 6 (0–20). From this rest

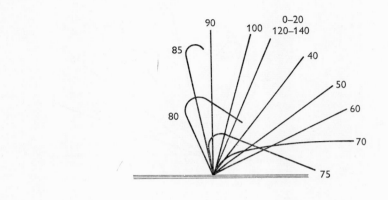

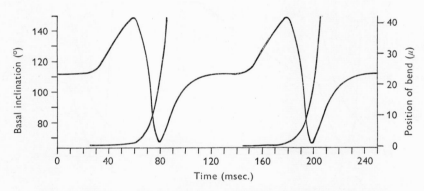

Fig. 6. The beat of a frontal cirrus of *Stylonychia mytilus*, filmed at 330 frames/sec. at 22° C.

position the cilium swings with a fairly quick effective stroke, and then a rapid return swing leads into the recovery phase whose flexure is propagated quickly to the ciliary tip during the early part of the next effective stroke. The compound cilium starts to move quickly at the beginning of the effective stroke, but gradually slows up as it approaches the resting position. The beat shows close similarities with that of the abfrontal cilium of *Mytilus*, except that the rest position is at a different place in the cycle.

Conspicuous among the diverse types of cilia on the cephalic tentacles of

Sabellaria are short thick compound cilia which sometimes stand perpendicular to the tentacle and sometimes lie along the tentacle surface. These cilia move from one position to the other at more or less random intervals. During the movements in both directions a bend is propagated

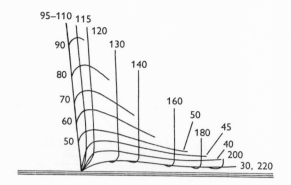

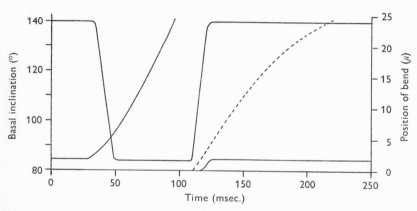

Fig. 7. The beat of a cilium from a cephalic tentacle of *Sabellaria alveolata*, filmed at 330 frames/sec. at 22° C.

along the flagellum from base to tip (Fig. 7), so that the cilium is never seen to move stiffly through the water in the extended effective-stroke position. The upward movement from the tentacle surface to the erect position is a typical recovery movement, but, when the basal bend occurs in the downward movement, the cilium does not remain straight distal to the bend— the distal region unrolls slowly from the base until it lies along the tentacle surface. The effective stroke is abnormal, with bends in both directions within its length; it is somewhat reminiscent of a flagellar beat.

The effective stroke of the cilium of *Opalina* (Fig. 8) is also not as stiff as that of a typical cilium; in fact this organelle could be described as a short flagellum with a slightly asymmetrical undulation. The close packing of these cilia on the surface of the organism probably has a considerable in-

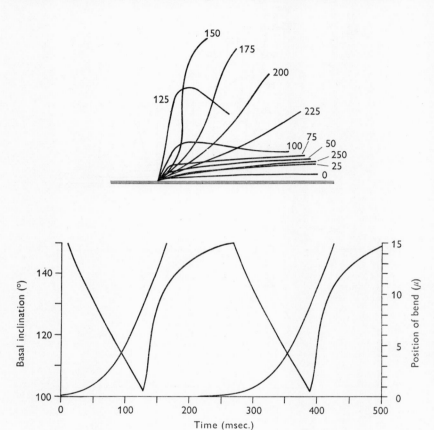

Fig. 8. The beat of a cilium of *Opalina ranarum*, filmed at 60 frames/sec. at 18° C.

fluence on the form of beat (Sleigh, 1960). For comparison, the movement of a typical flagellum is shown in Fig. 9, which is constructed from data given in an earlier paper (Sleigh, 1964); in other flagella there may be more complete waves within the flagellar length, and the rate of propagation of the waves (as well as amplitude) may increase or decrease towards the tip of the flagellum.

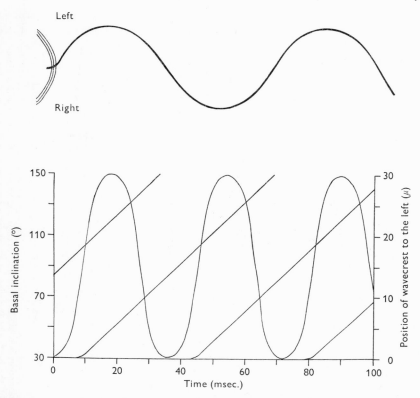

Fig. 9. The beat of a flagellum of *Codonosiga botrytis*, as reconstructed from photographs and stroboscope observations made at 18° C. (Sleigh, 1964.) The profile above indicates the position of the flagellum at 18 msec.

DISCUSSION

General comments on patterns of ciliary beating

The patterns of beat described fall into two main classes—those belonging to cilia from tracts in which the cilia are metachronally co-ordinated, and those of solitary cilia. The diagrams in Fig. 10 permit a comparison of the different beat cycles described here and of a few examples from the literature. The metachronal co-ordination of *Stentor* membranelles, *Jorunna* velar cilia, *Sabellaria* gill cilia (all compound cilia) and *Didinium* (simple cilia) is diaplectic, and all of these types show a similar beat which is very little different from the beat of *Pleurobrachia* comb plates (compound cilia), *Paramecium* cilia (simple) and the frontal cilia of *Mytilus* gill (simple), in which the metachronal co-ordination is antiplectic. The beat of the solitary 'flagellum' of the flagellate *Entosiphon* is unilateral and is more like

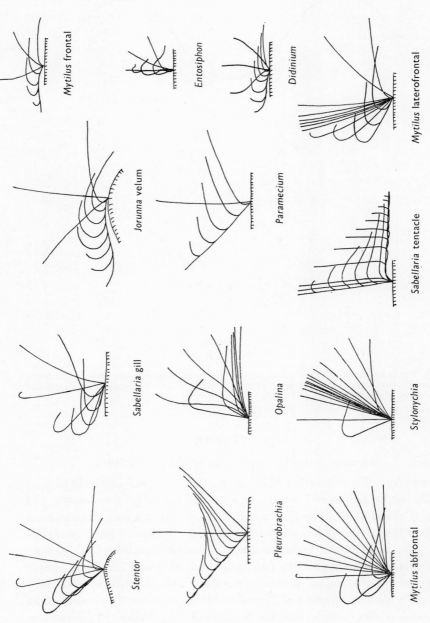

Fig. 10. Patterns of ciliary beating. Where the information is available, profiles in each sequence are drawn at equal time intervals to show up the slower and faster parts of the beat; the duration of these time intervals is different in different diagrams. The ciliary profiles were constructed from Figs. 1 to 8 above and from data in the literature as follows: frontal cilia of *Mytilus* from Gray (1922), flagella of *Entosiphon* from Jahn & Bovee (1967), cilia of *Didinium* from Parducz (1961), latero-

the beat of a typical cilium than is the beat of the ciliary organelle of *Opalina*. The other solitary organelles are compound cilia that tend to show individual peculiarities; e.g. they may stop in positions other than the beginning of the effective stroke, and the effective stroke may be very uneven in speed. The latero-frontal cilium of *Mytilus* behaves in this respect as if it were a solitary cilium, although Dral (1966) has described a form of diaplectic co-ordination of these latero-frontal cilia.

Parameters of the ciliary activity of the examples described in this paper are listed in Table 1. In terms of generalizations about the beating activity of cilia, this table gives rather little helpful information, but comparative data of this type are not available in the literature, and they may be of use in future discussions about ciliary movement. The following may be pointed out as being of general interest: (i) the angular swing of the effective stroke takes longer than that of the recovery stroke, (ii) the over-all duration of the recovery stroke is longer than that of the effective stroke, except in some solitary cilia where there is a rest or period of slow movement during the effective stroke, (iii) in some cilia there is a pause between the recovery stroke of one beat and the effective stroke of the next beat, and in other cases there is an overlap of adjacent beats, (iv) the rate of propagation of the flexure up the cilium is very variable, and does not appear to be correlated with any of the other parameters mentioned, though it does show a rough correlation with the number of ciliary shafts in the compound cilium. The general characteristics of the ciliary-beat cycle are probably best illustrated by *Stentor* membranelles, *Jorunna* velar cilia or *Pleurobrachia* comb plates, although in each case there are individual peculiarities.

The internal mechanism of ciliary movement

The observations of Satir (1965) on the arrangement of internal fibrils at the tips of cilia that are at the ends of their effective and recovery strokes, and the observations of Horridge (1965) concerning the cross-linking of the ciliary shafts and the degree of bending of macrocilia of *Beroe*, both suggest that the fibrils of the $9+2$ complex must slide over one another during the ciliary-beat cycle. As a result, it looks as if hypotheses of the mechanism of ciliary bending should be based on a system of sliding fibrils of constant length, and older hypotheses based on shortening of the fibrils (e.g. Sleigh, 1962) should be abandoned. The presence of the dynein ATPase system (Gibbons, 1965) in the form of arms projecting from one peripheral doublet towards the adjacent doublet makes a hypothesis based upon interaction between the peripheral doublets even more attractive.

If the fibrils of a cilium are all of the same length and are fixed in the basal body, changes in shape of the cilium must change the position of the

Table 1. Data on the cilia studied and their movements

	Pleurobrachia comb plate	Stentor membranelle	Joruma veliger	Sabellaria gill	Mytilus abfrontal	Stylonychia fr. cirrus	Sabellaria tentacle	Opalina	Codonosiga flagellum
1. Type of cilium	Compound	Compound	Compound	Compound	Compound	Compound	Compound	Simple	Simple
2. Simple or compound cilium	Antiplectic	Dexioplec.	Laeoplec.	Dexioplec.	Solitary	Solitary	Solitary	Symplec.	Solitary
3. Type of metachronism									
4. Cilium length (μ)	800	27·5	46	56	62	42	24	15	30
5. Temperature of observations (°C.)	17	22	22	20	20	22	22	18	18
6. Frequency of beat (cyc./sec.)	15·5	33	6·6	15	2·6	8·3	irreg. (4)	4	28
7. Angular swing of effective stroke (°)	96	67	100	77	118	82	56	48	120
8. Max. angular velocity during effective stroke (°/msec.)	10	9	3·3	5	2	2·3	5	2	15
9. Max. angular velocity of basal swing in recovery stroke (°/msec.)	27	14	5·2	25	6·6	9	3·8	0·5	15
10. Ratio of max. angular velocities 9/8	2·7	1·6	1·6	5·0	3·3	3·9	0·76	0·25	1·0
11. Duration of effective stroke (msec.)	11	9	38	40	225	98	15 (110)	140	18
12. Duration of basal swing in recovery stroke (msec.)	6	8	24	22	35	21	20	120	18
13. Ratio of durations of basal movements 12/11	0·55	0·9	0·63	0·55	0·16	0·21	1·33	0·85	1·0
14. Total duration of recovery stroke (msec.)	45	24	122	59	75	26	65	155	51
15. Ratio of total durations (recovery/effective) 14/11	4·1	2·7	3·2	1·5	0·33	0·27	0·6	1·1	2·8
16. Time for propagation of bend along cilium (msec.)	51	26	140	76	390	60	65	200	60
17. Max. propagation velocity of bend (μ/sec.)	16,600	1,200	500	800	1,200	4,000	450	160	500
18. Average propagation velocity of bend (μ/sec.)	15,700	1,060	330	740	160	700	340	75	500
19. Duration of pause (+) or overlap (−) between recovery and effective phases (msec.)	+9	−4	−8	−32	−40	−6	+15	−35	−33
20. Duration of pause during or at end of effective stroke (msec.), examples.	.	.	.	.	125	20	45	.	.

NOTES. The *Sabellaria* tentacle cilium beats irregularly; in the film the average frequency was 4 cyc./sec. In the effective stroke of this cilium the basal region completes its swing in 15 msec., but the distal part of the cilium does not reach the tentacle surface until 110 msec. The *Codonosiga* data is not based on filming; it is included for comparison only.

distal tips of the ciliary fibrils relative to one another (cf. Satir, 1965). The change in position of the tips of ciliary fibrils numbers 1 and 6 relative to a central fibril during the effective stroke of a cilium is shown in Fig. 11 a. The amount of sliding between opposite fibrils (1 and 6) depends only on the diameter of the fibril bundle and the angle between the regions of the cilium on either side of the bend, and not on the radius of the bend; if a

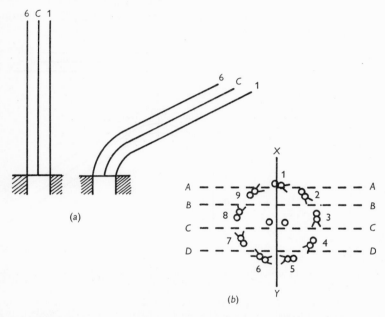

(a)

(b)

Fig. 11. (a) The change in position of the tips of peripheral fibrils 1 and 6 relative to a central fibril when a cilium bends during its effective stroke. (b) A transverse section of a ciliary shaft showing possible lines of sliding when the cilium bends in the plane XY.

cilium bends through 90°, the fibril at the inside of the bend will project about $\frac{1}{3}\mu$ further at the ciliary tip than the fibril at the outside of the bend. When a cilium bends at the base like this, the fibrils must slip by the same amount throughout the whole length of the cilium distal to the bend, but in the region of the bend the amount of sliding between adjacent fibrils will be limited by the basal attachment of the fibrils.

Let us consider the sliding of fibrils and its implications in a little more detail. Between each pair of peripheral doublets is a space across which the pairs of arms which project from one subfibril could form links with binding sites of the unarmed subfibril of the adjacent doublet, and these links could be used to exert a force between adjacent sliding doublets of fibrils comparable with that between the actin and myosin filaments of striated muscle. From a transverse section (Fig. 11 *b*) it can be seen that there are four lines (*A–A*, *B–B*, *C–C* and *D–D*) along which sliding may occur when a cilium bends in the plane *XY*, if we assume that each peripheral doublet slides along each of its neighbours (and there is a permanent link between fibrils 5 and 6). Horridge (1965) found that sliding could only occur along two of these lines in *Beroe*. If the amount of sliding between adjacent doublets is approximately the same along each of the four lines, then each doublet will slide on each of its neighbours by about 100Å. for every 10° of angular

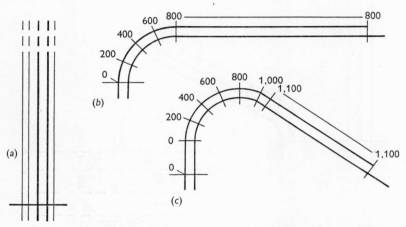

Fig. 12. The amount of sliding between adjacent fibril doublets at different times during the beat. (*a*) In the extended position the tips of all the ciliary fibrils are at the same level; only the two fibril doublets drawn with thicker lines are shown in the following diagrams. (*b*) The relative positions of the two doublets at the end of the effective stroke, the figures indicate (in Å.) the calculated amount of sliding between fibrils at the points indicated. (*c*) The relative positions of the two doublets when the flexure has moved a short distance up the shaft in the recovery stroke.

movement during the bending of a cilium (or each doublet slides on each neighbour by a distance equal to the interval between arms along the fibril for about every 20° of angular movement). During an average effective stroke each pair of arms in the distal region of the cilium may move about 800Å. along the adjacent doublet; the amount of slip between adjacent fibrils at various regions of such a flexed cilium is shown in Fig. 12*b*.

If new links capable of exerting a force are made between adjacent peripheral doublets which slide on each other, it is evident that during the effective stroke of a cilium new links can be formed throughout the length of the ciliary shaft, and the longitudinal pull exerted on the fibrils can act at the ciliary base to bend the shaft of the cilium in the region where the amount of sliding is limited; this cross-linking between the fibrils of the shaft could also account for the stiffness attributed to the cilium during its effective stroke. It is also important that new links could be formed between doublets all round the ring of 9 and not only on the inner side of the ciliary bend. As a result the whole of the energetic machinery throughout the length and diameter of the ciliary shaft can be brought into action during the effective stroke. It is of interest that the rate of slip of one fibril relative to its neighbour during the effective stroke would be between 1 and 10 μ/sec in the cilia described in this paper; the rate of sliding of myosin filaments along actin filaments is of the same order.

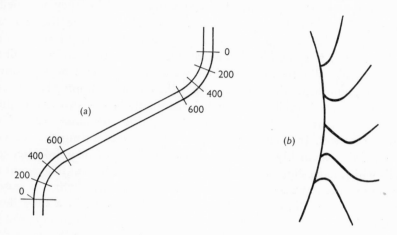

Fig. 13. Backward bending of the ciliary shaft during the effective stroke. (a) The amount of sliding between adjacent doublets (in Å.) at various points along the shaft of a cilium which bends backwards during the effective stroke (hypothetical). (b) During the effective stroke of a comb plate of *Pleurobrachia* the cilia may bend backwards and the position of the bend may travel up the cilium as seen in this tracing. The sequence of stages in the beat is from above downwards, with the effective stroke downwards; the backward bend is seen in the second, third and fourth profiles.

In this discussion it has been assumed that the distal part of the cilium remains straight during the effective stroke, so that the sliding of fibrils in the distal region must keep pace with the sliding at the site of bending. If the fibrils were to slide more slowly in the distal region than at the bend, the distal region of the cilium would bend backwards in order to accommodate fibrils which have slipped at the basal bend (Fig. 13a); one would expect that such a backward bend—indicating the extent of slipping or slipped fibrils—would be propagated up the cilium towards the tip. It appears that an extreme example of this may be seen in the 'effective stroke' of the cilia on the tentacles of *Sabellaria*, in which a backward bend travels very slowly (200–300 μ/sec) towards the tip of the cilium (Fig. 7). An obvious place to look for such a backward bend is in the very long cilia of ctenophore comb plates, and it appears to be there also (e.g. Fig. 13b); the rate of propagation of the backward bend in this case was about 30 mm./sec. If the linear speed of propagation of the extent of slipping were of this order in cilia of average length, the backward bend would reach the tip within an angular movement of 5° or so, and would hardly be noticed.

Further bending in the direction followed during the effective stroke, presumably accompanied by further slipping of the fibrils, occurs after the recovery stroke has started. At the beginning of the recovery phase the fibrils in the basal region start to slip back to the position they occupied at the beginning of the beat, and the cilium straightens out as the region of return slipping moves up the cilium and carries the ciliary flexure to the tip (Fig. 12c). It is significant that during the effective stroke the fibrils may normally slip throughout their whole length more or less simultaneously, but during the recovery stroke the region of slipping is restricted to the bent part of the cilium (provided that the angle of flexure of the cilium remains constant, which it usually does during the latter part of the recovery stroke). It is clear that some work is done during the recovery stroke, and presumably this involves the formation of new links between fibrils which have slipped back to their original position; to this extent the recovery stroke must be regarded as an active movement, which is reasonable since some cilia (e.g. *Mytilus* abfrontals) will rest in a fully flexed position from which they proceed to perform a vigorous recovery stroke— it seems unlikely that this is entirely elastic.

The sliding fibril hypothesis appears also to be applicable to the movement of a flagellum. In this case all parts of the flagellum that are parallel to the axis of the basal body (i.e. the crests of the waves) will be regions of zero slip between fibrils, and the straight regions between wave-crests will be regions of maximum slip (Fig. 14). In such an arrangement the fibrils will terminate unevenly at the distal end of the flagellum during most of the beat, but at the basal body there are no problems of accommodating fibrils that have slipped by different amounts. Incidentally, the resultant waveform would be expected to take the form of a sequence of circular arcs and straight regions as reported for flagella by Brokaw & Wright (1963) and for sperm tails by Brokaw (1965).

It is believed that this hypothesis should be applicable to the movement of all of the cilia and flagella described here in spite of the individual variations shown in every case. However, the hypothesis raises several problems, such as the mechanism of action of the arms in forming links and the part played by the radial connexions which could limit the amount of sliding. The mechanism required by a sliding fibril hypothesis of this type is simpler than that involved in a contraction hypothesis, and it is hoped that further observation and experiment will provide more tangible evidence in one direction or the other.

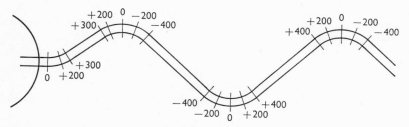

Fig. 14. The amount of sliding between adjacent doublets (in Å.) along the length of a flagellum. Positive values indicate sliding of the upper doublet to the right and negative values indicate sliding of the upper doublet to the left relative to the lower doublet.

SUMMARY

The cycles of beat of cilia which take part in metachronal waves are all of the same general type—the duration of the recovery phase is longer than that of the effective phase and the rest position is at the beginning of the effective stroke. Solitary cilia are much more variable; they may have a very slow effective stroke and may rest at other parts of the cycle, e.g. during or at the end of the effective stroke. These features are clearly seen in the graphs and the table which summarize the quantitative data obtained from the various types of cilium.

A hypothesis based upon the sliding of peripheral fibril doublets along one another is advanced to explain the observed movements of cilia and flagella. According to this theory, the formation of new links at the arms on the peripheral doublets produces the force which causes movement. During the effective stroke new links could be formed throughout the length and diameter of the ciliary shaft and could exert longitudinal forces acting at the ciliary base to bend the cilium as the ciliary fibrils slide along one another. The bend travels up the cilium during the recovery stroke, and the fibrils must slide back to the original position, forming new links again in the region of the bend. Flagella could be bent in a comparable manner.

Thanks are due to the Science Research Council for grants to provide equipment and assistance. I am also grateful to Miss Sheila Manning and Miss Margaret Nicholas who have helped in various parts of this work.

REFERENCES

BROKAW, C. J. (1965). *J. exp. Biol.* **43**, 155.

BROKAW, C. J. & WRIGHT, L. (1963). *Science, N.Y.* **142**, 1169.

DRAL, A. D. G. (1966). *Nature, Lond.* **210**, 1170.

GIBBONS, I. R. (1965). *Archs Biol., Liège* **76**, 317.

GLIDDON, R. (1965). Structure and function in *Euplotes eurystomus*. Ph.D. thesis, University of Bristol.

GRAY, J. (1922). *Proc. R. Soc.* B **93**, 104.

GRAY, J. (1930). *Proc. R. Soc.* B **107**, 313.

HOLWILL, M. E. J. (1966). *Physiol. Rev.* **46**, 696.

HORRIDGE, G. A. (1965). *Proc. R. Soc.* B **162**, 351.

JAHN, T. L. & BOVEE, E. C. (1967). In *Research in Protozoology*, vol. 1, 41. Ed. T. T. Chen. Oxford: Pergamon Press.

KINOSITA, H. & KAMADA, T. (1939). *Jap. J. Zool.* **8**, 291.

PARDUCZ, B. (1961). *Annls hist.-nat. Mus. natn. hung., Zool.* **53**, 267.

SATIR, P. (1965). *J. Cell Biol.* **26**, 805.

SLEIGH, M. A. (1960). *J. exp. Biol.* **37**, 1.

SLEIGH, M. A. (1962). *The Biology of Cilia and Flagella.* Oxford: Pergamon Press.

SLEIGH, M. A. (1964). *Q. Jl microsc. Sci.* **105**, 405.

YONEDA, M. (1960). *J. exp. Biol.* **37**, 461.

YONEDA, M. (1962). *J. exp. Biol.* **39**, 307.

DIFFERENCES OF A FUNDAMENTAL NATURE AMONG SEVERAL TYPES OF AMOEBOID MOVEMENT

By ROBERT D. ALLEN

Department of Biological Sciences, State University of New York at Albany, and The Marine Biological Laboratory, Woods Hole, Massachusetts

Since the majority of observations and experiments on amoeboid movement (usually defined as cell locomotion either by means of pseudopodia, or by internal cytoplasmic streaming), have been carried out using *Amoeba proteus* or *Chaos carolinensis* as material, it would be desirable to know the extent to which the conclusions reached can be generalized to other types of amoeboid cells. The primary aim of this paper is to summarize and examine some of the more important results obtained so far with the '*Amoeba–Chaos* group' and to call attention to some major differences in movement and behaviour among some of the groups of amoeboid cells.

The idea that all examples of amoeboid movement can be accounted for by one or at most two models (or 'theories') is widespread, either as a tacit assumption or as a firm conviction. We do not know for certain whether 'amoeboid movement' is a single phenomenon with numerous variations in detail or a collection of fundamentally quite diverse phenomena with superficial similarities. A second aim of this paper is to consider this question of the generality of mechanism in the light of present evidence.

CHARACTERISTICS OF MOVEMENT

The Amoeba–Chaos group

The following points constitute a summary of conclusions based on live observations and analysis of films by a variety of methods on the part of several members of my research group and students over the past half-dozen years. Much of the actual data will be published *in extenso* in the near future. The principal organism we have used has been the giant carnivorous amoeba, *Chaos carolinensis*, in prime physiological condition. Our studies have been carried out with various types of light microscopes using heat-filtered mercury green-line (546 nm.) illumination at a variety of light intensities. Great care has been taken to confirm in living material observations of phenomena first observed on film, where the vertical dimension of the optical image has been lost. Some of the observations are new, but there has been no systematic attempt to list and evaluate all 'new observations' reported in the recent literature, for some of these have turned out to be wrong or uncritical interpretations of commonplace events.

(1) Pseudopods of normal polypodial specimens form initially and continue to move independently of one another.

(2) Retracting pseudopods shorten slowly, while endoplasm within them is recruited from the walls of the ectoplasmic tube.

(3) The main body of endoplasm in a pseudopod often streams sporadically; spurts of streaming in different pseudopods are not synchronized.

(4) In addition to the main body of endoplasm streaming down the centre of a pseudopod there are 'streamlets' moving forward in channels through the ectoplasmic tube in many specimens (Goldacre, 1964; Jahn, 1964). These may stream either sporadically or continuously.

(5) The first indication of a spurt is detectable very near the pseudopod tip, and a wave of forward acceleration of endoplasmic particles spreads backward along the pseudopod away from the tip.

(6) Reversal of streaming direction under constant illumination apparently always begins at the *new* tip and spreads towards the old one. The old tip may initiate a few progressively weaker and finally futile attempts at 're-reversal' before the new direction of streaming is fully established.

(7) Hyaline caps are formed typically (but not always) before pseudopods appear, and at the onset of both spurts of streaming and abortive re-reversals.

(8) The pattern of streaming in a cylindrical pseudopod is generally that of a fountain with respect to the pseudopod itself, but when the plasmalemma and ectoplasmic tube are anchored to the substratum, most of the backward ectoplasmic movement relative to the pseudopod tip becomes stationary relative to the substratum (Allen, 1961b). Hence little if any backward movement relative to the substratum is seen in well-attached pseudopods, except near the tip, where it is attributable to slight ectoplasmic shortening. When it occurs, anterior ectoplasmic shortening is usually correlated with especially strong spurts in streaming velocity.

(9) The pattern of endoplasmic streaming in non-cylindrical pseudopods is most often an 'asymmetrical fountain' in which the ectoplasmic tube (the region of backward streaming relative to the pseudopod) has thick and thin regions within the same cross-section of pseudopod. In extreme cases of asymmetry, one may find a 'loop-pattern', especially in food-cup pseudopods, or a 'roller-towel pattern' in flattened sheet-like pseudopods, which we have named 'pharopodia' (Greek for 'shroud-feet'). If either the loop or roller-towel patterns are observed or filmed at a plane of focus that in-

cludes only the streaming endoplasm in the 'optical section', it is possible to gain the mistaken impression that all particles in the pseudopod are moving forward. This claim, advanced recently by Jahn (1964) and by Rinaldi & Jahn (1963), and based on film records, has not been confirmed in our studies, for, when living material is observed directly under these conditions, focusing up or down always reveals the other arm of the cytoplasmic loop or sheet: it takes the form of a bed of stationary ectoplasm occupying about half of the cross-section of the pseudopod.

(10) Endoplasmic streaming is not always undirectional as long assumed. Although we mentioned chance observations of 'counter-currents' of endoplasm in an earlier paper (Allen, 1961a), it is only recently that we have detected and analysed these movements in extensive film records in which the optical depth of field was accurately known. Mr A. C. Breuer has analysed velocity profiles of several examples of counter-current streamlets near the centre of the endoplasmic stream varying in volume in intact *Chaos carolinensis*, and has found negative velocity values in these counter-current streamlets that are comparable to the positive velocities found in the endoplasmic mainstream.

(11) Endoplasmic streaming has a periodic component that can be easily detected in compressed or tightly confined cells that are barely able to move (cf. Goldacre, 1964, for references to earlier work). Careful analysis of high-speed films by Mr A. C. Breuer has revealed the presence of this oscillation also in uncompressed or unconfined specimens about to change direction, and in specimens exhibiting rapid streaming. In the latter case the oscillation is seen as a slight periodic fluctuation in the velocity of streaming. The frequency of velocity fluctuation is approximately 1 cyc./sec., and the amplitude is of the order of 1 μ. The amplitude is greatest at the pseudopod tip, and diminishes toward the tail.

(12) Cytoplasm from *Chaos carolinensis* in a cell-free system produced by 'skinning' an amoeba inside a tight-fitting quartz tube shows organized streaming for periods of up to and slightly more than 1 hr. (Allen, Cooledge, & Hall, 1960; Griffin, 1964). Symmetrical fountain, asymmetrical fountain, and loop patterns of streaming have all been observed, depending on the history of the preparation. Various possible causes for this streaming were systematically examined, and the most likely was determined to be contraction, for both in the loop and fountain patterns a contractile deformation coupled with syneresis was detected by analysis of films. The cytoplasm shortens and thickens locally as it produces syneretic vesicles. More recently, Wolpert, Thompson & O'Neill (1964) have succeeded in preparing a cytoplasmic fraction from mass cultures of *Amoeba proteus* that imitates some of these movements *in vitro*.

Models applicable to the Amoeba-Chaos group

To aid in the interpretation of these observations, there is now an impressive (also confusing!) array of models. Many of these are not particularly successful in accounting for the observed complexities; others depend on processes (e.g. surface expansion model of Bell, 1961) or special ultrastructural features (the jet-propulsion model of Kavanau, 1963) that have never been demonstrated or seem inherently unlikely. The models based on cytoplasmic contractility have enjoyed the most widespread acceptance (Mast, 1926; Goldacre & Lorch, 1950; Landau, 1959; Allen, 1961 a, b; Jahn, 1964; Bovee, 1964; Griffin, 1964), although there is a lack of general agreement on where the contraction may take place. We know that cytoplasm contracts violently on direct exposure to calcium. On glycerination, ATP-induced contraction occurs in the presence of calcium ions, just as in muscle (Simard-Duquesne & Couillard, 1962).

The only purpose that models serve is to force us to test our understanding of a process by a formal comparison of evidence from observation and experimentation with the predictions of the model. As a first step toward the evaluation of two contractility models that have been much discussed in the past, I submit Table 1, which summarizes the facts that have been established about movement in *Chaos* and presents one observer's opinion as to the compatibility or incompatibility of the features of movement (described more fully in the text) with the frontal contraction model (Allen, 1961 a) and with the tail-contraction model (Mast, 1926; Goldacre & Lorch, 1950; Goldacre, 1964; Jahn, 1964). It should be noted, however, that various authors have proposed slightly different versions of the tail-contraction model.

The frontal and tail contraction models are the simplest ones that have been proposed, but, if Occam's razor can be disregarded, it is doubtless possible to suggest several more complicated hypotheses that might account for some or all of the complexities of movement. For example, one might consider an attempt to reconcile the frontal and tail contraction models with a suggestion either that (a) there might be two contractions, one in the front and the other in the tail, or (b) than an amoeba (of any species) might have both types of contraction in its repertory but normally use only one or the other for locomotion.

The main argument against this type of 'dual contraction hypothesis' comes from the study of the cycle of rheological changes in amoeboid cells. Although the significance of the so called 'sol-gel transformation cycle' is not understood in terms of what rheological state corresponds to what state of contraction, we assume that since opposite phases of the rheological cycle are situated at opposite poles of the cell, the opposite phases of the contraction cycle must be similarly polarized.

Another possibility, suggested by the 'sliding-filament' nature of muscle contraction, is that contraction in the amoeba might not take the form of 'bulk contraction' of a mass of cytoplasm, but rather of the opposite displacement of two bodies of cytoplasm perhaps containing different types of (hypothetical) filaments. One could imagine that the 'shear zone' of the amoeba was a site in which concentric cylindrical layers of cytoplasm were climbing over one another. Such a model would account for pseudopod extension or retraction, but would leave many of the complexities of movement and behaviour unexplained.

From Table 1 it should be apparent that at least one reviewer sees the frontal contraction model as entirely compatible with the available facts concerning the features of movement in *Chaos*. Claims to the contrary on the part of other authors (e.g. Jahn, 1964; Rinaldi & Jahn, 1963) do not, in my opinion, stand up to careful scrutiny. For example, the existence of 'streamlets' moving through (and even outside) the ectoplasmic tube had been claimed to invalidate the frontal contraction model. However, there is nothing in this model that would prevent streamlets moving in response to a tensile force applied at their destinations, or, for that matter, in response to secondary local hydrostatic pressure gradients established as a result of movement of the main mass of endoplasm. The frontal contraction model does require one important assumption, namely, that the endoplasm must have enough structure to transmit tensile forces. As we shall see later, there is good evidence that both the natural motive force and artificially applied tensile forces are transmitted.

The tail contraction model, on the other hand, is very clearly incompatible with points 9, 10 and 12 in Table 1, and requires some assumptions in connexion with points 1, 3, 5, 6, 7 and 8. These assumptions, referred to by letter in the Table, are as follows:

A. *That the entire ectoplasmic tube is contractile, and that the contractions always begin at the anterior rim of the tube and spread backward toward the tail.* This variation of the tail contraction model was proposed by Marsland (1964) in order to explain several events and spurts. Evidence from the analysis of films indicates some anterior shortening after the spurt, but not before it. There is very little if any shortening in the mid-region of pseudopods, but considerable shortening in the tail. Thus, there does not appear to be evidence supporting the notion of a propagated contraction in the ectoplasmic tube.

B. *That the hyaline cap is produced by syneresis from the anterior ectoplasm.* As pointed out under A, the sequence is opposite to that expected: hyaline cap formation precedes shortening. Interference micrographs presented at this society's symposium in 1965 (Allen & Francis, 1965) showed subtraction of water from a region of the anterior *endoplasm*.

Table 1. *Features of movement in the giant amoeba Chaos carolinensis*

	Compatibility of features with contraction models	
Features (summarized from the text)	Frontal	Tail
1 Independent pseudopod formation, extension, retraction in polypodial specimens	Compatible	Compatible (with Assumption A)
2 Pseudopods shorten on retraction; endoplasm recruited from walls of ectoplasmic tube	Compatible	Compatible
3 Streaming spurts are not synchronized	Compatible	Compatible (with Assumption A)
4 Streamlets move in channels through ectoplasmic tube	Compatible	Compatible
5 Spurt accelerations are propagated posteriorly from the tips of pseudopods	Compatible	Compatible (with Assumption A)
6 Waves of acceleration are propagated from tip in reversals and re-reversals	Compatible	Compatible (with Assumption A)
7 Anterior hyaline cap formation precedes spurts, reversals, and re-reversals	Compatible	Compatible (with Assumption B)
8 Backward movement in anterior ectoplasm, when it occurs, represents shortening	Compatible	Compatible (with Assumption A)
9 Three related patterns of streaming exist: fountain, loop, and 'roller-towel'	Compatible	Incompatible
10 Bi-directional streaming and counter-currents	Compatible	Incompatible (without Assumption C)
11 Oscillations in quiescent cells, periodic fluctuations in streaming velocity	Compatible	Compatible
12 Organized streaming continues in cell-free system showing fountain, loop patterns	Compatible	Incompatible (without Assumption D)

C. *That when counter-currents occur, they cannot be the result of the postulated hydrostatic pressure gradient, but of a directed force operating locally against the gradient.* There seems to be no evidence bearing on this point but if a directed force, such as tension from contraction, must be invoked to explain the counter-currents, then why should one not explain movement of the main mass of endoplasm in the same way?

D. *That cytoplasmic streaming in cell-free systems performs by some mechanism other than that operating in the living, intact cell, even though the patterns of streaming are similar.* Although we cannot rule out this possibility, it seems inherently unlikely that the cell would have evolved a separate mechanism for streaming in cell-free systems.

The other models not based on contractility will be omitted from consideration here because of space limitations. Perhaps it is preferable to suggest to the proponents of such models that a demonstration of the compatibility of their models with the known features of movement is desirable.

Our second step in the evaluation of these models has been to design experiments to test the models and weigh the impact of the evidence on them. Unfortunately, much of the evidence from experiments designed to test one model frequently turns out to be interpretable in more than one way. A notable and encouraging exception has been the cycle of birefringence changes recorded near *Chaos* pseudopod tips during sporadic streaming (Allen, Francis & Nakajima, 1965). These changes have not yet been reconciled with the tail contraction model, but are, so far, consistent with the location and sign of birefringence expected from the application of tensile and compressive forces to the endoplasm and ectoplasm respectively on the basis of the frontal contraction model. In essence, it has apparently been possible to use the amoeba's own cytoplasm as a sensitive photoelastic strain-gauge to detect and localize the minute tensile and compressive forces applied during pseudopod extension. The interpretation of birefringence as due to strain was considerably strengthened by the fact that birefringence changes were detected only during sporadic (i.e. not in continuous) streaming. An important feature of the film records of the birefringence changes was the propagation of positive birefringence from the tip some distance toward the tail. This is interpreted as support for the assumption required by the frontal contraction theory: that tensile forces can be transmitted by elastic elements in the endoplasm. Further support for this interpretation comes from unpublished results obtained in collaboration with Dr David Francis which show that positive birefringence was detectable even in the tail endoplasm during the application of a sharp suck from a micropipette at the tip of pseudopod. This detection was made both using photographic means whereby the exact location of birefringence could be visualized, and on chart paper records from a microbeam electronic birefringence detector developed in our laboratory (Allen, Brault & Moore, 1963; Allen, Brault & Zeh, 1966). Birefringence faded and elastic recoil took place in the endoplasm on release from suction.

Another result that still remains straightforward has been the finding that water is subtracted from a region of the anterior endoplasm, the approximate location proposed for the frontal contraction (Allen & Francis,

1965). Some of this water apparently contributes to the hyaline cap, while the rest is redistributed within the anterior portion of the pseudopod.

In general, we begin to see a consistent pattern in the evidence supporting the frontal contraction model. This is not to say, however, that we understand how this species of amoeba moves. At present we believe only that we understand how and where the principal force is applied. Control is quite another matter. We agree with Goldacre (1964 and earlier) that feedback systems of some kind must be operating to regulate the speed of movement and the shape of the cell. The fine control mechanisms required to bring about feeding and responses to stimuli remain mysterious but are perhaps eventually better explained in terms of a force applied and controlled in the front, where the behavioural events occur, than in the tail, but so far we have very little information on how movement is controlled. We hope to find this out.

Models applicable to Pelomyxa movement

It is ironic that observations on amoeboid movement in the giant herbivorous amoeba, *Pelomyxa palustris*, were not the basis for Mast's (1926) formulation of the tail contraction model, for movement in this species is rarely more than continuous progression at nearly constant speed by a monopodial organism that maintains a remarkably uniform shape. Nearly all of the complexities of movement found in *Chaos* (see Table 1) and *Amoeba proteus* are lacking, and a very simple model such as that proposed by Mast is all that is required to account for continuous monopodial progression (Cf. Mast, 1932; Allen, 1961a; Griffin, 1964). Dr J. L. Griffin began in my laboratory a comparative study of movement in *Pelomyxa palustris* and *Chaos carolinensis*, the results of which I followed with considerable interest, for I had previously assumed that amoeboid locomotion would not differ fundamentally from species to species. Table 2 is taken directly from Griffin's (1964) paper and points out very clearly the major differences in details of movement. His study leaves little doubt that *Pelomxya* and *Chaos* are quite different morphologically, cytologically, and physiologically, and that they occupy distinctly different ecological niches.

Griffin (1964) pointed out that the tail contraction model was adequate to account satisfactorily for the features of movement outlined in Table 2. It is perhaps noteworthy, after the discussion of movement and models to explain movement in *Chaos*, that none of the assumptions required by the tail contraction model for *Chaos* are required for *Pelomyxa*. While this might seem an ideal situation from a theoretician's point of view in that *Pelomyxa* conforms in every respect to the expectations of the traditional form of the tail contraction model, it should also be pointed out that other models cannot be ruled out on the basis of present evidence.

Further experimental work is clearly needed to test the tail contraction model with this material. Unfortunately, this species (and related ones) are difficult to raise in the laboratory, are easily damaged by experimental procedures and are optically opaque. Many, in fact, contain small jagged rocks, which apparently keep them weighted down in the mud of the lake bottom. Our best hope is that a hardier and more transparent related genus may be brought into successful culture.

Table 2. *Summary of observed differences in several giant amoebae related to movement*

Table II of Griffin (1964).

Property	C. carolinensis, C. illinoisensis, A. proteus	Pelomyxa palustris
1 Characteristic form in locomotion	Polypodial (alternate pseudopods), ectoplasmic ridges, wrinkled tail	Monopodial, cylindrical body
2 Initiation of movement	Many pseudopods, gradual decrease in number	Extrusion of hyaline fluid over surface, single pseudopod
3 Hyaline cap or layer	Forms at front	Forms at rear
4 Reversal of direction	Frequent, wave of reversal from pseudopod base to tip	Ectoplasmic barrier forms and hyaline material is extruded at old front
5 Large inclusions	Carried in tail	Carried at front
6 Ingestion of food	Anterior food cups, motile food	Algae pulled in at tail
7 Light sensitivity	In anterior fountain zone, rapid response	Relatively insensitive, slow response
8 A_t/A_s ratio	Greater than one	Apparently less than one at times
9 Behaviour of naked cytoplasm	Continues streaming in fountain and loop patterns	Contraction of tail of broken organisms, no streaming in naked cytoplasm

CHARACTERISTICS OF MOVEMENT IN THE TESTACEAN *DIFFLUGIA CORONA*

The testaceans, or shelled amoebae, are not among the most convenient organisms in which to study pseudopodial movement. Their pseudopods rarely extend far enough beyond the shell (or test) to be seen clearly with a high numerical aperture optical system. Mast (1931) studied two species of *Difflugia* and concluded that movement was very similar to that in *A. proteus*, for which species he had already proposed one form of the tail contraction model.

For several months one of our assistants, Mrs Eleanor Carver, managed to maintain a flourishing culture of one of the largest testaceans, *Difflugia corona*. Dr Alan Wohlman and I undertook a detailed study of movement and ultrastructure in these organisms, which proved to be splendid material because of their relatively long and transparent pseudopodia. This material was also extremely favourable for the study of pseudopod contraction; *D. corona* has a heavy test which it can carry about by this means. The following are some of the more interesting findings from our study, a report of which is now in the press (Wohlman & Allen, 1968).

Pseudopods tend to be cylindrical when first extended. They frequently point somewhat upward at first, and wave about before settling on to the substratum, where they establish one or two attachment points which are recognizable by local flattening. The pattern of streaming is, as far as one can tell, a fountain pattern nearly identical to that in the more perfectly cylindrical pseudopods of *Chaos*, but since the cytoplasmic particles are small and not very contrasty, it is more difficult to follow the pattern. Reversals and re-reversals occur as in *Chaos* (cf. Table 1). Sporadic streaming is observed with acceleration waves propagating toward the cell body. So far, counter-currents have not been observed. In polarized light, 'flashes' of positive birefringence have been seen near pseudopod tips in sporadically streaming specimens. These flashes suggest the development of tension and its subsequent relaxation as flow occurs, as apparently happens in *Chaos* (Allen *et al.* 1965).

The unique feature of movement in *D. corona* (and probably other testaceans as well) is the rapidity with which pseudopods, once they have attached to the substratum, are able to retract forcibly in order to transport the heavy test. This rapid shortening is quite different in character from pseudopod shortening in the naked amoebae. In polarized light one can see, soon after attachment, the rapid growth of an array of intracytoplasmic fibrils extending from the attachment point(s) to the cell body within the test. This array may be fully formed within 10–30 sec. of attachment. They are highly positively birefringent ($Br = +10^{-2}$), but during retraction they shorten and seem (in the polarized light image) to 'melt', disappearing about the time the retracting pseudopod disappears into the test. The retraction phase is far more dramatic than in *A. proteus* or *Chaos*, and is accompanied by the formation of extensive blebs of fluid with a lower refractive index than the original pseudopod cytoplasm, suggesting that the blebs contain syneretic fluid produced during contraction of material in or around the fibrils. Sometimes a pseudopod is extended with an extensive array of fibrils, but does not show much movement once formed; such pseudopods apparently serve as anchors to hold the organism to the substratum while inactive.

The fibrils are not only birefringent, but are visible in the differential interference microscope as phase-retarding structures of higher refractive index than their surround. It is thus not surprising that Dr Wohlman's electron micrographs showed bundles of 55–75Å. microfilaments corresponding to the fibrils seen in the light microscope. The large testaceans merit much further study as an almost ideal material in which to study the molecular basis of contraction and perhaps also pseudopod extension in amoeboid cells.

Models applicable to movement in Difflugia

The details of pseudopod extension are sufficiently similar to those in *Chaos* to allow us to suspect that the frontal contraction model may apply. Except for streaming behaviour during reversals and re-reversals, and acceleration waves progressing away from pseudopod tips in sporadic streaming, the ordinary details of streaming would be compatible also with the tail contraction model, assuming the 'tail' is often hidden within the test, but the flashes of birefringence during sporadic streaming are difficult to reconcile with the tail contraction model and suggest the deployment of forces expected according to the frontal contraction model.

The forcible retraction of pseudopods that brings about transport of the heavy test apparently represents a special mechanism not necessarily related to pseudopod extension. It is special in that a system of fibrils is layed down in the cytoplasm apparently to participate in the forcible contraction. Such fibrils are not found in *Chaos* or *A. proteus*, and the details of pseudopod retraction are dissimilar.

Some comments on the characteristics of movement in small, free-living amoebae

One investigator, who has observed and described many species of small, free-living amoebae, has remarked that they are far more varied in form, speed, manner of movement and behaviour than the more frequently studied giant amoebae, which he regards as 'stodgy' (Bovee, 1964). This view corresponds fully with my own, based in part on reading many accounts (cf. Bovee, 1964, for references, especially to his own copious work; also, Abé, 1961, 1962, and Penard, 1905, and others) and in part on numerous observations on living small amoebae and films made in my own laboratory.

Descriptions in the literature have been concerned chiefly with form changes of whole organisms and the gross movements of which their pseudopods are capable. These studies form an indispensable base line for the needed further research into detailed mechanisms of movement that should now be possible with modern optical, ultrastructural, and bio-chemical methods. It is perhaps not surprising that we now lack detailed information of the type available for the giant amoebae, because the smaller forms are between one and two orders of magnitude smaller.

The range of pseudopod shapes is considerable in the small amoebae: cylindrical or conical lobopodia, blunt or pointed filopodia (which may at times branch and fuse like the reticulopodia of Foraminifera), sheet-like 'pharopodia', slender filopodia that bend, wave, or suddenly coil (see especially Bovee, 1964, for drawings of the great variety of pseudopod forms and motions).

A common but by no means universal feature of the small amoebae is their hyaline pseudopods into which cytoplasmic particles, massed in the trailing cell body, seldom if ever invade. Many of these hyaline pseudopods move very slowly compared to pseudopods of the giant amoebae, and, since no particles are present to serve as markers, the pattern of streaming remains unknown. A remarkable exception comes from the work of Abé (1961, 1962, 1963) on *Amoeba (Thecamoeba) striata* and other amoebae of the *verrucosa* type, in which he worked out the pattern of streaming among islands of apparent gel. Abé concluded that the fundamental process in the movement of this species was the building forward of gel structures, especially at the front. If the change of state from the more fluid endoplasm ('sol') to gel were accompanied by a contraction, as we postulated to be the case in *Chaos*, then Abé's account would be readily interpretable in terms of the frontal contraction model. It is clear from Abé's (1963) discussion that tensile forces are required to bring about the observed events.

An interesting feature in many of the small amoebae is the occurrence of vigorous saltatory movement in the trailing cell body. (For reviews of the mechanism of saltatory motion, see Rebhun, 1963, 1964, 1967.) I have observed this especially in the mayorellids, where the direction of saltation seems to be random, and in the frontal region of 'eruptive' *limax*-type forms, where the saltations appear to be polarized parallel to the direction of movement and to be bi-directional. Shaffer (1964) has described similar motions in slime-mould amoebae. The functional relationship of saltation to amoeboid movement is not known.

I suspect that future studies on small amoebae with improved instrumentation will shed light on many forms of amoeboid movement and their evolutionary relationships to one another and to other types of movement (e.g. flagellar, euglenoid) found within the sarcodines and flagellates.

CHARACTERISTICS OF MOVEMENT IN THE
FORAMINIFERA AND RADIOLARIA

These marine organisms are capable of producing from a few to about 100 pseudopods in a spectrum of shapes from thick lobopodia to thin, sheet-like pharopodia, or long, slender filopodia that may branch and fuse to establish a web-like 'reticulopodial network'. Foraminifera, living generally on the bottom or attached to vegetation, extend their networks more or less in a single plane along solid surfaces, while the fewer pelagic Foraminifera and most Radiolaria (the majority of which are pelagic) extend their networks in three dimensions. The network of pseudopodia provides an efficient trap for bacteria, algae, protista and detritus from which some nutrient value may be gleaned.

It should be recognized from the beginning that the application of the term 'pseudopod' to these cytoplasmic extensions and to those of amoebae may draw us into a semantic trap. We should probably bear in mind that the differences in form and function may eventually force us to use a different terminology that recognizes these differences.

Most of the quantitative data regarding movement in these groups has been drawn from recent studies of two Foraminifera: *Allogromia laticollaris* (Arnold, 1955; Jahn & Rinaldi, 1959) and a smaller species, *Allogromia* sp. strain N.F. (Lee & Pierce, 1963; Allen 1964). Interesting descriptions of other forms are also to be found in the literature (Leidy, 1879; Doflein, 1916; Sandon, 1934; Jepps, 1942).

Movements in the two species of *Allogromia* are in general similar, but the summary that follows is based on the smaller organism isolated by Dr John Lee. It has the advantage of being very easily cultured on 2% agar in sea water, to which a pinch of dried yeast has been added to accelerate growth (Allen, 1964).

The foraminiferan reticulopodial network, for all its complexity, has some regularities in form and function that set it apart from other pseudopod types.

(1) Extending pseudopods (initially filopods) are stiffer than retracting ones of comparable dimensions; the latter may quiver, collapse or either fold or coil suddenly.

(2) Extending filopods branch most frequently at attachment points, often when tension on the pseudopod at that point has resulted in the pulling away of all but a slender thread of a pseudopod which then becomes a branch with increasingly active streaming.

(3) Streaming in virtually all parts of the network is bi-directional. Any given portion of the network typically shows particles moving in both

directions at more than a single velocity. The larger the diameter of the pseudopod (and the closer to the cell body) the larger the number of velocities that may be observed. There is a tendency for the velocities in a given direction to be roughly multiples of the lowest velocity. Individual particles in rows undergo similar changes in velocity in different portions of the network.

(4) In *Allogromia laticollaris*, Jahn & Rinaldi (1959) reported that particles move out to the very tips of pseudopods at the extremity of the network and return on a U-shaped path as if attached to a filament of that shape. We could not confirm this pattern of movement at the tip for the smaller species, but neither could we deny its occurrence. We did observe, however, that some particles frequently make an abrupt change in direction at attachment points, or regions where attachment points will soon reveal their presence.

(5) In addition to the small particles travelling along the network, there are hyaline 'droplets' that arise upon retracting pseudopods; these 'droplets' are carried about until they reach a portion of the network where pseudopod formation is in progress. Then their substances are somehow 'spun out' into filamentous pseudopods. We have given this 'fibre-droplet transition' a name but we do not yet understand its significance.

(6) If a substantial portion of the network is excised from the cell body, streaming continues for up to a few hours. 'Droplets' form along the network, however, and the pseudopods become progressively thinner, eventually showing mono-directional streaming and finally ceasing to stream at all. Accidental refusion of these degenerate excised networks with the intact network somehow 'infuses new life' into them, and bi-directional streaming is almost immediately resumed; the material in the 'droplets' is somehow speedily spun out into healthy new reticulopodial network.

Models applicable to pseudopodial movement in Foraminifera

These are perhaps only the salient factors of a very complex and detailed account of movement that has probably not been described in sufficient detail. The observations are difficult to interpret. The bi-directional nature of streaming in virtually all parts of the network argues convincingly against a mechanism based on hydrostatic pressure or any other physical or chemical gradient. Bi-directional streaming requires instead the application of the motive force locally, either at selected points in the network (such as attachment points and/or pseudopod tips) or in a diffuse manner throughout the entire network.

At this point, further interpretation is hampered by lingering uncertainties about the ultrastructure of the network. The pattern of streaming—

particles in files moving at widely separated velocities then turning about-face and returning—would seem almost to demand an ultrastructure consisting of filaments arranged in U-shaped loops, their bends located wherever reversals in direction are most frequently observed. Available ultrastructural evidence (Wohlfarth-Bottermann, 1961) does not offer confirmation for this view, and instead shows that the files of particles apparently move within membrane-bounded cytoplasmic strands packed with microfilaments ('plasmafilaments') and anastomosing with one another. We do not yet know for certain how well fixation has preserved the true morphology of these cells.

Two formal models have been proposed solely on the basis of observed details of movement. The 'active shearing' (or 'slidomatic') model (Jahn & Rinaldi, 1959) assumed the presence of U-shaped filaments within pseudopods and proposed a 'shearing' motive force generated at the apposing surfaces of the filaments. This model is consistent with our present knowledge of the details of movement, but unfortunately it demands an ultrastructure that differs from what has been found so far. In fact, the protoplasmic strands making up the pseudopod appear to be too far separated in space for shearing force to be developed between them.

The second model proposes that the motive force is generated by 'multiple contraction sites' spread throughout the network at pseudopod tips and at attachment points (Allen, 1964). If it is assumed that whatever the particles travel in or on is deployed as folded filaments with the bends at pseudopod tips and attachment points (this point has neither been demonstrated nor disproven), then the 'contraction-at-a-bend principle' can be invoked, as in the frontal contraction theory for *Chaos*, to explain displacement of material toward and away from each of the contraction sites.

The only evidence available concerning the deployment of forces in the foraminiferan reticulopodial network is contained in one of our unpublished time-lapse polarized-light films of *Allogromia* sp. strain N.F. In the film, it is possible to follow the development of moderately strong positive birefringence in selected portions of the network for brief periods. If this birefringence is caused by a tensile force or strain, then it is suggested that the forces are not transmitted over long distances, and therefore that the force-producing mechanism is quite decentralized. The polarized light evidence is consistent with the model but so far adds nothing to our poor understanding of how the forces are generated.

An interesting feature of the 'multiple contraction sites model' is that it is analogous in principle to the frontal contraction model for the *Amoeba–*

Chaos group. It seems at the present time our best hope for a general mechanism which is capable of accounting for the various types of movement in amoebae and Foraminifera.

CONCLUSION

1. It must be borne in mind that pseudopods, as locomotor organelles, are far less well organized than myofibrils, flagella, or cilia.

2. There appear to be classes of amoeboid cells that can be differentiated in terms of the details of movement. It therefore may be fallacious to search for a single mechanism of amoeboid movement.

3. In the giant carnivorous amoeba, *Chaos carolinensis*, the observed details of movement provide a fairly rigorous test for models intended to account for amoeboid locomotion. It seems well established that the motive force is developed by a bulk contraction of the cytoplasm near the tips of pseudopods as proposed in the frontal contraction model. This view is supported both by behavioural evidence and by the results of physical experiments designed to localize the site of application of the motive force.

4. In the giant herbivorous amoeba, *Pelomyxa palustris*, the work of Griffin has clearly shown major behavioural and physiological differences compared to *Chaos carolinensis*. The details of movement have been shown to be consistent with the tail contraction model.

5. In the giant shelled amoeba (testacean), *Difflugia corona*, pseudopod extension differs but little from that in *Chaos*, and polarized light observations suggest a deployment of forces identical to that proposed in the frontal contraction model. However, a separate mechanism not present in *Chaos* (or in *Pelomyxa*) has been added to allow rapid forcible pseudopod retraction in order to transport the heavy shell. Retraction is apparently aided by the rapid formation of a system of highly birefringent, refractile fibrils composed of electron-microscopically visible microfilaments.

6. There is an almost infinite variety of 'small amoebae' with a large range of pseudopod numbers, shapes, speeds of movement, and behavioural patterns. At this time one cannot even guess how many models may be required to account satisfactorily for movement in these cells.

7. In the Foraminifera and Radiolaria one encounters the greatest complexity and versatility in the 'reticulopodial network' with bi-directional streaming in all its parts. The motive force must be decentralized in this type of system and may be either distributed diffusely as proposed in Jahn & Rinaldi's (1959) 'active shearing' model, or may be distributed as 'multiple contraction sites' at bends of folded filaments of which the network seems (from its behaviour) to be composed (Allen, 1964).

8. It is probably too early to be certain whether amoeboid movement (as we originally defined it) is one phenomenon with variations or a collection of diverse phenomena with elements of similarity. We can already distinguish four surprisingly different types of movements, suggesting that a minimum of four models may be required to account for these cases. It would not be too surprising if the now baffling diversity among the less studied 'small amoebae' required us to resort to additional models. The selective advantage of movement for protista might lead us to expect the survival of cells that had independently evolved means for independent locomotion through several routes.

I wish to acknowledge support from Research Grants GM-08691 and GM-14891 from the Institute of General Medical Science, National Institutes of Health, and grant no. G 4551 from the National Science Foundation, and the important contributions of several former co-workers and students: Professor N. Kamiya; Drs H. Nakajima, C. D. Watters, A. Wohlman, D. Francis, and J. L. Griffin; Messrs A. C. Breuer, W. Reid Pitts, W. Burdwood, and S. L. Lloyd.

REFERENCES

ABÉ, T. (1961). *Cytologia* **26**, 378.
ABÉ, T. (1962). *Cytologia* **27**, 111.
ABÉ, T. (1963). *J. Protozool.* **10**, 94.
ALLEN, R. D. (1961a). *Expl Cell Res.* Suppl. **8**, 17.
ALLEN, R. D. (1961b). In *The Cell*, p. 135. Ed. J. Brachet and A. E. Mirsky. New York and London: Academic Press.
ALLEN, R. D. (1964). In *Primitive Motile Systems in Cell Biology*. Ed. R. D. Allen and N. Kamiya. New York and London: Academic Press.
ALLEN, R. D., BRAULT, J. & MOORE, R. D. (1963). *J. Cell Biol.* **18**, 223.
ALLEN, R. D., BRAULT, J. & ZEH, R. (1966). In *Recent Advances in Optical and Electron Microscopy*. Ed. R. Barer and V. Cosslett. New York and London: Academic Press.
ALLEN, R. D., COOLEDGE, J. W. & HALL, P. J. (1960). *Nature, Lond.* **187**, 896.
ALLEN, R. D. & FRANCIS, D. W. (1965). *Symp. Soc. Exp. Biol.* **19**, 259.
ALLEN, R. D., FRANCIS, E. W. & NAKAJIMA, H. (1965). *Proc. natn. Acad. Sci. U.S.A.* **54**, 1153.
ARNOLD, Z. M. (1955). *Univ. Calif. Publs Zool.* **61**, 167.
BELL, L. G. E. (1961). *J. Theoret. Biol.* **1**, 104.
BOVEE, E. C. (1964). In *Primitive Motile Systems in Cell Biology*, p. 189. Ed. R. D. Allen and N. Kamiya. New York and London: Academic Press.
DOFLEIN, F. (1916). *Zool. Jahrb. Abt. Anat. Ontog. Tiere* **39**, 335.
GOLDACRE, R. J. (1964). In *Primitive Motile Systems in Cell Biology*, p. 237. Ed. R. D. Allen and N. Kamiya. New York and London: Academic Press.
GOLDACRE, R. J. & LORCH, I. J. (1950). *Nature, Lond.* **166**, 497.
GRIFFIN, J. L. (1964). In *Primitive Motile Systems in Cell Biology*, p. 303. Ed. R. D. Allen & N. Kamiya. New York and London: Academic Press.

JAHN, T. L. (1964). In *Primitive Motile Systems in Cell Biology*, p. 279. Ed. R. D. Allen and N. Kamiya. New York and London: Academic Press.

JAHN, T. L. & RINALDI, R. A. (1959). *Biol. Bull. mar. biol. lab.*, Woods Hole **117**, 100.

JEPPS, M. W. (1942). *J. mar. biol. Ass. U.K.* **25**, 607.

KAVANAU, J. L. (1963). *J. Theoret. Biol.* **4**, 124.

LANDAU, J. V. (1959). *Ann. N.Y. Acad. Sci.* **78**, 487.

LEE, J. & PIERCE, S. (1963). *J. Protozool.* **10**, 404.

LEIDY, J. (1879). *U.S. Geol. Surv. Rept.* **12**, 324.

MARSLAND, D. (1964). In *Primitive Motile Systems in Cell Biology*, p. 331. Ed. R. D. Allen and N. Kamiya. New York and London: Academic Press.

MAST, S. O. (1926). *J. Morph. Physiol.* **41**, 347.

MAST, S. O. (1931). *Biol. Bull. mar. biol. lab.*, Woods Hole **61**, 223.

MAST, S. O. (1932). *Physiol. Zool.* **7**, 470.

NOLAND, L. E. (1957). *J. Protozool.* **4**, 1.

PENARD, E. (1905). *Arch. Protistenk.* **6**, 175.

REBHUN, L. I. (1963). In *The Cell in Mitosis*. Ed. L. Levine. New York and London: Academic Press.

REBHUN, L. I. (1964). In *Primitive Motile Systems in Cell Biology*, p. 503. Ed. R. D. Allen and N. Kamiya. New York and London: Academic Press.

REBHUN, L. I. (1967). *J. gen. Physiol.* **50**, 223.

RINALDI, R. A. & JAHN, T. L. (1963). *J. Protozool.* **10**, 344.

SANDON, H. (1934). *Nature, Lond.* **133**, 761.

SHAFFER, B. (1964). In *Primitive Motile Systems in Cell Biology*, p. 387. Ed. R. D. Allen and N. Kamiya. New York and London: Academic Press.

SIMARD-DUQUESNE & COUILLARD, P. (1962). *Expl Cell Res.* **28**, 85.

WOHLFARTH-BOTTERMANN, K. E. (1961). *Protoplasma*, **54**, 1.

WOHLMAN, A. & ALLEN, R. D. (1968). *J. Cell Sci.* (in the Press).

WOLPERT, L., THOMPSON, C. M. & O'NEILL, C. H. (1964). In *Primitive Motile Systems in Cell Biology*, p. 143. Ed. R. D. Allen and N. Kamiya. New York and London: Academic Press.

CELL SURFACE MEMBRANE AND AMOEBOID MOVEMENT

By L. WOLPERT and D. GINGELL

Department of Biology as Applied to Medicine,
The Middlesex Hospital Medical School, London, W.1.

1. INTRODUCTION

The cell surface membrane is a most fashionable organelle. In the study of amoeboid movement it has become a repository for a wide variety of functions which reflects, perhaps, both our ignorance of the mechanisms involved in amoeboid movement and our passion for the cell membrane, rather than deductions from persuasive evidence. In this paper we will attempt to examine critically the role of the cell surface membrane in amoeboid movement. Amoeboid movement is used here as a 'blanket' term for the locomotion of a wide variety of cells whose movement involves change in cell shape, flow of cytoplasm, and pseudopodal activity. It thus includes both the free-living amoeba, and tissue and embryonic cells. Surface membrane also requires some definition: by surface membrane we denote the typical triple layered unit membrane together with any outer surface coat—we do not include any structures beneath the unit membrane which are usually termed 'cortex'.

If we knew the mechanism of amoeboid movement, even in the crudest terms, the role of the membrane would pose less of a problem. However, there are at least four theories of movement current (reviewed Wolpert, 1965) and these are sufficiently different that even the location of the force for movement is not generally accepted. While most workers would probably accept that the force for movement is generated within the cytoplasm but would dispute its nature and location, several workers suggest that the site of the force for movement is in the membrane itself. In spite of these differences in interpreting the mechanism of amoeboid movement we have attempted to formulate some general principles relating to cell movement and cell contact with specific reference to embryonic and tissue cells (Gustafson & Wolpert, 1967) which do not rely on any specific mechanism for generating the force for movement. Briefly, these are: (i) cells move by pseudopodal extension, attachment and retraction; (ii) cells can generate tensile forces; (iii) isolated cells tend to be spherical but can form pseudopods; (iv) the degree of contact between cell and substratum is a function of the adhesive force and the mechanical properties of the cell; (v) contact with a substratum results in contact paralysis; (vi) cells may be polarized. We suggested that in considering cell movement and contact it is always necessary to consider the following factors: the shape of the cell, the forces it generates, the force of adhesion between cell and substratum, the mechanical properties of the cell and contact paralysis. For this paper, where we wish to include the large freshwater amoebae, some modification of (i) and (iii) are required. These amoebae are not spherical when not attached to a substratum; more important, they move in the direction of the extending pseudopod, whereas the above principles require that the cells move in the direction of the retracting pseudopod. One may still retain the general principle that amoeboid movement involves pseudopod extension and pseudopod retraction by recognizing that the spatial and temporal relation of these may vary with cell type. It should be pointed out that we regard the 'undulating membrane' at the anterior end of fibroblasts, which is probably the locomotory organ (Abercrombie, 1961), as reflecting pseudopodal activity, rather than the site for generating waves as suggested by Ambrose (1961).

If pseudopod extension and retraction can be regarded as a general and essential feature of amoeboid movement, then it is possible to consider the role of the membrane in this process. It is interesting to consider the possibility that much of the disagreement on the mechanism of cell movement comes from the tacit assumption that the same mechanism is involved in both pseudopod extension and retraction. We would suggest that it is likely that quite different mechanisms are involved and provide a new way of examining the problem. For example, pseudopod extensions might be due to a pushing process such as by microtubule assembly (du Praw, 1965; Tilney & Porter, 1967) or hydrostatic pressure (Goldacre, 1961, 1964). Retraction, on the other hand, might be due to contraction within the pseudopod (Allen, 1961). This distinction is of particular importance when considering the possible role of the membrane.

The role of the membrane will be considered from two main points of view: its mechanical role in movement; and its role in controlling movement, particularly in relation to electrical phenomena. We will try to show that the surface membrane is a relatively permanent structure which undergoes change in form as a result of forces generated within the cell. Contact between cell and substratum is particularly important in controlling movement and can result in contact inhibition and contact paralysis. We will suggest that surface electrostatic potential rather than transmembrane bioelectric potential may provide a transducing mechanism for the control of movement by environmental factors, including contact paralysis, phagocytosis, pinocytosis and chemotaxis.

Mechanical role of the membrane

Several workers suggest that the site for movement is the membrane itself. The two main ways in which the membrane could provide the force for movement are by active localized contractions and relaxations (Holtfreter, 1948) or by active expansion (Bell, 1961) due to formation of new cell surface (Shaffer, 1963, 1964, 1965). On the other hand the membrane may merely respond to forces generated within the cytoplasm.

Some insight into this problem can be obtained from a consideration of the manner in which the cell membrane behaves when a cell changes its shape. This is crucial to any understanding of the membrane's role in cell movement. There appear to be three main possibilities, shown in Fig. 1, where a cell is depicted withdrawing one pseudopod and extending another. (1) The membrane is stationary over most of the cell and change in shape involves resorption of existing membrane and formation of new membrane. This is an essential feature of the theories of Goldacre (1961), Bell (1961), and Shaffer (1964, 1965). (2) The membrane is reversibly extensible and changes in shape involve localized increases or decreases in surface area (Holtfreter, 1948; Ambrose, 1961). It is also possible that the membrane could behave in this manner, not by changes in surface area, but by reversible folding and unfolding of the membrane (Czarska & Grebecki, 1966). (3) The membrane is plastic and can flow in order to accommodate changes in cell shape (Fig. 1c) (Mast, 1926; Griffin & Allen, 1960; Wolpert & O'Neill, 1962).

The theories of Bell (1961), Goldacre (1961) and Shaffer (1964, 1965) require that the cell contents move through a stationary tube of membrane, new surface being formed at the front, while there is removal of membrane from the rear. On this basis the rate of turnover of the membrane between the surface and the interior must be high during movement, and the cell may be expected to renew its membrane completely each time it passes through its own length, namely about every 5 min., or about 20 %/min. for amoebae; this should be contrasted with mechanisms (2) and (3) which require a relatively permanent surface membrane. There is little evidence to justify this view, and most early investigations relied on the movement of particles attached to the cell surface. Contrary to Goldacre's (1961, 1964) theory, the movement of particles attached to the cell surface of large fresh-water amoebae such as *Amoeba proteus* and *Chaos chaos* give no indication of a stationary membrane, but move forward in a manner consistent with mechanisms (2) and (3) (Griffin & Allen, 1960; Mast, 1926; Abé, 1962; Czarska & Grebecki, 1966). Particles attached to the surface of some of the smaller amoebae (Pantin, 1923) and cells of the cellular slime mould

(Shaffer, 1963, 1964) remain stationary with respect to the substratum suggesting that the membrane is behaving as in (1). Experiments based on the movement of different particles may appear to give contradictory results on the same cell (Goldacre, 1961); for example, oil drops attached to the surface of *Amoeba proteus* do not move forward, while smaller particles do.

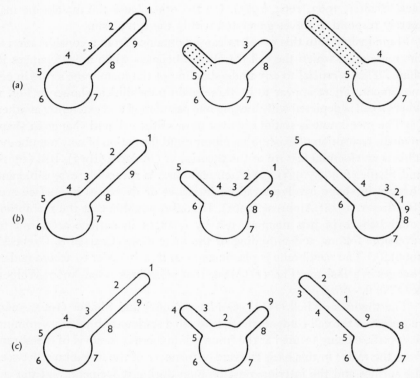

Fig. 1. Diagram showing pseudopod extension and retraction and the main ways in which the surface can behave during this change in shape. 1–9 are points on the surface. (*a*) Surface material is removed as the pseudopod is withdrawn and the extending pseudopod has new-formed surface, shown dotted. (*b*) Reversible extension of the surface. (*c*) Plastic flow.

We therefore considered that the problem might be resolved using a method free from the uncertainties inherent in the interpretation of particle movements. In our original experiments, such a marker was provided by an antibody specific to the cell surface to which a fluorescent dye had been coupled. This antibody was prepared from cell surface membranes isolated in bulk (O'Neill, 1964). Antisera to this fraction contain a single major antibody, together with two minor ones. The major antibody is almost certainly directed against the 2,000 Å. mucoprotein surface coat (Wolpert &

O'Neill, 1962; O'Neill, 1964). The labelled antibody may be applied to living amoebae in a concentration of 0·05 % globulin without damage for at least 5 min. and, after repeated washing, the cell surface alone can be seen in the fluorescent microscope to be brilliantly stained. Such cells appear to move and phagocytose quite normally. Fluorescence at the surface remained very strong during the first hour, but slowly decreased until, after 12 hr., it was no longer detectable. The half-life of the label was judged to be 5 hr., which corresponds to a turnover of 0·2 %/min. The, loss of the label from the surface was paralleled by the appearance of small fluorescent vesicles within the cell. Membrane loss probably occurs as the result of slow pinocytosis at the tail and this is supported by electron micrographs (Wohlfarth-Bottermann & Stockem, 1966). This observation almost conclusively demonstrates that the cell surface in amoeba is a rather permanent structure whose renewal, under normal conditions, is relatively slow. Similar results have been obtained using fluorescent labelled ribonuclease. It thus appears to invalidate any mechanism of amoeboid movement requiring continuous rapid turnover of the cell surface. Nevertheless, we have recognized that the fluorescent label is attached to the surface coat and strictly our conclusions only apply to this coat, and do not preclude rapid turnover of the underlying membrane. We have, however, argued that this is unlikely and know of no evidence to suggest rapid turnover of the unit membrane during locomotion of the large amoebae (Wolpert, Thompson & O'Neill, 1964; Wolpert & O'Neill, 1962; Wolpert, 1965). The observations of Nachmias (1966) on new membrane formation following treatment of the surface with alcian blue supports this view, since she has found that the labelled membrane is taken in at the tail by pinocytosis, and even here the time required for complete surface renewal is about 35 min. A second application of the dye results in a much longer time for renewal of the surface. A similar conclusion in relation to the turnover of the membrane during locomotion is reached by Czarska & Grebecki (1966), who have not only critically examined the literature but have carried out a variety of experiments involving vital stains and the attachment of particles to the membrane. It should, however, be noted that amoebae may, under special conditions not directly relevant to normal locomotion, form new surface quite rapidly (Jeon & Bell, 1964; Nachmias, 1966) and the most impressive demonstration of this occurs after treatment with high hydrostatic pressures (Landau & Thibodeau, 1962; Landau, 1965). Under high pressure the cell rounds up, without change in volume, and the surface is not convoluted; yet, pseudopod formation begins when the pressure is released. It is of interest that our estimate of a turnover rate of 12 %/hr. is similar to that obtained by

Chapman-Andresen (1963) in relation to recovery from pinocytosis. Marshall & Nachmias (1965) estimate the turnover in feeding *Chaos chaos* to be 70%/hr. under optimal conditions, but conclude that the basal rate of locomoting cells is about 1%/hr. Our figure of 12%/hr. is undoubtedly on the high side since the antibody promotes pinocytosis. One may conclude that the membrane is a relatively permanent structure in relation to movement.

All the above observations refer to large amoebae, having a thick surface coat, about 2,000Å. thick (Brandt & Pappas, 1962). It was thus of great importance to obtain data on a cell lacking such a coat. For this we chose the pre-aggregation cells of the cellular slime mould since they do not possess a surface coat as revealed by electron microscopy (Mercer & Shaffer, 1960), and Shaffer's (1963, 1964) observations on particle movements strongly suggest a stationary surface and rapid turnover; moreover the movement appears more typical of tissue and embryonic cells than that of the large amoebae. It has been possible to mark the surface of such cells with fluorescent labelled antibody directed against whole cells (Garrod & Wolpert, 1968). Observations on their movement show no evidence for a rapid turnover of membrane associated with cell movement, the surface remaining uniformly labelled even after the cell had moved several times through its own length. This observation is not easily reconciled with Shaffer's observations on particle movements. However, our own observations on particle movements have failed to confirm his results satisfactorily. We therefore concluded that the membrane of this cell, like that of the large amoebae, is a relatively permanent structure and that rapid formation and withdrawal of surface from the membrane does not accompany cell movement.

Having concluded that the membrane is a relatively permanent structure the question arises whether it has plastic or elastic properties and whether it can actively generate forces for movement. There is no evidence that surface membranes can actively and autonomously change their shape by expansion or contraction as suggested by Holtfreter (1948). In those cases where an active contraction at the surface has been established, as in cleaving sea-urchin eggs (Wolpert, 1963, 1966) and in the induced contraction of the surface of amphibian eggs (Gingell, 1967 b), the force is almost certainly in a cortical layer beneath the membrane, since in both cases the surface membrane itself becomes highly convoluted. The suggestion that surface membranes are capable of active contractions based on the extraction of an actomyosin-like system from isolated membranes, briefly reported by Neifakh, Avramov & Gaitskhoki (1965) and B. M. Jones (1966), is best left until more substantial evidence is forthcoming. In this connexion it is of interest to note the contradictory reports on the presence of a contractile protein in mitochondria (Conover & Bárány, 1966).

Few, if any, experiments have been carried out on amoeboid cells which provide a reliable means of assessing the relative contributions of elastic and plastic deformation to the membrane as indicated in Fig. 1 b–c. We thus have no alternative but to attempt to deduce the membrane properties from the behaviour of the membrane during amoeboid movement. From our studies with labelling the surface of the amoeba we concluded that this membrane underwent plastic deformation to accommodate changes in shape. However as Czarska & Grebecki (1966) have pointed out, membrane folding and unfolding may also play an important role; more important, we now recognize that we cannot exclude elastic deformations too. There appears to be at least some tension at the surface since amoebae round up under high hydrostatic pressure which breaks down cytoplasmic structures (Marsland, 1956; Landau, 1959). Unlike large amoebae, tissue cells when not in contact with any substratum tend to be spherical, although they may form pseudopods; they do not, however, take up the typical flattened or elongated shape of locomoting cells, which round up when freed from their substratum. This strongly suggests that the cell membrane is elastic and placed under tension when the cell is deformed. There is also little evidence relating to changes in surface area either in localized regions, as might be required by elastic deformation, or for the whole cell surface during amoeboid movement. For the large amoebae, we would agree with Czarska & Grebecki (1966) that the surface area remains more or less constant. By compressing tissue cells Rosenberg (1963) suggested that cells could undergo reversible changes in area of up to 50%; however, the details of his calculations are not given and he did not take into account membrane storage in foldings, convolutions and microvilli observed in most amoeboid cells. These can be very significant and, for example in the sea urchin egg, could account for at least a 30% increase in area above that estimated from cell diameter (Wolpert, 1963). (Rosenberg's observations are also consistent with the elastic properties of the membrane.) The postulated bi-molecular leaflet structure for the unit membrane would not be expected to permit significant changes in surface area without disruption. This, however, may be a tenuous argument in view of the uncertainties attached to membrane structure (Korn, 1966; Chapman, Kamat, de Gier & Penkett, 1968).

Studies on the membrane of non-amoeboid cells cannot necessarily be extrapolated, but are at least more or less consistent with an elastic membrane having some plastic properties. Careful studies on the red-cell membrane suggest that it has viscoelastic properties, the Young's modulus being about 10^7 dynes/cm.^{2} (Rand, 1964). Only elastic properties have been found for the sea-urchin egg (Mitchison & Swann, 1954) and its Young's modulus is about 5×10^6 dynes/cm.^{2} (Wolpert, 1963). The main resistance to deformation of the red-cell membrane is to stretching rather than bending (Rand & Burton, 1964) and a similar conclusion has been reached for the membrane of the sea-urchin egg (Wolpert, 1960). A particularly important feature of the red-cell membrane is that it cannot reversibly undergo increases in area of more than about 10% (Rand & Burton, 1964). There is no evidence for such a limitation in sea-urchin eggs, but it should be remembered that its surface is very convoluted.

We can now briefly consider the mechanical implications for amoeboid movement of an elastic convoluted relatively permanent membrane, whose total surface area remains constant over short periods of time. It is possible that this will result in the 'competition' between pseudopods that has been observed in tissue cells (Abercrombie, 1961). The stretching of the cell due to pseudopodal activity will cause a tension in the membrane, and the cell will not be able to form a new pseudopod unless the tension is released by, for example, the withdrawal of other pseudopods. The possibility that tension in the cell membrane can prevent pulsatory and pseudopodal activity has been suggested for the cells of the sea-urchin embryo (Gustafson & Wolpert, 1963). The mechanical properties of the membrane could thus play a very important role in controlling movement. One can also ask, but not answer, to what extent the properties of the membrane determine whether a cell has long thin pseudopods or short fat rounded ones. This could be due to the nature of the cytoplasmic forces or reflect the properties of the membrane.

Finally, it is of some interest to consider whether the estimated magnitude of the cytoplasmic forces could significantly deform an elastic surface membrane whose Young's modulus is about 10^6–10^7 dynes/cm^2. An estimate of the force involved in saltatory movement of a particle suggests that it is about 10^{-5} dynes, though cells can generate forces which are about 100 times greater (Wolpert, 1965). If this minimal force were exerted along the axis of a pseudopod $0.3\,\mu$ in diameter, extending it, the tension in the membrane would be 0.1 dynes/cm. and would result in a strain of about 5%. One can suggest that cytoplasmic forces are certainly adequate to alter the form of the membrane.

2. CELL CONTACT AND AMOEBOID MOVEMENT

Contacts between cell and substratum, which may be another cell, are of particular importance in amoeboid movement since a cell must not only make and break contact with the surface over which it is moving continuously, but its locomotion can be affected markedly by contact with other cells and the substratum.

Cell adhesion and cell movement

The conditions for the locomotion of a cell moving by pseudopodal extension and retraction are as follows. If a cell is to move from A to B, (i) a pseudopod must extend from A to B, (ii) the tension produced by the shortening pseudopod must be sufficient to break the contact between the cell and substratum at A and move the cell through the medium; (iii) the contact at B must be greater than at A; (iv) the substratum must be sufficiently rigid that points A and B are not drawn together. Movement by this type of mechanism is particularly clearly exhibited by the mesenchyme cells of the sea-urchin embryo—one of the few cells observed moving *in vivo* (Gustafson & Wolpert, 1963, 1967)—and the protozoan *Difflugia* (Mast, 1926). It is instructive to consider the effect on cell movement when the adhesiveness of the substratum varies and pseudopod formation is random. We have suggested that cell locomotion would take place in the direction of more stable adhesions, and that this mechanism can account for pattern formation by mesenchyme cells in the sea-urchin embryo, their distribution reflecting spatial variation in adhesiveness of the ectoderm over which they move, and other cases of directed movement and pattern formation (Gustafson & Wolpert, 1963, 1967).

Sea-urchin mesenchyme cells only make contact with the substratum, over which they move, at a few points—the tips of their long pseudopods. Restricted regions of contact have also been reported for other cells, even in fibroblasts where the cells appear to be spread out over the substratum, as demonstrated with the surface-contact microscope (Ambrose, 1961) and surface-reflexion microscope (Curtis, 1964). Bell & Jeon (1963) also showed this by viewing *Amoeba proteus* from the side. What determines the portion of the membrane which will adhere to the substratum and, how is this adhesion broken as the cell moves forward? To answer these questions satisfactorily we would require a knowledge of the mechanism by which cells adhere to each other or any other substratum, which is an active and controversial field (Curtis, 1962, 1966) beyond the scope of this paper, but some specific problems can be examined in the light of the two main current concepts of cell adhesion. The older suggests that adhesion results from the presence of a cementing substance at the outer surface of the cell which can be removed by treatment with trypsin and EDTA (Moscona, 1960; L. Weiss, 1962), for example. The other view holds that adhesion is determined by electrostatic repulsive forces and London–Van der Waals attractive forces acting at the surface, after the treatment developed by Verwey & Overbeek (1948) for lyophobic colloids (Curtis, 1962, 1966; Pethica, 1961). L. Weiss (1962) has suggested that active movement of two cells apart or loss of contact between cell and substratum in amoeboid movement is not limited by the strength of adhesions between the cell and substratum, but by the cohesive strength of the cell surfaces. Loss of adhesion and thus contact, would, he suggests, involve rupture of the surface involved and pieces of material may be expected to be torn away from the cell surface. He also discusses various mechanisms by which weakening of the surface cohesion could be brought about; for example, by enzyme action. To support this he has shown that when cells are removed from the glass surface on which they are growing, cell surface material is left behind (Weiss & Coombs, 1963), and he has suggested that this may also occur during normal amoeboid movement. Mechanical removal of cells is of course quite different from normal detachment during amoeboid movement. However, Bell & Jeon (1963) claim to have observed the detachment of pseudopodal fragments from the tail of amoebae, but our observations with labelled cells have not given any indication of this. Curtis (1962) could not find any evidence of material left behind on the glass when examining tissue cells with an interference–reflexion technique. We believe the colloid stability theory as developed by Pethica (1961), Curtis (1962) and Brooks, Millar Seaman & Vassar (1967) seems to provide a more satisfactory mechanism for making and breaking contacts since rupture of contacts would not damage the cell and changes in the adhesive force could, for example, be brought about by local changes in the charge at the surface. P. C. T. Jones (1966) has proposed a model along these lines. In this connexion it is important to remember that the degree of contact between cell and substratum depends not only on the adhesive forces which will tend to spread the contact, but also on the resistance of the cell to deformation, which will counteract such spreading (Gustafson & Wolpert, 1963, 1967). Carter (1967) has suggested that pseudopod extension might result from spreading forces between the cell and substratum, but this is certainly not the case for many tissue cells where pseudopods are extended directly into the medium (Taylor, 1966; Gustafson & Wolpert, 1963, 1967).

It is of some interest to compare the magnitudes of the forces holding cells together, as predicted from colloid stability theory, with the forces generated by cells and the forces required for amoeboid movement. Brooks *et al.* (1967) have examined in some detail the force that may be expected to hold cells together and calculate this to be about 10^{-7} dynes, if Hamaker's constant is in the range $1-5 \times 10^{-14}$ ergs. They conclude that this might be sufficient for freely moving cells and for reversible adhesion as in red-cell aggregation, but could not account for stronger cell adhesion in tissues. The value of 10^{-7} dynes obtained by Brooks *et al.* is for spherical particles $10\,\mu$ diameter with point contacts, but for $100\,\mu^2$ contacts a force of the order of 10^{-4} dynes has been calculated. As they point out, it has been extremely difficult to obtain reliable experimental data on the forces holding cells together. We have approached this problem from a slightly different point of view by trying to calculate the adhesive force between cell and substratum required in amoeboid movement. An estimate can be obtained from Stokes's equation, if the main resistance to movement lies in the viscous drag of the medium. For a cell $10\,\mu$ radius, moving at $10\,\mu/\text{sec.}$, through a medium 10 times as viscous as water, the force is 10^{-6} dynes and thus the adhesion would probably be adequate to move the cell forward on contraction of the pseudopod; cells can exert forces of about 10^{-3} dynes (Wolpert, 1965). It should be noted that the colloid stability theory predicts no resistance to shear between cell and substratum.

Contact inhibition and contact paralysis

One of the most important aspects of cell movement and cell contact arises from Abercrombie's work on contact inhibition (Abercrombie, 1961, 1964, 1965), which shows that when a cell comes into contact with the surfaces of surrounding cells its movement may be inhibited. 'The behaviour in question can be summed up by saying that, when contact inhibition is operative, a cell will not use another cell as substrate for its locomotion...' (Abercrombie, 1965). Contact inhibition thus refers to the overall behaviour of the cell and specifically whether it will move over another cell or not. We have introduced the term 'contact paralysis' to describe what we believe to be an important aspect not only of contact inhibition, but cell movement in general. Contact paralysis refers to the *local* inhibition in pseudopodal activity when a cell is in contact with another cell or substratum (Weiss, 1961; Gustafson & Wolpert, 1967). It is taken from Abercrombie's (1961) description of the behaviour of two approaching fibroblasts—the ruffled membrane at the leading edge stops moving when it makes contact with another fibroblast. Abercrombie (1961) has suggested that 'paralysis of the locomotory machinery brought about by close contact with the highly adhesive edge of another cell' occurs. We have proposed (Gustafson & Wolpert, 1967) that contact paralysis may be a very general feature of cellular behaviour, operative whether contact inhibition occurs or not. It can be shown that contact paralysis may be just one aspect of contact inhibition, and the occurrence of contact inhibition will depend on other factors such as the adhesive forces, the mechanical properties of the cell, the shape of the cell and the forces generated by the cell (Gustafson & Wolpert, 1967).

Contact paralysis can be observed in a variety of different situations in all of which pseudopodal activity seems to be suppressed where the cells are in contact with each other but continues at the free surface. Some examples are: reaggregation of amphibian blastula cells (Lucey & Curtis, 1959); ectodermal cells of the honey-bee embryo (du Praw, 1965); epithelial cell sheets (Vaughan & Trinkaus, 1966); the ectoderm of the sea-urchin embryo (Gustafson & Wolpert, 1967). Two cases may be described which illustrate some important aspects of the possible role of contact paralysis. The primary mesenchyme cells of the sea-urchin embryo move over the surface of the ectoderm cells by the formation and retraction of long pseudopods. Contact inhibition is clearly not operative yet contact paralysis is probably occurring at the tip of each pseudopod, for when the tip makes contact the pseudopod ceases to extend and appears to withdraw by contracting. The ability of the mesenchyme cells to move over the ectoderm is partly a consequence of the cells having, in contrast to fibro-blasts, long stiff and independent pseudopods. When the undulating membrane of a fibroblast makes contact with another cell, and the contact spreads (Abercrombie, 1961), then contact paralysis prevents further move-ment in that direction. With the primary mesenchyme cells only small contacts are made with the ectoderm and the contact paralysis of one pseudopod does not necessarily affect the others. It is of interest that con-traction is sometimes observed when the undulating membrane of a fibro-blast makes contact with another cell (Abercrombie, 1961). It is possible that contact paralysis is an essential feature of normal movement by pseudo-podal mechanism, since it may be involved in the cessation of pseudopod extension and the initiation of pseudopod retraction.

The other example concerns the behaviour of the cells in the migrating grex of the cellular slime mould (Garrod, 1968). There is good evidence that cells in the grex can move over each other and that there is thus no contact inhibition (Bonner, 1962). Detailed observations of cells in the grex suggest that when there is a free space between the cells, cells generally form pseudopods and move into it. This raises the question as to whether contact paralysis is operative in this system and pseudopod formation can only occur when cells are not in contact. So far it has been very difficult to resolve this issue.

It is a matter of some importance to establish whether contact paralysis requires a special mechanism or whether it simply reflects a mechanical blocking of pseudopodal activity. The cessation of pseudopodal activity where two cells are in contact might result from a local mechanical immobil-ization of the membrane due to adhesive forces (Abercrombie, 1961; Curtis, 1960) and the presence of a mechanical barrier. On the other hand a more subtle mechanism may be operative (Weiss, 1961). The possible role of changes in surface electrostatic potential in bringing about contact paralysis will be considered in a following section.

3. MEMBRANE PHENOMENA IN RELATION
TO THE CONTROL OF MOVEMENT

Goldacre (1961, 1964) has put forward a theory for the control of amoeboid movement in which the membrane plays a central role. He suggests that contact between the cell membrane and ectoplasmic gel in amoebae causes contraction of the gel, and he has described a hydrostatic feedback-regulating mechanism for controlling the site and force of contraction. This theory postulates the presence of a peripheral hyaline layer between membrane and ectoplasmic gel everywhere other than the tail. There is no evidence for this layer in tissue cells and its presence in the large amoebae is not well established. Moreover, there is considerable controversy concerning contraction of the tail (Wolpert, 1965). A different approach to control of movement involves the consideration of electrical phenomena.

Bioelectric potential and amoeboid movement

In view of the well-established role of bioelectric potentials across the membrane of muscle cells controlling contraction, it has long been tempting to speculate that a similar mechanism might operate at the cell surface membrane to control amoeboid movement. The first demonstration of such a relationship came from the work of Bingley & Thompson (1962) on *Amoeba proteus* using an intracellular electrode. Their striking discovery was that the membrane potential at the tip of an advancing pseudopod was about -30 mV. while that at the rear of the cell was about -70 mV. in Chalkley's medium. This implies a potential gradient in the cytoplasm of 1 V./cm. They suggested that this voltage gradient can govern the direction of movement by controlling the direction and rate of cytoplasmic streaming; the voltage gradient being determined by the permeability of the membrane. On this basis, quite a satisfactory theory for the control of movement by the membrane has been built up. A particularly attractive feature is that it provides a mechanism whereby environmental stimuli could modify amoeboid movement; for, as they point out, mechanical stimuli, to which amoebae are sensitive, could alter membrane permeability and the bioelectric potential. They predict that pseudopod extension will occur at a site of membrane depolarization. Unfortunately the theory as presented is open to several objections.

Tasaki & Kamiya (1964) used both intracellular and extracellular electrodes in their investigation of *Amoeba proteus* and *Chaos chaos*. The amoebae were in Kamiya's (1964) double chamber, held in the narrow constriction between the two chambers. With intracellular electrodes they recorded a variable potential, as large as -70 to -120 mV. This potential varied with time in two ways: it would gradually and usually irreversibly decrease, but occasionally there was a sudden transient depolarization lasting 1–20 sec. resembling intracellularly recorded action potentials in vertebrate neurones. Bingley (1966a) reports that mechanical stimulation of the rear regions produces a partial depolarization of the membrane and we agree with his view that the sudden depolarizations reported by Tasaki & Kamiya (1964) probably result from the mechanical constraints involved in their system for holding the amoebae: they have not been reported by other investigators such as Riddle (1962) or Gingell & Palmer (1967). It is of particular significance that Tasaki & Kamiya could detect no external current flow with extracellular electrodes which would be required if the potential gradient is generated by active ion transport across the membrane as suggested by Bingley & Thompson (1962). It therefore seems that such a gradient in potential could not be due to the passage of ions through the membrane. Bruce & Marshall (1965) in a comprehensive study of the permeability to ions and of bioelectric potentials in amoebae conclude that there is no evidence for active transport of any ion species directly across the cell surface membrane, and no other workers have as yet provided any evidence to the contrary. Furthermore, it is not easy to understand how the cell could maintain so steep a potential gradient within the cytoplasm. It can be calculated that the current which would have to flow, assuming a specific resistivity of cytoplasm of the order of 100 kΩ cm. (Bruce & Marshall, 1965; Loewenstein, 1966), is approximately 0·1 μA. If the potential gradient is not a membrane phenomenon the current must be maintained by cytoplasmic pumps. Although a potential difference has been repeatedly reported by Bingley (1966a, b) he has not produced convincing evidence that it is not an artifact due to progressive 'sealing' in of the electrode. Gingell & Palmer (1967) have found that locomotion can occur in the absence of a potential gradient when the electrodes are known to be sealed in. Bingley & Thompson (1962) found an inverse relationship between both membrane potential and the velocity of cytoplasmic streaming, and the logarithm of the external potassium chloride concentration, which they use to support their theory. In 0·01 mM-KCl the membrane potential was about −60 mV. and the rate of streaming 40 μ/sec.; whereas in 10 mM-KCl the potential was reduced to about −20 mV. and the rate of streaming to about 12 μ/sec. In view of the results of Brandt & Freeman (1967), Bruce & Marshall (1965) and Gingell & Palmer (1967), who found that added salt reduces membrane impedance, it may be that this is the significant event. The reduction in impedance may be brought about by reduction of the bioelectric potential or reduction of membrane surface potential. This is discussed more fully in the next section.

Surface potential and cell movement

The possibility that cell surface potential may play an important role in controlling amoeboid movement comes primarily from observations which show that altering the surface potential affects movement, particularly in *Amoeba proteus*. If surface potential does play a role then it could be an important factor in contact paralysis since it can be shown that the close approach of cells leads to an alteration in surface potential (Gingell, 1967 a).

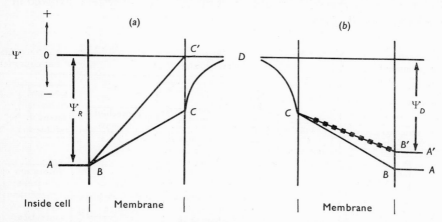

Fig. 2. (*a*) Schematic potential gradients through the plasma membrane due to bioelectric potential (Ψ_R) alone (BC'), and in the presence of additional fixed negative charges at the outer surface (BC). (CD) is the double-layer potential function. Decreasing the surface potential CC' by absorption of positive charges, for example, would make the gradient across the membrane steeper. (*b*) Change in potential gradient through the plasma membrane (BC to $B'C$) due to reduction of the bioelectric potential from Ψ_R to Ψ_D (from Gingell, 1967a).

A clear distinction should be drawn between two kinds of potential. A bioelectric or resting potential difference across the cell membrane is due mainly to the unequal distribution of diffusible ions across the membrane and is detectable between the internal and external bulk phases. Surface potential is a strictly localized phenomenon due to fixed electrostatic charges on the membrane and an associated diffuse layer of oppositely charged counterions. The potential profile across the membrane depends upon the summed effects of both bioelectric and surface potentials (Fig. 2). One of the purposes of this section is to suggest that there may be relationship between the two kinds of potential, since, if alterations in surface potential can bring about changes in membrane permeability, ensuing ionic fluxes may alter the bioelectric potential. The surface potential can be altered by changes in ionic strength of the medium, or by the absorption of polyelectrolytes on to the surface, or by the close approach ($\leqslant$ 20Å.) of surfaces bearing fixed charge of the same sign in physiological saline (Gingell, 1967a). Evidence obtained by Bangham and his co-workers (Bangham, Standish & Watkins, 1965; Bangham, Standish & Miller, 1965; Bangham & Papahadjopoulos, 1966; Papahadjopoulos & Bangham, 1966; Mueller & Rudin, 1968) from artificial membrane systems shows ionic permeability to be a function of surface potential, and some work described below suggests that this relationship may be quite widespread in biological membranes. This is clearly of great significance for cell movement since changes in membrane permeability might affect the cytoplasmic system involved in generating motile forces.

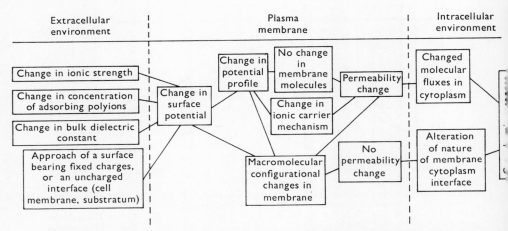

Fig. 3. Diagram to show some ways in which changes in the extracellular environment could, by altering the surface potential, bring about a cytoplasmic response. The transducing mechanism need not necessarily involve permeability changes.

There are a number of ways in which a change in membrane surface potential could become 'known' to a cell and lead to a cytoplasmic response (Fig. 3). The altered potential profile might, in the simplest case, make it easier or more difficult for ions to move across the electrostatic potential energy barrier, thus altering passive permeability. The fact that the average kinetic energy of ions in solution is about the same as the membrane electrostatic potential energy barrier makes such a scheme plausible. Permeability changes might on the other hand follow because of the altered electrostatic environment of charged ion carrier molecules involved in the translocation of ions between the aqueous phases bounding the membrane (Hodgkin & Huxley, 1952). Another possibility is that the changed electrostatic gradient in the membrane might bring about conformational allosteric changes in structural macromolecules of the membrane (Polissar, 1954; Hodgkin &

Chandler, 1965; Changeux, Thiery, Tung & Kittel, 1967). For example, charged groups and dipoles would be subjected to forces tending to re-orientate them and this might, in addition, trigger further structural changes. The magnitude of the field strengths expected makes the proposition reasonable (Polissar, 1954). Although a change in permeability might accompany an allosteric transformation, this is not necessarily so. It is important to realize that this could result in the presentation of new groups at the cytoplasmic interface (charges, co-enzymes, enzymes) and thus a mechanism for cytoplasmic response in the absence of permeability changes is also possible.

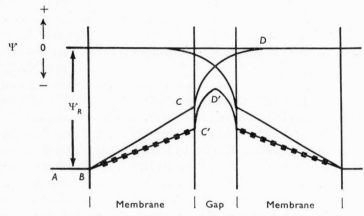

Fig. 4. Schematic representation of the potential changes predicted to occur on close approach of two identical membranes, under conditions of constant surface charge density. Each membrane bears fixed charges at its outer surface. The bioelectric potential across the membranes is Ψ_R, with respect to the bulk external phase and CD represents the double-layer potential function when the membranes are at infinite separation. As they come together the potential profile changes from $ABCD$ to $ABC'D'$ and the potential gradient in each membrane changes from BC to BC' (from Gingell, 1967a).

The relationship between bioelectric potential changes and surface electrostatic changes can best be understood with the aid of the simplified diagrams (Figs. 2, 4). In the absence of fixed charges the potential falls to zero across the membrane. The potential gradient is reduced if fixed negative charges are present outside (Hodgkin & Chandler, 1965). Reduction in the bioelectric potential, which is known to cause a permeability increase in nerve cell membranes, can be exactly paralleled in theory by hyperpolarization of the outer surface of the membrane, which might follow the close approach of two charged membranes (Fig. 4 and Gingell, 1967a) in physiological saline or dilute media. The adsorption of charged molecules to the outer surface of the cell membrane as well as a change in ionic strength of the medium would alter the surface potential and hence the potential profile across the membrane. If a change in membrane permeability were to follow, the bioelectric potential might also be changed.

All the above considerations assume that the primary molecular event takes place within the unit membrane. It may well be that local potential gradient in the outermost region of the cell surface—the surface coat— which may be freely permeable to counter ions, could also trigger off macromolecular configurational changes whose effect might be transmitted to the unit membrane. Some evidence that this may in fact occur in the surface coat of amoebae will be presented when considering pinocytosis.

Some evidence which supports these arguments will now be presented. The addition of substances, which change the surface potential, to the medium in which the amoebae *Chaos chaos* and *Amoeba proteus* are moving brings about a striking change in the membrane impedance and motility. Brandt & Freeman (1967) found in *Chaos chaos* that 10 mM-NaCl, ribonuclease or lysozyme produced a 10- to 20-fold decrease in membrane impedance and that this was accompanied by the cessation of amoeboid movement and the initiation of pinocytosis. We have calculated that the addition of 10 mM-NaCl would approximately halve the surface potential by an ionic strength effect. The fall in impedance is highly dependent on the calcium concentration; when the cells have a low impedance a tenfold increase in Ca^{2+} concentration returns the impedance to the control value or higher and halts pinocytosis. The low impedance of the membrane is associated with a doubling of the thickness of the electron-transparent lamella of the unit membrane, suggesting structural change in the membrane. Similar changes in impedance (Fig. 5) have been found by Gingell & Palmer (1967) using *Amoeba proteus*. They also noted a correlation between impedance changes and pseudopod activity, and they point out that substances which bring about the lowering of the impedance are those which reduce the surface potential (Gingell, 1967a). Addition of NaCl reduces the surface potential by increasing the ionic strength of the medium, while polylysine and ribonuclease, which are positively charged macromolecules, bind to the surface of amoebae and similarly reduce the negative surface potential. Application of 0·05% polylysine results in a rapid fall in impedance and cessation of pseudopod formation. If the polylysine in the medium is washed away, the impedance remains unaltered, but if negatively charged polyglutamate is added a few minutes after the initial addition of polylysine the impedance rises again and streaming and movement begin. Studies with fluorescent labelled polylysine show that it binds to the surface of the amoeba and that it is not removed by polyglutamate. A similar result attends the action of ribonuclease. Treatment of the cells with 0·5%

ribonuclease in low calcium causes a fall in impedance and cessation of movement. Washing in culture medium does not result in restoration of movement, but washing rapidly in 0·1 M-NaCl to remove bound ribonuclease (revealed by fluorescent studies) and then culture medium does

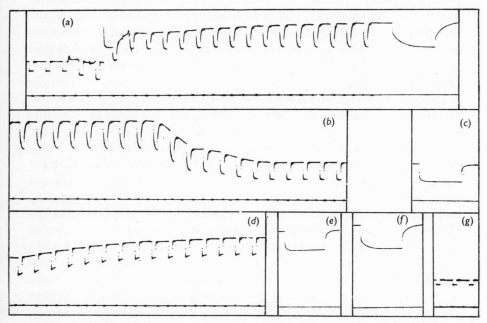

Fig. 5. Electrical potential and cell membrane impedance changes preceding motile responses of *Amoeba proteus* through the action of sodium chloride. Recorded with a single intracellular microelectrode. Voltage pulses for resistance measurements appear as upward displacements of the potential (upper) trace (ordinate). The lower event marker trace also serves as a reference potential. Time (abscissa) runs left to right in each insert. Recording scale: 0·25 cm./sec., normal; 2·5 cm./sec., fast. (*a*) Penetration of the microelectrode into a streaming cell: as it 'sealed in' the rounded capacitative impedance pulses and negative potential recorded increased to steady values. (*b*) Addition of NaCl to a final concentration of 8·5 mM (event marker) caused a rapid fall in potential to zero and the impedance decreased, becoming less capacitative (*c*) A fast pulse immediately following the previous insert shows reduced capacity and impedance (cf. fast pulse in *a*): locomotion had practically ceased. (*d*) Two minutes after (*c*), NaCl was washed away with Chalkley's medium: the potential rose steadily. (*e*) and (*f*) show fast pulses during recovery: movement began at (*f*) 4 min. after washing began. (*g*) shows the potential after removal of the electrode. Zero had hardly altered but the lower pulse (cf. before penetration in *a*) indicated slight electrode breakage (from Gingell & Palmer, 1967).

restore impedance and motility. One can perhaps reinterpret Bingley & Thompson's (1962) observations, referred to earlier, relating bioelectric potential to movement: it is very likely that the primary effect of KCl was to reduce membrane impedance. In fact Gingell & Palmer (1967) have not found a consistent correlation between bioelectric potential and movement. While the potential invariably falls when the impedance falls and movement stops, the subsequent initiation of movement is associated with a rise in impedance, but the potential does not always rise in parallel.

It thus appears that there is a very good correlation between surface potential changes, membrane impedance changes and alteration in the pattern of cellular motile behaviour. It will be noticed that reduction in negative surface potential appears to trigger permeability increases in the membranes of free-living cells in dilute media. This may be in direct contrast to the situation in tissue cells and other living cells in physiological saline, a possibility which will be considered later in relation to the induction of pinocytosis.

Special consideration must be given to the role of Ca^{2+} in relation to membrane permeability and impedance. It is well established for excitable membranes that Ca^{2+} is necessary for the maintenance of membrane impedance and may control permeability of K^+ and Na^+ ions (Koketsu, 1965; Loewenstein, 1966). Loewenstein (1966) has also shown that the removal of Ca^{2+} leads to a fall in the impedance of non-excitable cell membranes such as epithelia and this has also been observed with the early amphibian embryo (C. Roberts & J. F. Palmer, 1967, personal communication) and amoebae (Bruce & Marshall, 1965). It is thus clear that the effect of Ca^{2+} is different from that of other cations and, as pointed out above, Ca^{2+} can counteract the effect of NaCl. The mechanism by which calcium exerts its effect is not known but it is possible that it acts predominantly in the deeper region of the membrane increasing the degree of condensation of phospholipid (Shah & Schulman, 1965), a suggestion which is also in agreement with L. Weiss's (1967) finding that the removal of calcium increases membrane deformability.

A rather different system which provides evidence for the relationship between surface potential and cytoplasmic motility is the localized contraction that results from the local application of adsorbing polycations and ionic detergents to the surface of the eggs of *Xenopus laevis* (Gingell, 1967b). Local application of polylysine or ribonuclease causes a contraction at the surface as manifested by the accumulation of pigment granules. Electron micrographs show that in such regions the membrane is highly convoluted and it appears that the site of contraction is almost certainly in the cortical cytoplasm. (The appearance is very similar to that seen in gastrulation and neural plate formation (Baker, 1965; Baker & Schroeder, 1967).) Contraction induced by polylysine is reversed by treatment with the negative polyions polyglutamate and heparin as well as by increasing the ionic strength with salt. There is a striking correlation between these changes and the impedance of the egg membrane, contraction being associated with a fall and relaxation with a rise in impedance (Fig. 6) (Gingell & Palmer, 1968).

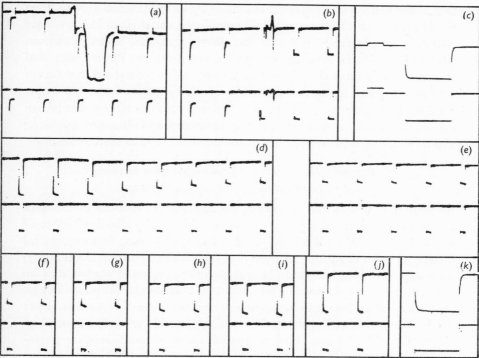

Fig. 6. Electrical potential and cell membrane impedance changes preceding reversible contraction of *Xenopus laevis* egg in response to the action of polyelectrolytes applied to the cell surface, recorded with two intracellular microelectrodes. Voltage pulses for current measurement appear as periodic downward displacements of lower trace. Voltage pulses for resistance measurements appear as displacements of the upper potential trace (ordinate). Time (abscissa) runs from left to right in each insert. Scale: normal, 0·25 cm./ sec.; fast, 2·5 cm./sec. (*a*) Negative potential was apparent on penetration of the recording electrode into an untreated fertilized egg. (*b*) Increased resistance due to membrane impedance became apparent on insertion of the stimulating electrode into the egg. (*c*) Capacitative membrane impedance was shown by a fast pulse A (−) 1·0 mV. calibration appears on the trace. (*d*) On addition of polylysine the membrane impedance fell from 260 kΩ to 120 kΩ and the potential changed from (+) 10 mV. to (+) 12 mV. The impedance pulse squared off, indicating reduction in membrane capacitance. Contraction in the treated region began. (*e*) Excess polylysine was washed out and polyglutamate was added with no immediate effect other than a slight increase in membrane capacitance (*f–i*). Inserts show progressive recovery of potential and impedance over a period of about 4 min. (Note: the potential trace was moved to 10 mV. in a negative direction to accommodate increasing pulse height before the next record.) (*j*) Six minutes after the application of polyglutamate the impedance was 280 kΩ and the potential had recovered to (+) 16 mV. Relaxation was by now well under way. (*k*) A fast pulse which shows recovery of capacitance (cf. insert *c*). Note: due to the unknown value of the microelectrode tip potential, potentials quoted are not absolute values.

Again calcium or divalent cations are crucial. Application of ribonuclease or polylysine to the surface in the presence of trace amounts of calcium leads to a fall in impedance but not to contraction; as soon as additional calcium or magnesium is added contraction ensues. These results suggest that if the cell surface potential is altered by environmental factors, then the impedance of the membrane will be reduced and this fall in impedance may reflect an increased permeability, allowing, say, the influx of calcium ions which induces localized cytoplasmic contraction. Reversibility and localization of contraction, however, are not easily understood in terms of calcium entry and it may be that the site of calcium action is the membrane itself. In general terms, we suggest that alterations in surface potential can act as a transducing mechanism whereby environmental influences can bring about changes within the cytoplasm and thus evoke cellular motile responses.

Surface potential as a transducing mechanism in contact paralysis, phagocytosis, pinocytosis and chemotaxis

As pointed out in an earlier section, the approach of two cell membranes results in localized contact paralysis manifested by the inhibition of pseudopod formation. While the mechanism involved may be a mechanical intervention, more subtle processes may be involved. Weiss & Scott (1963) have suggested that localized pH changes at the region of contact may be responsible. They do not suggest why pH changes should occur but an analysis of close intercellular approach suggests a small reduction in pH would occur (Gingell, 1967a). This might provide a mechanism, since Taylor (1962) has shown that lowering pH causes a cessation of the movement of tissue cells. Another mechanism is conceivably provided by a change in surface potential due to the close approach of two electrostatic double layers. Gingell (1967a) has given a theoretical treatment of this problem on the basis of the Verwey–Overbeek theory (1948) of lyophobic colloids. He considers surface charges to be fixed rather than reversibly absorbed and in consequence a model of interaction at constant surface charge, but variable surface potential is obtained. It can be shown that surface potential is a function of the distance separating charged membranes. As cells come into close contact, $\sim$ 20Å. separation in physiological saline, their surface potentials undergo a local rise (Fig. 7). The approach to 12Å. separation might be expected to increase the surface potential from -25 to $-39\cdot36$ mV. This calculation is based on the assumption of an impenetrable surface layer. For a 14Å. penetrable layer, with a degree of impenetrability of 0·8, the absolute increase is $-9\cdot83$ mV. (Gingell, 1968). Much higher potential increases are predicted at still closer interaction distances. It has already been argued that the increase in surface potential due to close approach of two cell membranes may produce a change in the gradient through the membrane similar to that following reduction of the bioelectric resting potential across the membrane of an isolated cell. The potential changes calculated might be significant, since depolarization of a nerve cell membrane by about 15 mV. is sufficient to trigger cation permeability changes. It is thus clear that the theory provides a reasonable basis for contact paralysis. The theory may be objected to on the grounds that electron-microscope evidence does not

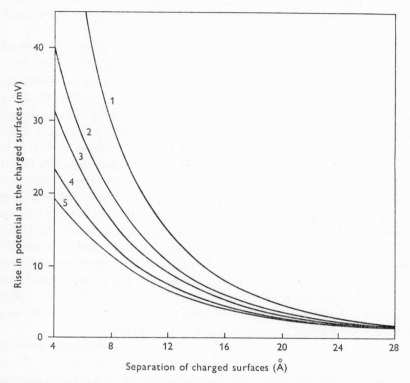

Fig. 7. This figure shows computed rises in potential ($\delta\psi_0$) in the plane of fixed charges borne at the surfaces of approaching membranes in physiological saline. In the first model (i) fixed charges reside at an interface which is impermeable to counterions, while in subsequent cases, fixed charges are located at the outer boundary of a partly permeable layer (e.g., protein) at the surface of the membrane. The thickness of this layer is (d') and its degree of impenetrability is (α). The values of these parameters are as follows: (ii) $\alpha = 0.8$, d' = 10Å; (iii) $\alpha = 0.8$, d' = 20Å; (iv) $\alpha = 0.4$, d' = 10Å; (v) $\alpha = 0.4$, d' = 20Å. Values of surface charge density are calculated in each case such that the surface potential (ψ_0) at infinite separation of the membranes is − 25mV (from Gingell, 1968).

support the widespread approach of cell membranes as closely as 20Å. However, in view of the controversial nature of the cell surface, and the nature and dimensions of the surface coat (e.g. Lesseps, 1967) at the present time, the approximations required by the theory need not be regarded as a major obstacle. It should not be assumed that only changes in potential at the major permeability barrier, as represented by the triple-layered unit membrane seen with the electron microscope, are likely to be of significance. Local potential gradients in the outermost region of the cell surface, which may be freely permeable to counterions, might also trigger off macromolecular configurational changes whose effect may extend to the less permeable part of the membrane. In addition, recent reports suggest that separations between moving cells are not always greater than 150Å. and much smaller distances are now being found (Lesseps, 1963; Trinkaus & Lentz, 1967; Trelstad, Hay & Revel, 1967).

Some support for the suggested mechanism comes from the work of Loewenstein and his co-workers on functional coupling between cells, (Loewenstein, 1966). Close contact between cells in certain tissues results in a large (10^4) drop in the membrane resistance in that region. We have suggested that this functional coupling may result from the close approach of two membranes, increasing surface potential, which increases local membrane permeability (Gingell, 1967a; Gingell & Wolpert, 1968). It is thus of great interest that Loewenstein & Penn (1967) have possibly found a correlation between the cessation of cell movement and the re-establishment of functional coupling in the epidermal cells of newt skin during wound healing. He does, in fact, suggest that functional coupling may be involved in contact inhibition. Potter, Furshpan & Lennox (1966) have found functional coupling between fibroblasts in culture, and Loewenstein (1967) has found that when sponge cells make contact during reaggregation they develop a functional coupling within about 20 min. This latter observation is particularly encouraging since Mookerjee & Ganguly (1964) have reported that when sponge cells meet, the area of contact spreads and pseudopods are formed away from the area of contact.

It is obviously tempting to extend this approach to phagocytosis since the theory provides a basis for the cell 'knowing' that there is a particle at the surface. A review of this field is beyond the scope of this paper but the report by Christiansen & Marshall (1965) on phagocytosis in *Chaos chaos* is particularly relevant and supports the view that one aspect of phagocytosis is a localized contact paralysis. Christiansen & Marshall conclude that the stimulus for food cup formation in the capture of *Paramecium aurelia* involves direct contact between the paramecium and the cell membrane, and that this contact must be longer than that involved in a simple collision. They propose 'that the membrane area directly stimulated by the prey organism becomes attached to the underlying cortical gel. With that region held fast, the surrounding cytoplasm flows outward around the food object'. The similarity between this behaviour following contact and that of localized contraction of the amphibian egg, and contact paralysis, suggests that surface potential may be acting as a transducer in all three cases.

One of the best pieces of evidence for the general significance of cell-membrane surface potential as a transducing mechanism in relation to cellular responses comes from a consideration of the agents which cause pinocytosis in amoebae (Gingell & Wolpert, 1967). Proteins on the acid side of their isoelectric points, where they are net positive, as well as cationic dyes and inorganic salts are known to induce pinocytosis in those cells (Chapman-Andresen, 1958, 1962). Cationic protein and cationic polyelectrolytes bind electrostatically to the negatively charged cell surfaces and acting in this way they would reduce the negative surface potential to zero or positive values. Increase in concentration of inorganic salts would lower the surface potential towards zero by supplying additional diffuse double-layer counterions (Gingell, 1967a). Thus both salts and polyelectrolytes that induce pinocytosis probably reduce the surface potential. It is thus very interesting that the same agents bring about a marked reduction in membrane impedance as discussed in §3 above (see Josefsson, 1966). Brandt & Freeman (1967) showed this could lead to cytoplasmic changes leading to pinocytosis. It is of great interest that Brandt & Pappas (1962) have found that ferritin, which also induces pinocytosis, attaches to the filamentous coat of amoebae, and does not penetrate the 200Å. homogeneous zone overlying the unit membrane. This implies that the effect of the binding of the ferritin may be transmitted by the surface coat to the unit membrane. This clearly has very great implications for the possible role of the surface coats of membranes.

The situation in tissue cells living in physiological saline is not so clear, but there is evidence which suggests that pinocytosis is initiated by an increase in negative surface potential. Pulvertaft & Weiss (1963) found that diluting the saline medium of embryonic chick cells while maintaining osmolarity with sorbitol appeared to cause pinocytosis. Reduction in ionic strength would increase surface potential (Gingell, 1967a). Cohn (1966) and Cohn & Parks (1967a, b) have shown that negatively charged substances cause pinocytosis in macrophages. Adsorption to the cell surfaces was not demonstrated. Similarly Nordling, Vaheri, Saxen and Pettinen (1965) showed that negatively charged polymers inhibit cell attachment and conclude that surface adsorption occurs, but the role of serum proteins in most of the experiments which have been performed remains ambiguous.

The chemotactic responses of cells are reviewed by Rosen (1962). The chemotaxis of *Amoeba proteus* to *Hydra* tissue and also to a cationic protein extracted from crude papain has been described by Jeon & Bell (1964), who found a positive motile chemotactic response to these substances. In an earlier paper, Bingley, Bell & Jeon (1962) using an intracellular microelectrode described a reduction of the bioelectric resting potential of amoebae by these materials as well as by heparin. Surprisingly, the chemotactic responses found by Jeon & Bell (1964) were not interpreted in terms of depolarization of the resting potential, a concept previously provided by Bingley & Thompson (1962) for the control of movement, but in terms of local surface extension. Certain features of this work can be contrasted with our results. Wolpert & O'Neill (1962) found that fluorescent labelled antibody applied locally to *Amoeba proteus* always ended up at the surface of the tail. This was confirmed using fluorescent labelled ribonuclease as well as polylysine; the cells responded to these enzymes with strong negative chemotaxis. Polyglutamate and heparin elicited no definitive response. It is possible that the different results reported with polycations might be due to qualitatively different responses at very low concentrations. Jeon & Bell (1965) have pointed out that higher concentrations of their protein immobilize amoebae.

It has already been emphasized that the primary action of surface-bonding cationic substances is probably to reduce the negative surface potential, which is followed by a decreased membrane impedance and a cessation of locomotion. A change in resting potential invariably follows presumably because of altered transmembrane ionic fluxes, and this may provide the signal for cytoplasmic contraction and negative chemotactic response.

Polycations which bind to the cell surface thus appear to induce a tail when applied locally. This is particularly interesting in relation to the discovery that the surface of an extending pseudopod of *Naegleria gruberi* has a higher negative surface charge density than the rest of the cell (Forrester, Gingell & Korohoda, 1967) as determined by cell electrophoretic mobility measurements. Whether the difference is the cause or result of pseudopodal protrusion is unknown, but it provides a possible physiological correlate with polarized motile behaviour, and may provide a clue to the control of movement. It is tempting to associate normal locomotion of cells which live in dilute media with increased pseudopodal negativity, and the negative chemotactic response to surface binding cations with reduction of surface negativity. However, the evidence at present renders such a suggestion no more than plausible.

SUMMARY AND CONCLUSIONS

On the evidence currently available it appears that the surface membrane does not provide the force for movement and is, with respect to amoeboid movement, a relatively permanent structure which is deformed by forces generated within the cytoplasm. It is probable that it undergoes both elastic and plastic deformations but the relative contributions are not known; nevertheless the tension developed when it is deformed could play an important role in controlling movement by restricting the possibility for pseudopod extension.

Amoeboid movement requires continued making and breaking of contact with the surface over which it is moving. The nature of the adhesive forces are controversial and the mechanisms for making and breaking contact unknown, but the possibility that surface charge plays an important role is attractive. There is evidence that pseudopod extension is prevented when cells are in contact—contact paralysis—but it is not known whether this is purely a mechanical effect or whether a more subtle mechanism may be operative.

The possibility that bioelectric potentials control amoeboid movement—pseudopod extension occurring where the potential across the membrane is lowest—is of great interest, but the experimental data are still controversial. A somewhat different mechanism involving surface potential is put forward. This is based on experiments which show that altering the electrostatic surface potential of amoebae and of the surface of an amphibian egg can bring about a change in impedance of the membrane and a cytoplasmic response. In general terms it is suggested that the surface potential can provide a transducer mechanism whereby external stimuli can bring about a response in the cytoplasm. While this could provide an explanation of a variety of phenomena including contact paralysis, pinocytosis, and chemotaxis, it is not clear whether changes in surface potential play any role in normal movement; thus it may be very significant that pseudopod formation in some cells is associated with an increased negative surface charge density. If the formation and retraction of pseudopods were controlled by surface potential there might be the exciting possibility of developing a theory which could encompass not only normal movement but also cell adhesion and contact, intercellular interaction, and the responses to environmental stimuli. Until very much more experimental work has been done, the feasibility of such a possibility cannot be seriously assessed.

This work has been supported by the Nuffield Foundation.

REFERENCES

ABÉ, T. H. (1962). *Cytologia* **27**, 111.
ABERCROMBIE, M. (1961). *Expl Cell Res.* Suppl. 8, p. 188.
ABERCROMBIE, M. (1964). *Archs Biol. (Liége)* **75**, 351.
ABERCROMBIE, M. (1965). In *Cells and Tissues in Culture*, vol. 1, p. 177. Ed. E. N. Willme. New York: Academic Press.
ALLEN, R. D. (1961). *Expl Cell Res.* Suppl. 8, p. 17.
AMBROSE, E. J. (1961). *Expl Cell Res.* Suppl. 8, p. 54.
BAKER, P. C. (1965). *J. Cell Biol.* **24**, 95.

BAKER, P. C. & SCHROEDER, T. E. (1967). *Devl Biol.* **15**, 432.

BANGHAM, A. D. & PAPAHADJOPOULOS, D. (1966). *Biochim. biophys. Acta* **126**, 181.

BANGHAM, A. D., STANDISH, M. M. & MILLER, N. M. (1965). *Nature, Lond.* **208**, 1295.

BANGHAM, A. D., STANDISH, M. M. & WATKINS, J. C. (1965). *J. molec. Biol.* **13**, 138.

BELL, L. G. E. (1961). *J. theoret. Biol.* **1**, 104.

BELL, L. G. E. & JEON, K. W. (1963). *Nature, Lond.* **198**, 675.

BINGLEY, M. S. (1966*a*). *Expl Cell Res.* **43**, 1.

BINGLEY, M. S. (1966*b*). *J. exp. Biol.* **45**, 251.

BINGLEY, M. S., BELL, L. G. E. & JEON, K. W. (1962). *Expl Cell Res.* **28**, 208.

BINGLEY, M. S. & THOMPSON, C. M. (1962). *J. theoret. Biol.* **2**, 16.

BONNER, J. T. (1962). *Am. Nat.* **86**, 79.

BRANDT, P. W. & FREEMAN, A. R. (1967). *Science, N.Y.* **155**, 383.

BRANDT, P. W. & PAPPAS, G. D. (1962). *J. Cell Biol.* **15**, 55.

BROOKS, D. E., MILLAR, J. S., SEAMAN, G. V. F. & VASSAR, P. S. (1967). *J. cell. Physiol.* **69**, 155.

BRUCE, D. L. & MARSHALL, J. M. (1965). *J. gen. Physiol.* **49**, 151.

CARTER, S. B. (1967). *Nature, Lond.* **213**, 256.

CHANGEUX, J. P., THIERY, J., TUNG, Y. & KITTEL, C. (1967). *Proc. natn. Acad. Sci. U.S.A.* **57**, 335.

CHAPMAN, D., KAMAT, V. B., DE GIER, J. & PENKETT, S. A. (1968). *J. mol. Biol.* **31**, 101.

CHAPMAN-ANDRESEN, C. (1958). *C. r. Trav. Lab. Carlsberg* **31**, 77.

CHAPMAN-ANDRESEN, C. (1962). *C. r. Trav. Lab. Carlsberg* **33**, 73.

CHAPMAN-ANDRESEN, C. (1963). In *Progress in Protozoology*, p. 267. Ed. J. Ludvik, J. Lom and J. Vavra.

CHRISTIANSEN, R. G. & MARSHALL, J. M. (1965). *J. Cell Biol.* **25**, 443-457.

COHN, Z. A. (1966). *J. exp. Med.* **124**, 557.

COHN, Z. A. & PARKS, E. (1967*a*). *J. exp. Med.* **125**, 213.

COHN, Z. A. & PARKS, E. (1967*b*). *J. exp. Med.* **125**, 457.

CONOVER, A. & BÁRÁNY, B. (1966). *Biochim. biophys. Acta* **127**, 235.

CURTIS, A. S. G. (1960). *Am. Nat.* **94**, 37.

CURTIS, A. S. G. (1962). *Biol. Rev.* **37**, 82.

CURTIS, A. S. G. (1964). *J. Cell Biol.* **20**, 199.

CURTIS, A. S. G. (1966). *Sci. Progr., Lond.* **54**, 61.

CZARSKA, L. & GREBECKI, A. (1966). *Acta Protozool.* **4**, 201.

DU PRAW, E. J. (1965). *Devl. Biol.* **12**, 53.

FORRESTER, J. A., GINGELL, D. & KOROHODA, W. (1967). *Nature, Lond.* **215**, 1409.

GARROD, D. (1967). In preparation.

GARROD, D. & WOLPERT, L. (1968). *J. Cell Sci.* (in Press).

GINGELL, D. (1967*a*). *J. theoret. Biol.* **17**, 451.

GINGELL, D. (1967*b*). In preparation.

GINGELL, D. (1968). *J. theoret. Biol.* (in Press).

GINGELL, D. & PALMER, J. F. (1967). Unpublished observations.

GINGELL, D. & PALMER, J. F. (1968). *Nature*, **217**, 98.

GINGELL, D. & WOLPERT, L. (1968). In preparation.

GOLDACRE, R. J. (1961). *Expl Cell Res.* Suppl. 8, p. 1.

GOLDACRE, R. J. (1964). In *Primitive Motile Systems*, p. 237. Ed. R. D. Allen and N. Kamiya. New York: Academic Press.

GRIFFIN, J. L. & ALLEN, R. D. (1960). *Expl Cell Res.* **20**, 619.

GUSTAFSON, T. & WOLPERT, L. (1963). *Int. Rev. Cytol.* **15**, 139.

GUSTAFSON, T. & WOLPERT, L. (1967). *Biol. Rev.* **42**, 442.

HODGKIN, A. L. & CHANDLER, W. K. (1965). *J. gen. Physiol.* **48**, 27.

HODGKIN, A. L. & HUXLEY, A. F. (1952). *J. Physiol., Lond.* **117**, 500.
HOLTFRETER, J. (1948). *Ann. N.Y. Acad. Sci.* **49**, 709.
JEON, K. W. & BELL, L. G. E. (1964). *Expl Cell Res.* **33**, 531.
JEON, K. W. & BELL, L. G. E. (1965). *Expl Cell Res.* **38**, 536.
JONES, B. M. (1966). *Nature, Lond.* **212**, 362.
JONES, P. C. T. (1966). *Nature, Lond.* **212**, 365.
JOSEFSSON, J. O. (1966). *Acta physiol. scand.* **66**, 395.
KAMIYA, N. (1964). In *Primitive Motile Systems*, p. 257. Ed. R. D. Allen and
    N. Kamiya. New York: Academic Press.
KOKETSU, K. (1965). *Proc. 23rd Int. Cong., Physiol. Sci., Tokyo,* vol. IV, p. 521.
KORN, E. D. (1966). *Science, N.Y.* **153**, 1491.
LANDAU, J. V. (1959). *Ann. N.Y. Acad. Sci.* **78**, 487.
LANDAU, J. A. V. (1965). *J. Cell Biol.* **24**, 332.
LANDAU, J. V. & THIBODEAU, L. (1962). *Expl Cell Res.* **27**, 591.
LESSEPS, R. J. (1963). *J. exp. Zool.* **153**, 171.
LESSEPS, R. J. (1967). *J. Cell Biol.* **34**, 173.
LOEWENSTEIN, W. R. (1966). *Ann. N.Y. Acad. Sci.* **137**, 441.
LOEWENSTEIN, W. R. (1967). *Devl Biol.* **15**, 503.
LOEWENSTEIN, W. R. & PENN, R. D. (1967). *J. Cell Biol.* **33**, 235.
LUCEY, E. A. & CURTIS, A. S. G. (1959). *Med. biol. Illust.* **9**, 86.
MARSHALL, J. M. & NACHMIAS, V. T. (1965). *J. histochem. cytochem.* **13**, 92.
MARSLAND, D. (1956). *Int. Rev. Cytol.* **5**, 299.
MAST, S. O. (1926). *J. Morph.* **41**, 347.
MERCER, E. H. & SHAFFER, B. M. (1960). *J. biophys. biochem. Cytol.* **7**, 353.
MITCHISON, J. M. & SWANN, M. M. (1954). *J. exp. Biol.* **31**, 461.
MOOKERJEE, S. & GANGULY, B. (1964). *Wilhelm Roux Arch. EntwMech. Org.* **155**,
    525.
MOSCONA, A. A. (1960). In *Developing Cell Systems and Their Control*, p. 45.
    Ed. D. Rudnick. New York: The Ronald Press Co.
MUELLER, P. & RUDIN, D. O. (1968). *Nature* **217**, 713.
NACHMIAS, V. T. (1966). *Expl Cell Res.* **43**, 583.
NEIFAKH, S. A., AVRAMOV, J. A. & GAITSKHOKI, V. S. (1965). *Biochim. biophys.*
    Acta **100**, 329.
NORDLING, S., VAHERI, A., SAXEN, E. & PETTINEN, K. (1965). *Expl Cell Res.* **37**,
    406.
O'NEILL, C. H. (1964). *Expl Cell Res.* **35**, 477.
PANTIN, C. F. A. (1923). *J. mar. biol. Ass. U.K.* **13**, 24.
PAPAHADJOPOULOS, D. & BANGHAM, A. D. (1966). *Biochim. biophys. Acta* **126**, 185.
PETHICA, B. A. (1961). *Expl Cell Res.* Suppl. 8, p. 123.
POLISSAR, M. J. (1954). In *The Kinetic Basis of Molecular Biology*. Ed. F. H.
    Johnson, H. Eyring and M. J. Polissar. New York: John Wiley and Sons.
POTTER, D. A., FURSHPAN, E. I. & LENNOX, E. J. (1966). *Proc. natn. Acad. Sci.*
    U.S.A. **55**, 328.
PULVERTAFT, R. S. V. & WEISS, L. (1963). *J. Path. Bact.* **85**, 473.
RAND, R. P. (1964). *Biophys. J.* **4**, 303.
RAND, R. P. & BURTON, A. C. (1964). *Biophys. J.* **4**, 115.
RIDDLE, J. (1962). *Expl Cell Res.* **26**, 158.
ROSEN, W. G. (1962). *Q. Rev. Biol.* **37**, 242.
ROSENBERG, M. D. (1963). *J. Cell Biol.* **17**, 289.
SHAFFER, B. M. (1963). *Expl Cell Res.* **32**, 603.
SHAFFER, B. M. (1964). In *Primitive Motile System*, p. 387. Ed. R. D. Allen and
    N. Kamiya. New York: Academic Press.
SHAFFER, B. M. (1965). *J. theoret. Biol.* **8**, 27.

SHAH, D. O. & SCHULMAN, J. H. (1965). *J. Lipid Res.* **6**, 341.

TASAKI, I. & KAMIYA, N. (1964). *J. cell. comp. Physiol.* **63**, 365.

TAYLOR, A. C. (1962). *J. Cell Biol.* **15**, 201.

TAYLOR, A. C. (1966). *J. Cell Biol.* **28**, 155.

TILNEY, L. G. & PORTER, K. R. (1967). *J. Cell Biol.* **34**, 327.

TRELSTAD, R. L., HAY, E. D. & REVEL, J. P. (1967). *Devl Biol.* **16**, 78.

TRINKHAUS, J. P. & LENTZ, T. L. (1967). *J. Cell Biol.* **32**, 139.

VAUGHAN, R. B. & TRINKHAUS, J. B. (1966). *J. Cell Sci.* **1**, 407.

VERWEY, E. J. & OVERBEEK, J. TH. G. (1948). *The Theory of the Stability of the Lyophobic Colloids.* Amsterdam: Elsevier.

WEISS, P. (1961). *Expl Cell Res.* Suppl. 8, 260.

WEISS, L. (1962). *J. theoret. Biol.* **2**, 236.

WEISS, L. (1967). *J. Cell Biol.* **33**, 341.

WEISS, L. & COOMBS, R. R. A. (1963). *Expl Cell Res.* **30**, 331.

WEISS, P. & SCOTT, B. I. H. (1963). *Proc. natn. Acad. Sci. U.S.A.* **50**, 330.

WOHLFARTH-BOTTERMANN, K. E. & STOCKEM, W. (1966). *Z. Zellforsch. mikrosk. Anat.* **73**, 444.

WOLPERT, L. (1960). In *Int. Rev. Cytol.* **10**, 163.

WOLPERT, L. (1963). In *Cell Growth and Cell Division*, p. 277. Ed. R. J. C. Harris. New York: Academic Press.

WOLPERT, L. (1965). *Symp. Soc. gen. Microbiol.* no. XV, p. 270.

WOLPERT, L. (1966). *Expl Cell Res.* **41**, 385.

WOLPERT, L. & O'NEILL, C. H. (1962). *Nature, Lond.* **196**, 1261.

WOLPERT, L., THOMPSON, C. M. & O'NEILL, C. H. (1964). In *Primitive Motile Systems*, p. 143. Ed. R. D. Allen and N. Kamiya. New York: Academic Press.

THE MECHANISM OF CYTOPLASMIC MOVEMENT IN A MYXOMYCETE PLASMODIUM

By N. KAMIYA

Department of Biology, Faculty of Science, Osaka University

INTRODUCTION

Recently considerable efforts have been devoted to elucidating the physical, chemical and structural bases of cytoplasmic movement in the plasmodium of myxomycetes. In particular, the plasmodium of *Physarum polycephalum* has been a subject of extensive study.

Movement of the myxomycete plasmodium has various outstanding features. The rate of flow (Kamiya, 1950a) as well as the amount of endoplasm carried along with the streaming (Kamiya, 1950b) are exceedingly great compared with the ordinary cytoplasmic streaming in plant cells or in amoebae. When a part of the strand is excised and hung in the air, it exhibits peculiar torsional movements (Kamiya & Seifriz, 1954).

In a major strand of the plasmodium of *Physarum* we observe sol endoplasm flowing vigorously in the tube with a wall of gel ectoplasm. The endoplasm flows back and forth with a certain period along the capillary tube, the speed being greatest at the axial region of the tube. The analysis of the velocity distribution of the endoplasmic streaming in the capillary tube, which coincides with that of the so-called plug flow of a non-Newtonian fluid, shows that the endoplasm in a capillary tube is based on a pressure-flow mechanism (Kamiya & Kuroda, 1958). The motive force responsible for the endoplasmic streaming along the strand, or the capillary tube, is then the differential pressure established in one and the same plasmodium.

The absolute amount of the motive force which is measurable by the double-chamber technique changes with a period of about 2 min. and an amplitude of about 15 cm. of water column under normal physiological conditions. Taking advantage of the double-chamber method, various physical, chemical and physiological aspects of the motive force production have been revealed (Kamiya, 1959); but their details cannot be given here. The purpose of the present study is to relate some aspects of the cytoplasmic movement of the slime mould to the behaviour of its glycerol model and to the structural differentiation of the cytoplasm revealed by electron microscopy.

THE RESPONSE OF THE GLYCEROL MODEL OF
THE PLASMODIUM TO ATP

If the *Physarum* plasmodium is treated with glycerol under proper conditions and its 'model' is made, it contracts with the addition of ATP (Kamiya & Kuroda, 1965). Plate 1 *a*, *b* shows a lobule of the plasmodium before and after ATP has been added. The material was treated with 40% glycerol containing 10 mM EDTA, 10 mM-KCl and 10 mM Tris buffer (pH 7·1) at −5° C. for 1 day and then at −15° C. for 15 days. After washing with 60 mM-KCl several times at room temperature the material was treated with the experimental solution containing 5 mM ATP, 5 mM-MgCl$_2$ and 30 mM-KCl. It has been pointed out that the magnitude and direction of contraction are different according to the loci of the plasmodium. Clear contraction is observable in the strand region and the peripheral zone of the fan-shaped expanse, where the sol and gel parts were intricately interwoven when the plasmodium was alive. In the strand part, contraction occurs only laterally. In other words, the strand is hardly shortened, but becomes thinner on addition of ATP. At the advancing margin of the fan-like expanse, the contraction takes place in the main radially, not tangentially to the margin (Plate 1, Fig. 1). The maximal relative linear contraction is approximately 30% in both cases. Recently Dr Kuroda and I continued a further series of experiments on glycerol models of the plasmodium. Although the experiments are still in progress a brief description would be relevant.

When a strand part of the plasmodium is excised and suspended vertically in moist air by holding it by one end, the free lower end, to which a small weight is attached, gradually shows periodic twists around the axis of the strand concomitantly with contraction and elongation of the strand. For some time after the thread has been hung in the air, its spontaneous twisting is rather insignificant and irregular, but after about 1 hr. the strand gradually manifests conspicuous oscillatory contractions and torsions (Kamiya & Seifriz, 1954; Kamiya, 1965).

If a piece of the strand is treated with glycerol soon after it has been taken out from the plasmodium creeping on the substratum, it does not contract longitudinally but laterally as was stated before. However, the strand, which has been hung in moist air for 1 hr. or longer under an appropriate tension (*c*. 20 g/cm.²) and has become as thin as 100 μ in diameter before it is treated with cold glycerol, contracts by about 10% in the longitudinal direction on addition of ATP. This evidence suggests that contractile fibrous elements in the strand, which were at first circularly orientated in the wall of the strand, have gradually given way to the tension applied so that they reorientate themselves longitudinally to the axis of the strand. That this actually occurs can be demonstrated by electron-microscopical investigations, which will be discussed later.

One of the characteristic features of the movement of the myxomycete plasmodium is its rhythm. Not only endoplasm flows back and forth, but also the hanging strand twists to the right and left, or contracts and elongates with a constant period. Although the cause of the oscillation of

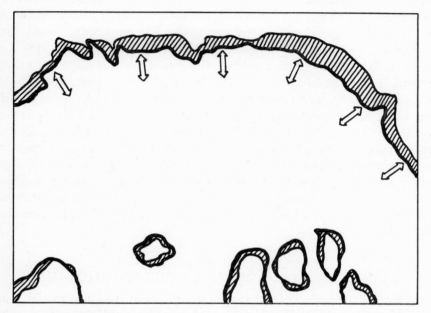

Fig. 1. Contraction of the fan-like expanse of the glycerol-treated plasmodium. The shaded areas represent parts where the margin of the plasmodium has retreated after addition of ATP. The double arrows show the direction of contraction and loci where distinct contraction occurs.

these movements is still utterly unknown, there is a possibility that it is due to an intrinsic character of the contractile protein of this organism. If so, it is expected that under proper conditions the glycerol model may also oscillate just as in the cases of ciliary and flagellar motions (Hoffmann-Berling, 1960, 1961) and in the contraction of insect flight muscle (Jewell & Rüegg, 1965).

Our preliminary experiment in collaboration with Dr Kuroda was performed using calcium buffer prepared according to the method of Jewell & Rüegg. For this kind of experiment there are many technical problems which should be overcome. Though the experiment has just begun, the results are promising. We selected for the material to be tested the plasmodial strand hung in the air under a constant tension. What we can say at present is that glycerol-treated models of the strands did exhibit oscillatory twisting motion on addition of $1-2 \times 10^{-3}$ M ATP containing about $10^{-7}-10^{-8}$ M-Ca^{2+}. The strand of such a model was not only thin ($120\,\mu$) but had exhibited vigorous oscillatory twisting motion before it was treated with 20% glycerol for 3 weeks at $-5°$ C. One cycle of swings took about $1 \cdot 5$ min., which is about the same as the period of movement of the living strand, and the angle of the swing was about $50°$ immediately after ATP was applied. The angle of the swing, however, gradually diminished until oscillation stopped completely after 25 min. The amplitude, period and duration of oscillation are quite different according to the sample. It is our impression that the essential condition for a good result is the use of a thin strand, a considerable part of which is occupied with contractile fibrils aligned regularly. The rest of the water-insoluble materials in the model may work simply as obstacles to this movement. Though details about the oscillatory motion induced in the plasmodium-model await further study, the fact that a glycerol-treated plasmodial strand can oscillate spontaneously under appropriate conditions has the important implication that the rhythm of the movement is based on the intrinsic character of the protein molecules themselves. It shows that a simple system composed of contractile protein, ATP and some simple ions can make a feed-back loop which produces the oscillatory motion.

FIBRILLAR STRUCTURES IN THE PLASMODIUM

Fibrillar differentiation of the ground cytoplasm in the slime mould was first demonstrated with the electron microscope by Wohlfarth-Bottermann (1962), and later by Porter *et al.* (1965), McManus (1965), McManus & Roth (1965), Rhea (1966), and by ourselves (Nagai & Kamiya, 1966).

The plasmodia of *Physarum* used for our observations were fixed with 4% osmic acid for 2 min., then with 4% glutaraldehyde with additives of 0·05 M-NaCl, 0·01 M-KCl and 0·007 M-$CaCl_2$ at the final concentrations for 25 min. Then they were postfixed for 15 min. with 2% OsO_4 in the presence of the same salts at the same concentrations, embedded in Epon 812, sectioned with a glass knife on an LKB ultramicrotome, doubly stained with uranyl acetate and lead citrate and observed with a model JEM-7 electron microscope.

A tiny part of a plasmodium transplanted onto the surface of agar gel spreads out into a ramified system of protoplasmic strands with fan-like expanses at its terminals. The channels of flow in the fan-like expanses divide off repeatedly into smaller channels as the marginal zone is approached. Our observations on the normal plasmodium are well in conformity with the observations that Wohlfarth-Botterman (1962, 1963, 1964 a, b, 1965) made using the electron microscope. Fibrillar structures are observable where the cytoplasm is in the gel state; they may be seen for example in the wall of the capillary tube and in the zone close to the advancing front. They are more or less spongy in structure since there are minute channels of streamlets in them. As pointed out by Wohlfarth-Bottermann, the fibrils are composed of bundles of numerous filaments with a mean diameter of 70 Å. put together without geometric array (Plates 1 c, 2 a). These fibrils seem to be identical to those described by Wohlfarth-Bottermann and correspond to type I or II described by McManus (1965) and McManus & Roth (1965). In the fan-like expanse the dominant orientation of these fibrils is radial. In the wall of the capillary tube their major orientation is circular rather than longitudinal when the capillary tube is creeping on the substratum. But when it is hung in the moist air and a proper tension is given to it for an hour or two with a weight (c. 5 mg.) attached to its lower end, the orientation of most of the filaments becomes longitudinal. Under these conditions the filaments tend to gather in a dense layer just below the surface membrane and in contact with the vacuolar membrane (Plate 2 b). Thus the orientation of the fibrils coincides neatly with the direction of ATP-induced contractions in the specimen treated with glycerine. These facts suggest that the fibrillar structures in question are intimately correlated with the ATP-induced contractions of the glycerol model.

In glycerol-treated specimens or models filamentous structures can be seen more clearly. Plate 3 a shows the marginal region of a glycerol-treated small lobule sectioned in parallel to its spreading surface. This specimen was kept for 10 days at $-15°$ C. in 40% glycerol with 10 mM EDTA, 10 mM-KCl and 10 mM Tris buffer (pH 7·1) added at their final concentrations. Single filaments lie nearly parallel with one another to form denser or looser bundles. These bundles form delicate networks as they are interconnected with some of the filaments of which they are composed. In order to know the role played by the filaments in the process of the contraction of the plasmodium, it is extremely important to observe their behaviour when ATP is added. Their reaction to ATP is quite distinct. In the presence of 1×10^{-3} M ATP the fibrils gather more closely to one another to form localized and compact bundles (Plate 3 b). The compact bundles are joined to adjacent ones with the filaments coming out of them to form ramified structures. At the same time some filaments are seen to have free ends without forming a network. In the ATP-treated specimens, more free ends of unit filaments are seen than in the control specimens, probably due to their mechanical breakdown in the process of aggregation induced by ATP. Though the effect of ATP on the aggegation pattern of the filaments is quite remarkable, there is no clear indication that each filament is shortened or becomes thicker in this process. The reaction of the filaments in response to ATP resembles a certain phase of super-precipitation of muscle actomyosin *in vitro* (Ikemoto, Kitagawa & Gergely, 1966).

The presence of actomyosin-like contractile proteins in the plasmodium of *Physarum polycephalum* was first pointed out by Loewy (1952). Later Ts'o *et al.* (1965*a*, *b*, 1957*a*, *b*) and Nakajima (1960) conducted detailed studies on the proteins extracted from the slime mould. Recently Hatano & Oosawa (1966*a*, *b*), and Hatano & Tazawa (1968), who further improved the method of extraction, succeeded in isolating and purifying contractile proteins similar to muscle myosin B, myosin A and actin separately from the same material. Like Nakajima's data, purified myosin B of the plas-modium shows superprecipitation at low salt concentrations and a viscosity drop at high salt concentrations on addition of ATP. The sedimentation pattern of this protein in 0.5 M-KCl solution gives a single peak. On addition of ATP, this peak is divided into two peaks in the presence of Mg^{2+}. It was ascertained that the slow component is myosin A. This means that the myosin B-like protein is not a single protein but a com-pound protein, one component of which was known to be plasmodium myosin A.

Close investigation of electron micrographs of glycerinated plasmodium reveals that there are many small particles attached to the filaments, par-ticles which disappear on addition of ATP. Using a negative staining tech-nique, Dr Nagai and I recently had an opportunity to investigate plas-modium myosin B and native F-actin *in vitro* with the collaboration of Dr Hatano. From their dimensions and form, and comparing the bio-chemical data of Hatano, Totsuka & Oosawa (1967), we suppose the fila-ments described above represent plasmodium F-actin and that the small particles, which dissociate from the filaments with ATP in the presence of Mg^{2+}, are probably plasmodium myosin A (R. Nagai & N. Kamiya, unpublished).

ARTIFICIAL MODIFICATION OF THE DISTRIBUTION OF ENDOPLASM

The next problem is to try to correlate the generation of the motive force with the fibrillar differentiation of the cytoplasm. We shall discuss our recent experiments using uneven external pressure to change the endo-plasm-ectoplasm ratio, so modifying the motive force. Chemical agents are therefore avoided. Such an experiment not only helps us to understand an important aspect of the nature of the fibrils mentioned above, but also demonstrates the presence of self-regulatory mechanism in the production of the motive force in the plasmodium.

When the two halves of a plasmodium in a double chamber were subjected to a sufficiently large difference in air pressure—for example, a water pressure of 30 cm.—the endoplasm rushed along the capillary tube connecting the two halves from the higher to the lower pressure. With this procedure, a considerable part of the endoplasmic sol in one half of the plasmodium is carried to the other half while the ectoplasmic gel is left behind. Thus we have a dumbbell-shaped plasmodium with endoplasm-rich and endoplasm-poor halves connected by a single strand. Figure 2 shows this state diagrammatically, where the right half of the plasmodium

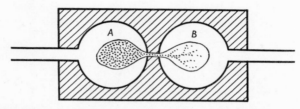

Fig. 2. A plasmodium in a double chamber under pressure gradient. Air pressure in B is made higher than A by a water pressure of 30–40 cm. Most of the endoplasm in B is dislocated to A (Takata, Nagai & Kamiya, 1967).

in compartment B has withered away losing its endoplasm while the left half in compartment A has swollen with the inflowing endoplasm. Since the spreading area of each half of the plasmodium does not change appreciably in this case, the endoplasm-rich half becomes thick and opaque with the inflowing endoplasm while the endoplasm-poor half becomes thin and transparent.

If the pressure gradient is removed between A and B in such a situation, the endoplasm always tends to come back rapidly. This tendency can be shown more exactly in terms of the balance-pressure. In Fig. 3, which represents the result of an experiment of this kind, the initial part (a) of the curve up to 12·5 min. shows spontaneous changes of the motive force under normal conditions. Then a constant air pressure amounting to 30 cm. of water was applied to compartment B for 17·5 min., during which period the endoplasm flowed mostly from B to A. After this, measurement of the motive force was re-started. It can be seen in Fig. 3 (b) that the motive force of the backward streaming was high immediately after the constant one-sided pressure ceased to be applied and was replaced with the balance-

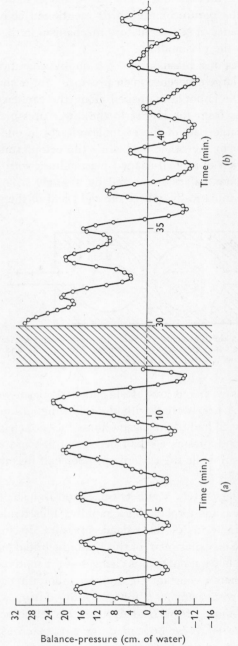

Balance-pressure (cm. of water)

Time (min.)

(a)

Time (min.)

(b)

Fig. 3. The motive force production in a plasmodium whose endoplasm is dislocated by the externally applied pressure gradient. Curve *a*: control; the shaded part: period during which air pressure amounting to 30 cm. of water column was applied to *B* for 17·5 min. (time scale is discontinued). Curve *b*: the motive force after the distribution of endoplasm has been polarized (Takata, Nagai & Kamiya, 1967).

pressure. It took 5·5 min. before the undulating curve came down and crossed the base line. It is to be remembered here that this curve was obtained when the endoplasm was held quiet at the connecting strand between endoplasm-rich and endoplasm-poor halves. This simple experiment shows clearly that the forced translocation of the endoplasm augments the motive force of the backward streaming, and that the augmented motive force is readjusted sooner or later even though no back streaming was allowed to take place.

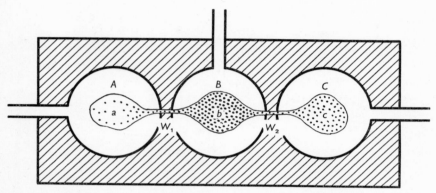

Fig. 4. Triple chamber consisting of three compartments, A, B and C, in series with partition walls W_1 and W_2 between A and B, and B and C respectively. Showing diagrammatically the state of the plasmodium in which protoplasmic blob a was made endoplasm-poor and b endoplasm-rich while c remained normal in the endoplasm–ectoplasm ratio (Kamiya & Yoneda, 1967).

For further analysis of this phenomenon a chamber consisting of three compartments, a triple chamber, was constructed (Kamiya & Yoneda, 1967). In Fig. 4 three parts of a plasmodium (a, b, c) connected with one another by single strands in series are placed in compartments A, B and C. The motive forces of the flow between a and b and between b and c were measured simultaneously by two observers who applied balance-pressures to A and C by watching the flow at W_1 and W_2 through a specially designed optical system. Compartment B was left open to the atmosphere throughout the experiment. When we applied to A a sufficiently large constant air pressure, either positive or negative, the plasmodial part b became abnormally rich or poor in endoplasm. The streaming between b and c was, however, arrested without interruption so that the endoplasm–ectoplasm ratio was kept normal at c. Under such a situation, the balance-pressure in C represents the motive force of the flow between the endoplasm-rich (or -poor) part (b) and the normal part (c). A series of experiments of this kind, an example of which is shown in Fig. 5, revealed that the endoplasm-rich

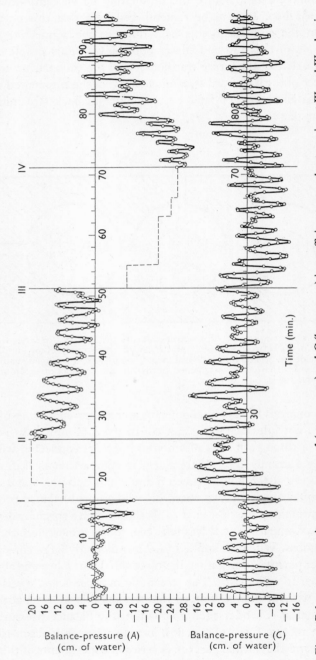

Fig. 5. Balance-pressures in compartments A (upper curve) and C (lower curve) just sufficient to stop the streaming at W_1 and W_2, showing the effect of dislocation of the endoplasm from a to b, and then from b to a (cf. Fig. 4). Broken lines show the pressure applied to A to dislocate the endoplasm from a to b or from b to a (Kamiya & Yoneda, 1967).

part of the plasmodium had always a higher internal pressure at first than the normal part of the same plasmodium, while the endoplasm-deficient part of the plasmodium had always an internal pressure lower than that of the normal part (Kamiya & Yoneda, 1967). This fact shows that both endoplasm-rich and endoplasm-poor halves are responsible for the generation of the counter motive force as stated in the foregoing (cf. Fig. 3).

In order to gain further insight into the physiology of endoplasm-rich and endoplasm-poor plasmodia, an attempt was next made to measure the

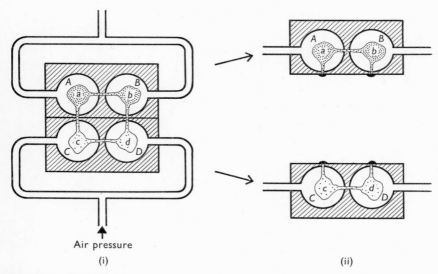

Air pressure

(i)   (ii)

Fig. 6. Quadruple-chamber system composed of a pair of identical double-chambers (i). After the major part of the endoplasm in protoplasmic blobs c and d has been transported to a and b through application of positive pressure to compartments C and D the quadruple chamber is decomposed into two double chambers to measure the motive forces of the endoplasm-rich and endoplasm-poor plasmodia separately (ii) (Kamiya & Takata, 1967).

motive force of each (Kamiya & Takata, 1967). For this purpose, a chamber with four compartments, a quadruple chamber, was made (Fig. 6). It consisted of a pair of detachable identical double chambers put together to make an air-tight unit. Four small masses (a, b, c and d) of the plasmodium were placed in the four compartments (A, B, C and D) and connected with one another by single strands as is shown in Fig. 6 to the left. As is the case in ordinary double-chamber technique, the construction is such that the partition walls between adjacent compartments are sealed air-tight and yet the plasmodial strands penetrate them without impeding the endoplasmic flow. With this set-up, if we apply a higher air pressure to compartments C and D evenly, the endoplasm in c and d is forced to move toward *a* and *b*. After *a* and *b* have been sufficiently swollen with the inflowing endoplasm while *c* and *d* have wilted away with the outflowing endo-plasm, the two double chambers were detached from each other. The orifices of the broken strands between *a* and *c*, and *b* and *d* were sealed with petroleum jelly. The motive forces of the two dumbbell-shaped plasmodia in the two double chambers—one rich in endoplasm distributed evenly in both halves (*a* and *b*) and the other poor (*c* and *d*)—were then

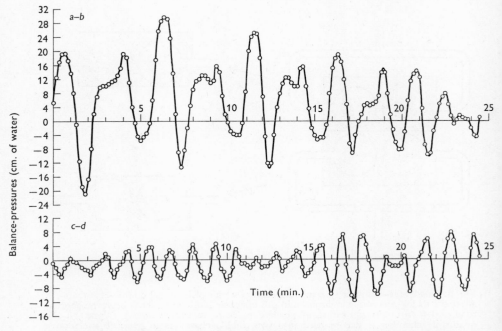

Fig. 7. Balance-pressures obtained from endoplasm-rich (top) and endoplasm-poor (bottom) plasmodia (Kamiya & Takata, 1967).

measured simultaneously and independently by two observers. Figure 7 shows one of the results thus measured. The upper waves show the motive force generated in the endoplasm-rich plasmodium while the lower wave-train represents that of the endoplasm-poor plasmodium. Differences in magnitude and in period of the motive force curve are obvious. A further point to be noticed in this figure is that the amplitude and period of the upper waves diminished with time while those of the lower waves increased so that the difference between the two groups of waves became gradually inconspicuous.

When a plasmodium is expanded with the inflowing endoplasm, one might think that the elastic force of the ectoplasm is heightened. When it shrinks with the outflowing endoplasm, it may be that the elastic force at the cortex is diminished. The above curves were obtained, however, from the dumbbell-shaped plasmodia, the two halves of which were both endoplasm-rich or both endoplasm-poor, and hence, simple changes in elastic tension of the cortex must have been cancelled out on both sides. Nevertheless there is a big difference in motive force production between the two states of the plasmodia. From this experiment, it is reasonable to suppose that the counter motive force accompanying the forced dislocation of the endoplasm (cf. Figs. 3 and 5) does not represent a simple elastic rebound of the ectoplasmic gel. Generation of the counter motive force is likely to be a response caused by a more deep-seated mechanism.

Generation of the motive force and its relation to the fibrillar structures

With the expectation that there may be a correlation between the motive force production and the development of the ATP-sensitive fibrils, we investigated next the fine structures of the endoplasm-rich and endoplasm-poor plasmodia. The material was fixed at various times after the one-side constant external pressure had been replaced with the balance-pressure.

Electron micrographs revealed a clear difference in the development of fibrils between the two states of the plasmodium, one over-abundant in endoplasm and the other deficient in it. In the ectoplasmic layer of the endoplasm-rich half of the plasmodium we found well-developed fibrillar bundles, which are hardly distinguishable from those in the normal plasmodium. Also we often encountered cases in which the fibrillar bundles were attached to the vacuolar membrane and plasmalemma at their terminals, an observation which was made by Wohlfarth-Bottermann (1964a, b, 1965) in the normal plasmodium. Plate 4a shows a part of the endoplasm-rich half of the plasmodium close to its advancing front in a section parallel to the agar substratum. Here filament bundles branch off from those running along the membrane.

In the endoplasm-poor half, on the other hand, we can observe scarcely any fibrillar differentiations in the cytoplasm at first. Instead, there are aggregates of what appear to be globular substances or rather entangled masses of filament. They are not only similar in staining to those of the fibril bundles, but also they are found in regions just where fibrillar bundles are likely to have been present, especially frequently around the vacuole (Plate 4b). From these facts we are inclined to believe that, when the endoplasm has been sucked out to disturb the normal endoplasm–ectoplasm ratio, the filaments composing the fibrillar bundles are converted into another state, which we should like to term the 'skein state'.

As already stated in the foregoing pages, fibrillar differentiation in the plasmodium probably represents the formation of bundles of plasmodium F-actin to which plasmodium A is attached. It is especially worthy of note in this connexion that Hatano, Totsuka & Oosawa (1967) showed recently that there is, besides F-actin, another state of the actin polymer, the 'Mg-polymer', which is formed in the presence of Mg^{2+}. Mg-polymer of the actin is low in viscosity compared with plasmodium F-actin, suggesting that it is globular rather than fibrillar. Though uncertain, the dense region around the vacuole in Plate 4b, or what we call skein state, may correspond to the aggregate of Mg-polymer made *in vitro* by Hatano, Totsuka & Oosawa (1967).

We have shown that (1) when endoplasm is translocated from one part of the plasmodium to the other by an external force a strong counter motive force is generated to bring the translocated endoplasm back, and (2) this polarity in motive force generation tends to be neutralized gradually. After 10 min., when the polarity of the motive force curve (cf. Kamiya, 1959) approaches the normal level, we see fibrous structures develop in the cytoplasm from the skein state (Plate 5). Judging from the evidence so far obtained, it is safe to say, as already stressed by Wohlfarth-Bottermann through his extensive observations, that the fibrillar structures revealed by electron microscopy are the structural basis of the motive force. Further it may be said that the production of the motive force is regulated by the capacity of the plasmodium to control the state of fibrillar differentiation, this capacity being sensitive to changes in endoplasm–ectoplasm ratio.

CONCLUDING REMARKS

We have discussed some physiological and structural aspects of the plasmodial movement in the foregoing pages. High correlation of fibril formation to motive force production is well in accord with the view that the fibrils in question are the structural basis for the plasmodium to move, a view which has been stressed before by Wohlfarth-Bottermann (1963, 1964a, b, 1965). If this is actually the case, the next problem is how they work so that the endoplasm flows back and forth in the living plasmodium. Ambiguities still remain however as to the role or functional aspect of the fibrils in generating the motive force. The unit filaments, represented probably by F-actin, may possibly slide with one another being intermediated by myosin molecules in such a way that the bundles themselves shorten and exert pressure on the endoplasm. Alternatively, the sliding force is established between the fibrils and the surrounding matrix, which in turn brings forth the streaming of the endoplasm. In the latter case, the direct cause for the pressure flow is not to be found in contraction of the fibrils *per se*. In this connexion, it should be remembered that in the glycerinated specimen of the plasmodium, filaments tend to gather in response to ATP to form denser bundles locally and that there is no indication of unit filaments contracting or becoming thicker. Rhythmic contraction, which is so obvious in the living plasmodium on the macroscopical level, is still obscure as far as molecular events involved in it are concerned. Success in making the glycerinated strand oscillate with a natural physiological period in an appropriate medium containing ATP will provide us with a new means of approach for gaining insight into the cause of oscillation of the cytoplasmic movement of the slime mould.

SUMMARY

1. Glycerinated specimens of the plasmodium of *Physarum polycephalum* can be reactivated by ATP, sometimes even with a spontaneous rhythm.

2. The magnitude and direction of contraction in the glycerol model are different according to loci and treatment (tension) before glycerination.

3. Fibrillar differentiations described by previous authors in the *Physarum* plasmodium have been confirmed. Their distribution and orientation coincide well with the loci and directions of contraction in the glycerol model.

4. Unit filaments of the glycerol model gather closer to form more compact aggregates on addition of ATP. There is no indication of each filament being shortened or becoming thicker.

5. These filaments are presumed to be plasmodium F-actin, to which plasmodium myosin A is probably attached in the absence of ATP or detached in the presence of ATP.

6. When the distribution of the endoplasm is polarized, a counter motive force is generated to induce the restitutional streaming.

7. In the ectoplasmic layer of the fan-like expanse where the endoplasm was made over-abundant, fibrillar structures are well developed. In that part of the fan-like expanse from which the endoplasm is pushed out, most fibrils disappear, being converted to aggregates of another state which we call here the 'skein state'.

8. The plasmodium possesses a capacity of regulating the production of the motive force and also the endoplasm-ectoplasm ratio.

9. This regulatory capacity is closely associated with reversible formation and dissociation of the fibrillar structures in the cytoplasm.

I should like to express my hearty thanks to Drs K. Kuroda and R. Nagai of our Department who co-operated with me in various experiments described or cited here. This work was supported by Grants-in-Aid for Scientific Research from the Japanese Ministry of Education and also by a Research Grant from the Takeda Foundation for the Promotion of Science.

REFERENCES

HATANO, S. & OOSAWA, F. (1966a). *Biochim. biophys. Acta* **127**, 488.

HATANO, S. & OOSAWA, F. (1966b). *J. Cell Physiol.* **68**, 197.

HATANO, S. & TAZAWA, M. (1968). *Biochim. biophys. Acta* (in Press).

HATANO, S., TOTSUKA, T. & OOSAWA, F. (1967). *Biochim. biophys. Acta* **140**, 109.

HOFFMANN-BERLING, H. (1960). In *Comparative Biochemistry*, vol. II, p. 341. Ed. M. Florkin and H. S. Mason. New York and London: Academic Press.

HOFFMANN-BERLING, H. (1961). *Ergebn. Physiol.* **51**, 98.

IKEMOTO, N., KITAGAWA, S. & GERGELY, J. (1966). *Biochem. Z.* **345**, 410.

JEWELL, B. R. & RÜEGG, J. C. (1965). *Proc. R. Soc.* B **164**, 428.

KAMIYA, N. (1950a). *Cytologia* **15**, 194.

KAMIYA, N. (1950b). *Protoplasma* **39**, 344.

KAMIYA, N. (1959). *Protoplasmatologia* **8**, 3a, 1.

KAMIYA, N. (1965). In *Proc. IVth Int. Cong. Rheology*, 1963, Brown University, U.S.A. John Wiley and Sons.

KAMIYA, N. & KURODA, K. (1958). *Protoplasma* **49**, 1.

KAMIYA, N. & KURODA, K. (1965). *Proc. Japan Acad.* **41**, 837.

KAMIYA, N. & SEIFRIZ, W. (1954). *Expl Cell Res.* **6**, 1.

KAMIYA, N. & TAKATA, T. (1967). *Proc. Japan Acad.* **43**, 537.

KAMIYA, N. & YONEDA, M. (1967). *Proc. Japan Acad.* **43**, 531.

LOEWY, A. G. (1952). *J. cell. comp. Physiol.* **40**, 127.

McMANUS, M. A. (1965). *Amer. J. Bot.* **52**, 15.

McMANUS, M. A. & ROTH, L. E. (1965). *J. Cell Biol.* **25**, 305.

NAGAI, R. & KAMIYA, N. (1966). *Proc. Japan Acad.* **42**, 934.

NAKAJIMA, H. (1960). *Protoplasma*, **52**, 413.

PORTER, K. R., KAWAKAMI, N. & LEDBETTER, M. C. (1965). *J. Cell Biol.* **27**, 78A.

RHEA, P. R. (1966). *J. Ultrastructure Res.* **15**, 349.

TAKATA, T., NAGAI, R. & KAMIYA, N. (1967). *Proc. Japan Acad.* **43**, 45.

TS'O, P. O. P., BONNER, J., EGGMAN, L & VINOGRAD, J. (1956a). *J. gen. Physiol.* **39**, 325.

TS'O, P. O. P., EGGMAN, L. & VINOGRAD, J. (1956b). *J. gen. Physiol.* **39**, 801.

TS'O, P. O. P., EGGMAN, L. & VINOGRAD, J. (1957a). *Arch. Biochem. Biophys.* **66**, 64.

TS'O, P. O. P., EGGMAN, L. & VINOGRAD, J. (1957b). *Biochim. biophys. Acta* **25**, 532.

WOHLFARTH-BOTTERMANN, K. E. (1962). *Protoplasma* **54**, 514.

WOHLFARTH-BOTTERMANN, K. E. (1963). *Zellstrukturen und ihre Bedeutung für die amöboide Bewegung.* Köln and Opladen: Westdeutscher Verlag.

WOHLFARTH-BOTTERMANN, K. E. (1964a). *Int. Rev. Cytol.* **16**, 61.

WOHLFARTH-BOTTERMANN, K. E. (1964b). In *Primitive Motile Systems in Cell Biology*, p. 79. Ed. R. D. Allen and N. Kamiya. New York and London: Academic Press.

WOHLFARTH-BOTTERMANN, K. E. (1965). *Wilhelm Roux Arch. EntwMech. Org.* **156**, 371.

PLATE I

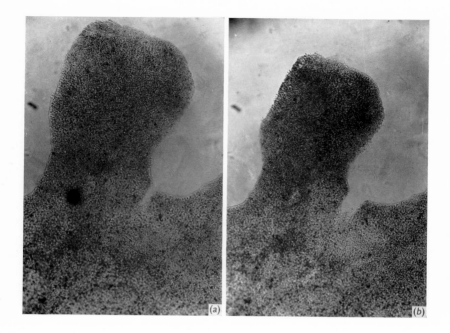

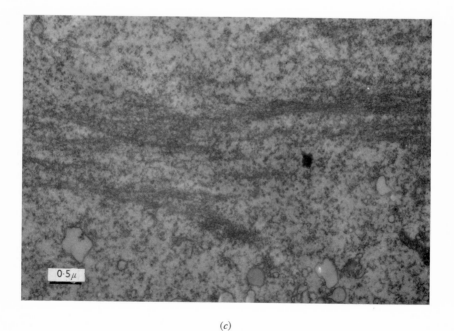

(c)

Glycerinated lobule-like expanse of the plasmodium before (a) and after (b) application of
ATP. (c) Fibrillar differentiation of the cytoplasm composed of bundles of filaments. The
section of the fan-like expanse parallel to the spreading surface near the advancing front.

(facing p. 214)

PLATE 2

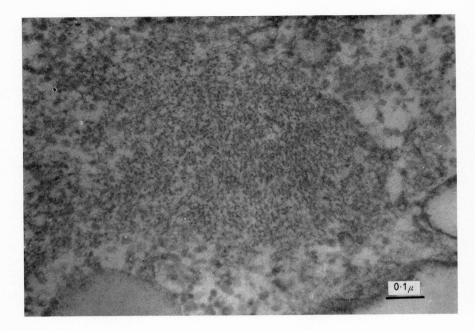

(a)

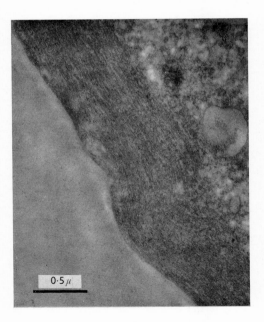

(b)

(a) A filament bundle in cross-section near the advancing front of the fan-like expanse of the plasmodium (Nagai & Kamiya, 1966). (b) Longitudinal section of the plasmodial strand hung in the air under tension. The filaments run longitudinally in parallel to the vacuolar membrane. The lower left represents the vacuolar space.

PLATE 3

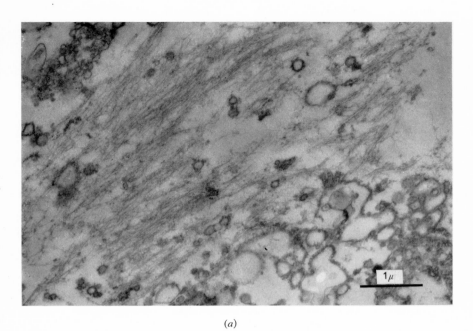

(a)

(b)

(a) Fibrillar structures in the glycerol-model of the plasmodium. The section parallel to the spreading surface of the plasmodium near the margin of the lobule in the solution consisting of 5 mM. MgCl$_2$ + 30 mM. KCl (Nagai & Kamiya, 1966). (b) A similar part of the same lobule of the plasmodium after application of 5 mM. ATP.

PLATE 4

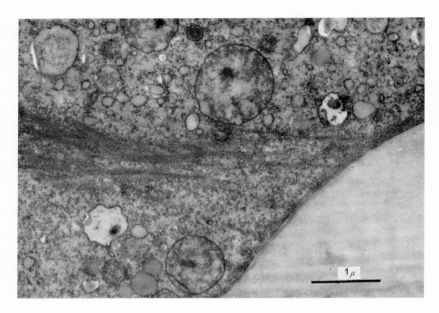

(a)

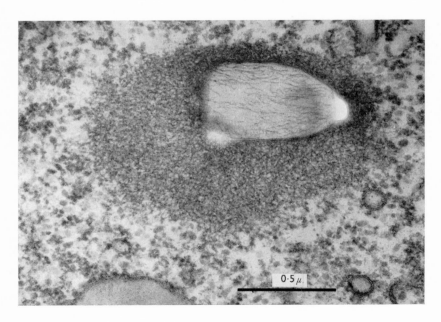

(b)

(a) Fibrillar differentiation of the cytoplasm near the periphery of the endoplasm-rich half of the plasmodium (Takata, Nagai & Kamiya, 1967). (b) Aggregate of globular-like cytoplasmic components around the vacuole in the endoplasm-poor half of the plasmodium (Takata, Nagai & Kamiya, 1967).

PLATE 5

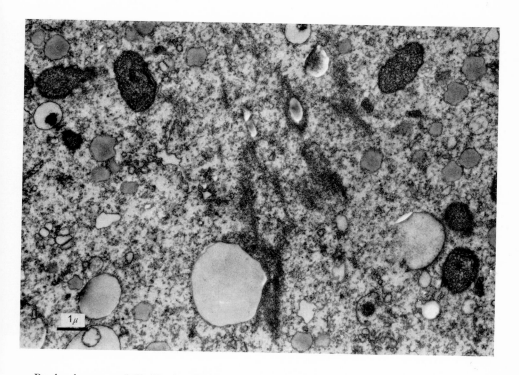

Re-development of fibrillar bundles in one half of the plasmodium where the fibrillar structures are supposed to have been converted into the skein state through application of one-sided pressure 45 min. before. The one-sided constant pressure was then followed by the balance-pressure so that the endoplasmic inflow was arrested for 45 min.

STRUCTURE AND FUNCTION OF
BACTERIAL FLAGELLA

By J. LOWY and M. SPENCER

M.R.C. Biophysics Research Unit, Department of Biophysics,
King's College, 26–29, Drury Lane, London, W.C. 2

STRUCTURAL STUDIES

Introduction

The advent of the sliding-filament theory of contraction for striated muscle has undoubtedly stimulated researches on non-muscular systems, many of them undertaken with the object of providing support for the idea that all types of contractile systems operate according to similar principles. Seen from this 'unitary' viewpoint it was to be expected that in studying non-muscular contractile systems investigators would look for chemical and structural features known to exist in muscle. In particular, such researches have set out to demonstrate that, as in muscle, the other systems also contain actin-like and myosin-like proteins, that the energy for locomotion is derived from ATP, and that the myosin-like protein functions as an ATPase. Gibbons & Rowe (1965) have prepared a protein with ATPase activity from the cilia of *Tetrahymena pyriformis* and a myosin-like protein was isolated by Loewy (1952) from the slime mould plasmodium. Recently the structural as well as the chemical identification of actin in plasmodium has been claimed (Hatano, Totsuka & Oosawa, 1967). Though there is relatively less information about the contractile mechanism underlying amoeboid locomotion, some investigators have deduced from the available evidence that an actomyosin-like system is involved (see review by Wolpert, 1965). The situation appears to be quite different in bacterial flagella, and that is one of the main reasons why these organelles have been so intensively studied during the past few years.

By the term 'bacterial flagellum' we have in mind its main portion, which is a helical filament. The complete flagellum comprises at least three regions which can be distinguished in the electron microscope: a basal portion associated with the cytoplasmic membrane, a proximal hook, and the main helical filament (Abram, Koffler & Vatter, 1965; Abram, Vatter & Koffler 1966).

The helical filament is composed of only one structural protein, called flagellin. The evidence for this comes from chemical studies (Weibull, 1960; Abram & Koffler, 1964; McDonough, 1965; Martinez, Brown &

Glazer, 1967), as well as from serological and genetical experiments (Stocker, 1956). It has so far not been possible to detect ATPase activity in bacterial flagella (de Robertis & Franchi, 1951; Barlow & Blum, 1952; Newton & Kerridge, 1965), nor is there any evidence for the presence of a high-energy phosphate compound like ATP (Weibull, 1951). Clearly, from what is known about muscle, it can be argued that bacterial flagella may not be capable of transforming chemical into mechanical energy. Such a view has in fact been put forward on other grounds, mainly by Pijper in a series of papers from 1930 to 1964 (reviewed by Holwill, 1966). From an analysis of cinematographic films showing flagella (very likely representing many of them organized into 'bundles') on living, moving organisms, Pijper concluded that locomotion is due to undulations of the body, which he believed to have a spiral shape. The arguments against Pijper's views and in favour of flagellar motility are presented in a number of papers and reviews (Hodge, 1949; Stocker, 1956; Weibull, 1960; Holwill & Burge, 1963; Holwill, 1966). *So far the issue has not been resolved and therefore remains the most important problem concerning bacterial flagella.*

We have proceeded on the assumption that these organelles are in fact 'monomolecular muscles' (in the phrase coined by Astbury, Beighton & Weibull, 1955), and from that viewpoint studied the structure of some of them in the hope that the results might give clues about their functioning. This approach has had some measure of success in that it has enabled us to suggest one possible model for the functioning of bacterial flagella as active motor organelles. The first part of the paper presents a general review of certain structural features. Our model is described in the second part.

Large-scale structure

The essential facts about the large-scale structure of bacterial flagella are summarized in the reviews by Stocker (1956) and Weibull (1960). Only certain points relevant to the presentation of our model will be considered here.

Bacterial flagella are cylindrical filaments which have a uniform diameter for a given species and strain. *In vivo*, and when detached from the cell and examined in 'wet' preparations, they have a helical shape. In the process of drying them on to a plane they are flattened and their helical shape is distorted into an approximately sinusoidal wave (see also p. 226).

From electron microscope and X-ray diffraction studies, values obtained for the flagellar diameter range from about 120 to 200Å. This depends on the species and strain, as does the number of flagella per cell, which can vary from one to many hundreds. The flagella can be situated either at one or both ends of the cell, when they are called polar flagella, or all over the surface, when they are called peritrichous flagella. Both polar and peritrichous flagella can organize into bundles large enough to be seen by dark-field light microscopy. This has made it possible to establish their helical shape in living material. A recent example of such a study is that by Mitani & Iino (1965). Their micrographs clearly show the alternation of dark and bright parts along the helix of flagellar bundles in living specimens of *Salmonella abortivoequina*. Flagella detached from the bacterial body can aggregate in a side-to-side manner to form bundles. By appropriate focusing with a phase-contrast microscope Weibull (1950, 1960) observed the helical shape of such bundles and showed that in the strains of *Proteus vulgaris* and *Bacillus subtilis* which he studied the helix is left-handed.

There is reasonably good agreement between the values for the pitch of the flagellar helix as measured in living material and the figures for the sinusoidal wavelength obtained from flattened preparations either stained and examined in the light microscope (see Leifson, 1960) or studied in the electron microscope by shadowing or negative contrast methods.

In many species the pitch of the flagellar helix is constant and lies between 1·5 and 2·5 μ. Its radius is about 0·5 μ. (The figure for the radius is for the *flattened* helix, see p. 230.) The number of pitch lengths is generally between 3 and 6, the over-all length of the flagellum being several times that of the cell. In the extreme case of *Spirillum volutans*, Reichert (1909) reports a length of 72 μ, containing six pitch lengths.

Species are known in which the normal pitch of the flagellar helix can be reduced by about half as a result of genetic changes (Iino, 1962) or by altering the pH of the medium (Leifson, Carhart & Fulton, 1955). This phenomenon has been called 'biplicity' (Pijper, Neser & Abraham, 1956), or 'curlyness' (Leifson, 1960).

ULTRASTRUCTURE

General features

Bacterial flagella may provisionally be placed into two categories: those which appear to be made only of the globular protein flagellin, and those which show structural features suggesting that they contain other components in addition to flagellin.

In the first category there are flagella which, in certain cases, show a distinct surface structure in the electron microscope. For instance, the flagella of *Salmonella typhimurium* have a predominantly 'beaded' surface appearance (Plates 1, 2); those of *Pseudomonas fluorescens* and *Bacillus pumilus* show a predominantly 'lined' surface (Plates 3, 4) (Lowy & Hanson, 1965; Champness & Lowy, 1968). Beaded and lined flagella will be described in the following two sections of the paper.

The evidence suggests that, as hitherto prepared for chemical studies, the flagella of *S. typhimurium* and *B. pumilus* contain only flagellin which, in both species, has a M.W. of about 40,000 (see respectively McDonough, 1965, and Abram & Koffler, 1964). Other flagella which have been examined (e.g. *Proteus vulgaris*) do not show a surface appearance which can straightforwardly be described as either beaded or lined. The type of surface structure appears to be constant for a given species and strain; and beaded and lined structure are not present along the length of the same flagellum (Lowy, 1965). However, in *Bacillus stearothermophilus* more than one kind of surface structure has been seen along a single flagellum (Abram, Vatter & Koffler, 1966).

The extra feature seen in the second category appears as a banded structure around otherwise normal-looking flagella. Here two types have so far been recognized. Some flagella of *Pseudomonas rhodos* have around them close-fitting helically wound 'bands' (thickness about 25 Å.), and in negatively stained preparations the lined structure of the flagellum can sometimes be seen through the bands (Lowy & Hanson, 1965). These flagella have also been studied in shadowed preparations by Marx & Heumann (1963), who deduced the presence of two left-handed helices, the pitch of each being about 200 Å. Another example of close-fitting helical bands was found in the case of flagella belonging to an unknown strain of *Proteus vulgaris* (Lowy & Hanson, 1965).

In the second type, the banded structure may be described as a sheath. It appears to be less intimately associated with the flagellum in that it is not nearly so close-fitting (Plates 5a, 7) and can often be seen isolated as a coherent structure (Plates 5b, 8). Around the flagella of *Treponema microdentium*, Bladen & Hampp (1964) reported the presence of a sheath showing bands with an axial spacing of about 60 Å. Such a sheath has also been seen around flagella of *Treponema zuelzerae*. Here the axial spacing of the bands is about 50 Å., the over-all width of the sheath about 300 Å., and the diameter of the beaded flagellum about 150 Å. (Plates 5a, b).

Flagella surrounded by similarly banded sheaths have been seen in two other (as yet unidentified) organisms, one of which is shown in Plate 6. Here the flagellum itself has a lined surface appearance (Plate 7).

The nature and function of the two types of banded structures remain unknown. In the case of *Vibrio metchnikovii* the flagellum is surrounded by a sheath which, according to studies of sectioned material, has the same layered structure as the cell wall and is continuous with it (Glauert, Kerridge & Horne, 1963). It is conceivable that such a sheath could act as a diffusion barrier. From the structural point of view this does not appear very likely in the case of the close-fitting helically wound bands.

Our main interest so far has been in flagella which appear to consist of flagellin only, and we have concentrated on studies of the beaded flagella from *S. typhimurium*, and the lined flagella of *B. pumilus*. Both forms have been investigated by electron microscopy and X-ray diffraction. The results which are relevant here are summarized in the next two sections of the paper.

'BEADED' FLAGELLA

Electron microscopy

The beaded flagella of *S. typhimurium* were first studied with the negative contrast method by Kerridge, Horne & Glauert (1962). Using partially disintegrated flagella, it appeared that these flagella are made up of approximately globular units (diameter about 45 Å.) which form the walls of a cylinder (outside diameter about 120 Å.) and are arranged on its surface in a hexagonal pattern.

Kerridge *et al.* determined the M.W. of *Salmonella* flagellin to be between 30,000 and 40,000 and deduced by calculation that such molecules would have a volume equal to a sphere of diameter about 45 Å., and therefore could constitute the globular units seen in the electron microscope. Support for this idea came from the finding that the structure of the flagella-like filaments, formed when flagellin molecules (prepared from *S. typhimurium*) reaggregate *in vitro*, is indistinguishable in negatively stained preparations from the structure of the native flagella (Lowy & McDonough, 1964).

Two alternative models were proposed for the flagellum of *S. typhimurium* (Kerridge *et al.* 1962). One had globular units arranged in three helical subfilaments, the other five longitudinal rows of globular units running parallel to the flagellar axis. On both models transverse sections would show a regular pentagonal arrangement of globular units. According to Kerridge *et al.* such appearances have actually been seen in sectional material.

Provided the globular units are roughly spherical, both models suggest the existence of a central 'core'. An appearance which indicates the presence of such a core is seen in preparations where phosphotungstate is used as the contrasting agent (Plate 2). This was first noted in sonicated material by Kerridge *et al.* (1962). On that evidence the core could be empty or contain material which is positively stained with phosphotungstate.

Lowy & Hanson (1965) also studied flagella of *S. typhimurium* and found that very often the globular units were arranged along rows making an angle greater than 45° with the flagellar axis (Plates 1, 2). The axial spacing of these oblique rows was about 50 Å. and did not vary appreciably with the preparative procedure. In many instances globular units connected along rows running parallel to the flagellar axis were also seen. In such cases it was possible to count 4 or 5 of these longitudinal rows, spaced about 40Å. apart, but this spacing, and the diameter of the flagellum (about 140Å.), were both found to vary considerably with the preparative procedure. A model was proposed that consisted of eight rows of spherical units close-packed to form a cylindrical shell. In this model the outside diameter of the cylinder is 163Å., the effective diameter of the space of core inside the cylinder is about 60Å., and the longitudinal rows of units are 43Å. apart.

X-ray diffraction

Fibre preparations have been used to obtain X-ray diffraction patterns from flagella of *S. typhimurium* (Champness & Lowy, 1968). The results confirm, and in some respects extend, those obtained by electron microscopy. Thus the reflexions in the meridional direction can all be indexed as orders of an axial repeat of about 52Å. (Table 1). As mentioned above, this

Table 1. *Meridional diffraction pattern from bacterial flagella* (*Champness & Lowy, 1968*)

Axial spacings (in Ångstroms) recorded at, or near, saturation humidity. 'L' denotes a layer line, 'M' an apparently meridional reflexion, and 'A' an arced reflexion. Orders of 52Å. are also shown for comparison with the observed reflexions.

Salmonella typhimurium		Bacillus pumilus		Orders of 52
(L)	51·10±0·70	(L)	c. 50	52·00
(M)	25·97±0·20	(M)	25·98±0·10	26·00
(L)	17·24±0·35	(L)	17·18±0·20	17·33
(A)	12·69	(M)	12·97±0·10	13·00
(A)	10·25	(L)	10·30±0·10	10·40
(A)	8·58	(M)	8·62	8·67
(A)	7·29	(L)	7·35	7·43
(A)	6·36	(L)	6·47	6·50
(A)	5·72	(M)	5·80	5·78
(A)	5·13	(L)	5·20	5·20
(A)	4·68		4·71	4·73
(A)	4·23		4·32	4·33
			4·02	4·00
			3·71	3·71
			3·48	3·47
			3·27	3·25
			3·07	3·06

periodicity has also been observed in the electron microscope (Lowy & Hanson, 1965). The first and third layer lines contain definitely off-meridional diffraction, and the X-ray pattern is therefore consistent with the general 'staggered-row' configuration proposed in the models of Kerridge *et al.* (1962) and Lowy & Hanson (1965). However, measurements of the maximum on the first layer line show that the spacing between longitudinal rows is about 60Å. and not 43Å. as predicted on the Lowy & Hanson model. The arrangement indicated by the X-ray pattern could result from a close-packing of ellipsoidal units rather than of the spherical units indicated in the model (Champness & Lowy, 1968).

A first-order equatorial reflexion at 190Å. shows that the diameter of the flagellum is likely to be somewhat larger than is suggested by the electron-microscope measurements. Also, the whole equatorial pattern changes markedly when the specimen is dried. In comparison, the pattern in the meridional direction is very little affected by drying, all the spacings showing a decrease of only 1–2%. These results are in line with the electron-microscope observations, which show that both the lateral spacing of the longitudinal rows of subunits and the diameter of the flagellum are appreciably affected by the preparative procedure, whereas the 50Å. axial spacing of the subunits is not. Thus it is possible to conclude that the organization of subunits is more rigidly maintained in the axial than in the lateral direction.

'LINED' FLAGELLA

Electron microscopy

Lowy & Hanson (1965) have described flagella of Ps. fluorescens and B. subtilis. These rarely show globular subunits or helical connexions. Instead, an appearance of predominantly longitudinal lines running parallel to the flagellar axis is seen (Plates 3, 4).

With a uranyl acetate preparative method one sees five or six lines in Ps. fluorescens and the outside diameter of the flagellum is about 170Å. Using the same method we find that the flagella of B. pumilus also show a predominantly lined surface appearance; as in B. subtilis, one sees four or five lines and the outside diameter of the flagellum is about 140Å.

Based on studies of partially disintegrated preparations, a model has been reconstructed for the flagella of B. pumilus in which ovoid subunits are arranged in the form of six fibres coiled around an empty core (Abram, Vatter & Koffler, 1964; Abram, Koffler & Vatter, 1966).

X-ray diffraction

Patterns have been obtained from fibre preparations of flagella from B. pumilus (Champness & Lowy, 1968) and also from B. subtilis and Ps. fluorescens (Champness & Lowy, unpublished results). As in the case of Salmonella, all the reflexions in the meridional direction can be indexed as orders of about 52Å. This is shown for flagella of B. pumilus and S. typhimurium in Table 1. The patterns given by the flagella from the Bacilli also demonstrate that the second layer line contains meridional, the first and third layer lines off-meridional diffraction. This distribution of reflexions is consistent with a 'staggered-row' configuration of subunits. Comparison between these patterns and that given by the flagella of *Salmonella* shows intensity differences (e.g. the first-order reflexion is much stronger in the latter suggesting that the structure of the subunits is different in the two forms).

Low-angle equatorial patterns given by the flagella of *B. pumilus* show a first-order reflexion at about 130Å., indicating that the diameter of these flagella is smaller than that of the flagella of *Salmonella*.

DISCUSSION

The X-ray results have revealed the existence of a 52Å. axial periodicity in the lined flagella where, unlike in the beaded form, this feature could not be seen in electron-microscope preparations. The presence of a 52Å. periodicity can also be deduced from the X-ray pattern given by flagella of *Proteus vulgaris*, whose surface appearance is not clearly beaded or lined (Champness & Lowy, unpublished results). We have already pointed out that the X-ray results from beaded and lined flagella suggest a 'staggered-row' configuration of the subunits in both forms.

The intensity differences mentioned above suggest that there is a difference between the structure of the subunits in the flagella of *S. typhimurium* and *B. pumilus*. It could explain the respective beaded and lined surface appearance seen when the two forms are examined by the same uranyl acetate negative staining method. The observed differences in surface structure do not appear to depend on the staining procedure. Thus it was found that when phosphotungstate at about pH 7 is used, the main difference (relevant to the present considerations) is that the globular units in beaded flagella and the lines in lined flagella are seen less clearly than in uranyl acetate preparations (Plates 1–4) (Lowy & Hanson, 1965). The mobility of *S. typhimurium* and *Ps. fluorescens* does not appear to be appreciably affected in distilled water containing 1 % potassium phosphotungstate adjusted to pH 7.

It is interesting to note that the same differences in surface appearance are still seen in the flagella-like filaments which can be prepared by re-aggregation of flagellin monomers. Thus such filaments prepared from flagellin monomers of *S. typhimurium* and *B. pumilus* show beaded and lined surface structure respectively, and (in the electron microscope) are each respectively indistinguishable from the native flagella (Lowy & McDonough, 1964; Champness & Lowy, unpublished results). As might be expected from these results, synthetic filaments prepared from monomers of *B. pumilus* flagellin give an X-ray diffraction pattern which is identical with that obtained from native *B. pumilus* flagella (Champness & Lowy, unpublished results).

As a working hypothesis we suggest that the surface appearances seen in the electron microscope reflect differences in the structure of the subunits, but that the geometrical arrangement of these units is basically the same in all types of flagella.

From this point of view, the main differences in the surface appearance of the two forms we have studied are that the helical connexions between the subunits apparent as oblique rows (when only the upper flagellar surface is contrasted, see Lowy & Hanson, 1965) are more emphasized in beaded flagella, whereas the interconnexions between subunits apparent as longitudinal rows are more emphasized in lined flagella. But just as longitudinal rows of subunits can be observed in beaded flagella, rows of units (with an axial spacing of about 50Å.) are sometimes visible in lined flagella (Plate 3).

Preparations in which phosphotungstate is used to obtain the negative contrast effect show an important feature common to the two forms and illustrated for beaded flagella in Plate 2. Abram, Vatter & Koffler (1964) first noted that in detached flagella and also in flagella still attached to the cell body the distal end can be distinguished from the proximal end, thus indicating the existence of structural polarization. Flagella-like filaments prepared from flagellin monomers also show this structural polarization, as well as the appearance of a stain-filled central canal (Abram, personal communication; Lowy, unpublished results).

The lined flagella of *Ps. fluorescens* show an additional feature of great interest. In preparations described by Lowy & Hanson (1965) it was found that the lines are interrupted at fairly regular intervals (600–800Å.), and that the lines on either side of each interruption are displaced by half a line spacing relative to one another (Plate 9). We shall refer to this appearance as a 'line shift'. In a personal communication Dr A. Klug first pointed out to us that such a pattern could arise from seeing two sides of the cylindrical shell of subunits in superposition, the longitudinal rows of subunits running at a small angle to the cylinder axis. It seems therefore that in addition to the helical connexions between subunits represented by the appearance of oblique rows which we shall call the 'small-scale subunit helix', there may exist helical connexions between subunits which are represented by the appearance of approximately longitudinal lines. We shall call this helix (which has a much larger pitch) the 'large-scale subunit helix'. Assuming the same underlying geometry for the subunit arrangement in beaded and lined flagella, this means that the longitudinal rows of subunits seen in the beaded form should also run at a small angle to the flagellar axis. Such an arrangement is to be expected when one considers ways of organizing the subunits to form the helical filament. This will be discussed in detail in a later section of the paper.

There remain a number of unsolved structural problems. Two of them are of particular interest. One concerns the question as to whether or not the core of the flagellum is empty; the other relates to the number of approximately longitudinal rows of subunits in any particular type of flagellum. Both problems can probably be tackled by further study of X-ray diffraction patterns. As regards the number of longitudinal rows, very tentative estimates are available from studies of negatively stained preparations: thus the number could be 7, 8 or 9 in flagella of *S. typhimurium*; and 9, 10 or 11 in those of *Ps. fluorescens* (Lowy & Hanson, 1965).

Clearly, more detailed chemical and structural information is needed before it will be possible to establish a definite model for bacterial flagella made of only one structural component and showing beaded and lined surface appearances. But we have considered it worth while at this stage to see whether the structural results so far available for such flagella might suggest anything about their mode of functioning.

A MODEL FOR FLAGELLAR LOCOMOTION

Introduction

Two hypotheses have recently been put forward to explain locomotion of flagellated bacteria in terms of the rotation of a helically shaped flagellum. Jarosch (1964) put forward the idea that the helical shape of the flagellum is due to the intertwining of helical subfilaments each having a slightly different pitch which is much smaller than that of the flagellar helix. He proposed that helical waves are propagated along the flagellar helix as the result of small periodic changes in the pitches of the constituent helical subfilaments. Jarosch's model is based on the proposition that flagella consist of two or three subfilaments. This is not consistent with the structural evidence we have discussed. Another hypothesis has been proposed by Doetsch (1966). It assumes that the helically shaped flagellum is rotated by a mechanism located around its base within the cell body. Apart from the absence of any evidence for the existence of such a mechanism within the cell body, the main difficulty about this idea is that it requires rotation of the flagellum relative to the body during locomotion. A mechanism which avoids this was first proposed by Bütschli (1883) and later elaborated by Reichert (1909). It is referred to by Weibull (1951) and again by Astbury et al. (1955).

In the Bütschli–Reichert hypothesis, the flagellum is considered to be a cylindrical rod which has a hypothetical 'line-of-contraction' running helically round its surface. When this line is shortened relative to other lines running parallel to it on the surface of the cylinder, the rod adopts a helical shape. Movement in a definite sequence of the line-of-contraction around the surface of the cylinder leads to apparent rotation of the helically shaped flagellum, though it does not rotate relative to the body. Forward propulsion will be produced just as it is with an Archimedean screw. We attempt to show here that this hypothesis is consistent with our present structural knowledge of flagella which have a constant flagellar helix pitch, show either beaded or lined surface structure, and are believed to be made of flagellin only. We are not yet in a position to test the hypothesis directly; the argument is at present purely geometrical.

If the Bütschli–Reichert line-of-contraction has any reality it should be possible to visualize subunits of flagellin being interconnected to form such a line. The interconnexion need not represent the strongest bonding direction: it is only necessary that the geometrical arrangement of the subunits is such as to allow the postulated line-of-contraction to form. Briefly, we propose that the line-of-contraction follows the large-scale subunit helix defined above, and that during activity the state of contraction is transferred from one of these helical rows of subunits to the neighbouring ones.

The flagellar helix seen in low-resolution electron micrographs has well-defined dimensions. It is therefore possible to work out the pitch angle of the Bütschli–Reichert line-of-contraction, knowing the diameter of the flagellum. If our assumption about the line-of-contraction is correct, it follows that this calculated pitch angle should correspond closely to the observed pitch angle of the large-scale subunit helix.

The use of radial projections

To make quantitative predictions from the observed structure, it is convenient to think in terms of radial projections which can also usefully be applied to the construction of paper models to illustrate three-dimensional aspects of the problem. In the case of a thin cylindrical shell, a radial projection may be regarded as the result of cutting open the cylinder and unrolling it. A radial projection such as Fig. 1a corresponds to a cylinder in which longitudinal rows make a small angle with the axis, as in Fig. 1b. The cylinder has in this example been cut parallel to the longitudinal rows in order to make the projections.

Now consider what happens if some longitudinal rows are shortened relative to their neighbours. The radial projection of Fig. 1a will change on contraction to a projection which may be represented by Fig. 1c, where the row AB is the shortest and XY the longest of the group. The corresponding three-dimensional structure is that of Fig. 1d. This is a helical rod whose shortest filament AB follows that path on the 'inside' of the helix which maintains a minimum distance from the helix axis. If the angle between the filaments and the rod axis decreases to zero, the helix will collapse into a coil.

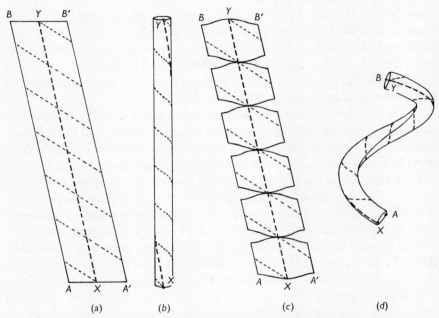

(a)   (b)   (c)   (d)

Fig. 1. a, Radial projection of a cylindrical shell in which longitudinal rows of subunits (one of which is represented by the long dashed line XY) make an angle with the axis. (The short dashed lines represent another of the possible ways of connecting the subunits to form a small-scale subunit helix.) b, Cylindrical structure corresponding to the projection of a. c, Radial projection of a cylindrical shell in which some longitudinal rows of subunits are shorter than others. AB is the shortest row and XY the longest. The rows also make an angle with the axis as in a. d, Helical rod corresponding to the projection of c. The drawing is not intended as a scale representation of a bacterial flagellum, which has a much smaller rod diameter in relation to its pitch.

The interpretation of electron micrographs

When a helical flagellum is flattened on to a supporting film for electron microscopy, a variable amount of distortion will inevitably be introduced. We must therefore consider how this distortion can be allowed for in testing a three-dimensional model. Two examples will serve to illustrate the range of likely appearances.

If flattening develops from one end and progresses down the helix, the flagellar helix may 'unwind' (with local distortion of the packing of sub-

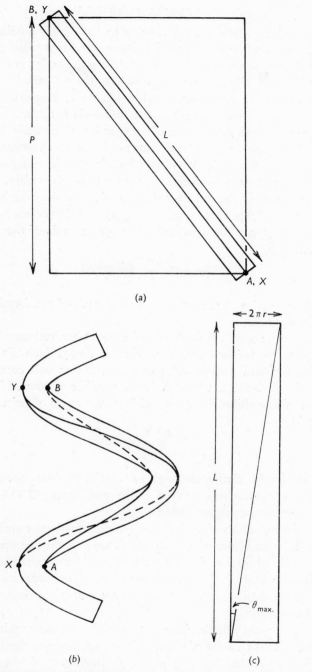

Fig. 2. *a*, Radial projection of a helical rod, corresponding to an unwound helix. The projections of all longitudinal rows of subunits are parallel to each other, and the projections of the shortest row AB and the longest row XY coincide. (L = length of rod forming one turn of the flagellar helix; P = pitch.) *b*, A flattened helical rod, corresponding to a projection from one side of the helical structure in Fig. 1*d*. The longitudinal rows AB and XY are shown by solid lines when on top of the rod, and by dotted lines when underneath. *c*, Illustrates the calculation of θ_{max}; each longitudinal row goes once round the rod (radius r) for each turn of helix. L is the length of the rod forming one turn. For further explanation see text.

units) so that the rows of subunits appear to run exactly parallel to the rod axis. This unwound appearance would correspond to a radial projection of the original structure on to a cylinder enclosing the helix; in the projection shown in Fig. 2a, *all filaments run parallel to the rod axis*.

If, on the other hand, the flagellum is held at both ends so that untwisting is prevented, and if the region between the ends is flattened, the general appearance will be similar to that of a projection of the helix from one side on to a plane (not a radial projection). Figure 2b illustrates the result expected with such a projection of our model; *each filament goes once round the rod for every turn of the helix*. It may be shown from Fig. 2c, which is a radial projection of the rod after straightening out the helix and 'cutting' parallel to the rod axis, that the angle θ_{max} (averaged over one turn) between the projection of any filament and the projected axis of the rod is given approximately by

$$\theta_{max} = \frac{360r}{L} \text{ (degrees)} \tag{1}$$

where r is the radius of the rod and L the length of rod forming one turn of the flagellar helix.

To deduce the apparent angle of twist from observations of the 'superposition patterns' referred to above, consider Fig. 3. Each 'line-shift' seen on viewing top and bottom rows in superposition will correspond to a rotation of π/N radians, where N is the number of rows. If the average separation of line shifts along the rod is S, the angle of twist is given approximately by

$$\theta' = \frac{180r}{NS} \text{ (degrees).} \tag{2}$$

(A similar formula relating the angle of twist to the line shift period of the superposition pattern was derived earlier and conveyed to us by Dr A. Klug in a personal communication.)

By calculating values of θ_{max} and θ' (using equations 1 and 2) from observed or deduced values of r, N, S and L, we may thus compare the value of θ_{max}, predicted by our model for a flagellar helix of the observed dimensions, with the angle θ' deduced from independent observations of superposition patterns. θ' *should be between zero and* θ_{max}, depending on the degree of distortion.

Secondly, we can calculate the degree of shortening required to turn a cylindrical rod into a helix of given dimensions. Imagine the helical rod of Fig. 4 to be bounded by two cylinders having radii $R+r$ and $R-r$ (Fig. 4a). R is the mean radius of the helix and P its pitch. If these two cylinders are unrolled and the resulting flat sheets superimposed as in Fig. 4b,

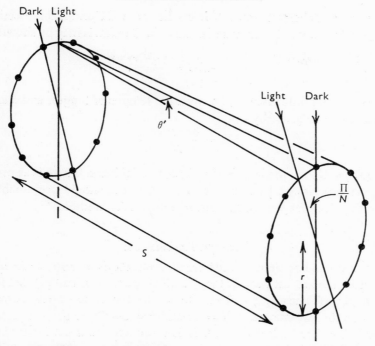

Fig. 3. Interpretation of superposition patterns. A section of rod is shown whose length, S, incorporates one line-shift. N is the number of longitudinal rows per rod (shown here with $N = 10$) and θ' the angle between such a row and a projection of the axis on to the surface of the cylinder.

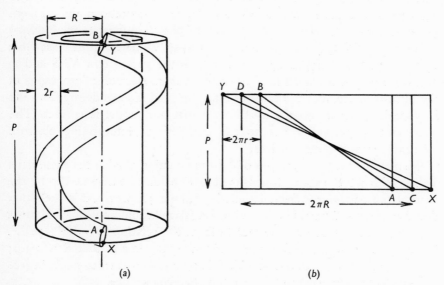

Fig. 4. a, A helical rod enclosed by two cylinders of radii $R+r$ and $R-r$. The longitudinal row of subunits AB lies on the inner cylinder and XY on the outer one. b, Superimposed radial projections of the cylinders in a (scale $\times \frac{1}{2}$). AB represents the shortest longitudinal row in the rod and XY the longest. (P = pitch.)

the longest and shortest filaments in the helix are XY and AB respectively. If $R \gg r$, which is normally true for bacterial flagella, it may be shown that

$$XY - AB = \frac{8\pi^2 Rr}{CD}.$$

The percentage difference, Δ, between the lengths of longest and shortest filaments is then given by

$$\Delta = \frac{800\pi^2 Rr}{L^2}, \tag{3}$$

where $L \; (= CD)$ is the length of rod per turn of helix. There is at present no direct experimental check of this value, but Δ should presumably be only a few per cent for the model to be physically credible.

Numerical calculations

Our electron micrographs of lined flagella from *Ps. fluorescens* (strain 10038) show stretches at least 2000 Å. long in which some rows run parallel to the flagellar axis (Plates 3, 4). From the results for these flagella (Lowy & Hanson, 1965) we may take $N = 10$ and $r = 0.0085\,\mu$. From equation 2 θ' must therefore be less than $1°$. If it is assumed that the separation of line-shifts (S) is between 0.07 and 0.1 μ (see caption to Plate 9), one can calculate from equation 2 that θ comes to 1.5 to 2.2°. Since the value of r used is the outer radius of the cylinder, it will give an upper limit to θ': its true value is probably less. For these flagella values for L range from 2 to 2.5 μ (where 30 measurements from shadowed preparations and 40 from material negatively stained with potassium phosphotungstate were taken) so the value of θ_{max} (from equation 1) is 1.2–1.5°. There is thus reasonable agreement (considering the uncertainties in the parameters N, S and r) between the maximum value of θ' deduced from electron micrographs of the ultrastructure, and the value of θ_{max} deduced independently from the large-scale structure on the assumption that our model is correct. The uncertainties are partly due to the difficulty of interpreting electron micrographs of flattened helices.

We may next calculate values of Δ from equation 3 using the same data. Values of R for the three-dimensional helix cannot be assumed to be the same as those measured from flattened specimens; however, it is likely that L and P are less distorted in flattening long flagella containing several turns of helix. We may therefore calculate from the relation $L^2 = P^2 + 4\pi^2 R^2$. For *Ps. fluorescens* values for P range from 1.7 to 2.2 μ so that $R \leqslant 0.3\,\mu$; equation 3 then shows that $\Delta < 4\%$. It is clear that no unreasonable degree of contraction is needed to produce the observed shapes.

Activation of the flagellum

As mentioned earlier, apparent rotation of the model requires that a small contraction be progressively transferred from one large-scale subunit helix to the neighbouring ones. We are not yet in a position to explain how this happens; however, a few tentative suggestions may be made.

We have seen that a relative shortening of only a few per cent is required. One might reasonably assume, in the absence of evidence to the contrary, that the contraction would be induced along one large-scale subunit helix

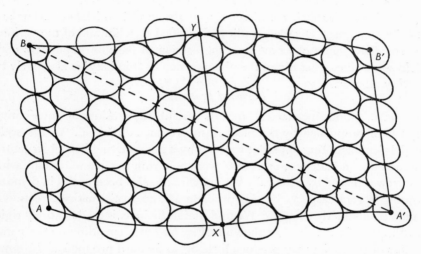

Fig. 5. Radial projection of part of a flagellar helix (cf. Fig. 1c). Subunit projections are represented by ellipses. The ellipse axes along lines parallel to the dotted line $A'B$ are all of equal length; the axes at right angles to this line vary periodically, repeating once every ten subunits. Projections of subunits lying on any one line parallel to AB or XY are all identical.

by some form of polarization which resulted in a small shape change in each subunit making up the helix. It is of interest in this connexion that (as mentioned on p. 223) both intact flagella and reconstituted flagella-like filaments show a structural polarity. The contraction would presumably have to be initiated at one end of the flagellum. However, this idea is hard to reconcile with the other observation that filaments reconstituted from flagellin monomers in the absence of any form of attachment to bacteria still have an appearance in the electron microscope which suggests that they are flattened helices (Ada, Nossal, Pye & Abbot, 1963; Abram & Koffler, 1964; Lowy & McDonough, 1964; Asakura, Eguchi & Iino, 1966).

An alternative hypothesis is that there is something inherent in the structure of flagellin which makes it pack into a shell that is not quite cylindrical but has the helical form observed. This might arise from periodic variations in the orientation of subunits (assumed to be non-spherical) within the shell. There are several possible ways of producing the same effect. Figure 5 is a radial projection which illustrates one way of building up the helix. The diagram corresponds to one section only of the projection of Fig. 1c, which is that of a helical rod as demonstrated earlier. For apparent rotation to occur, there would have to be transference of a given orientation from each longitudinal row to its neighbour. This transference would have to be controlled from the base, *but there would still be a static helix after detachment of the flagellum from the body*.

The difficulties facing a direct test of the model which we favour are clearly very great. Detailed studies of purified flagellin and of the various intermediate stages observed in reaggregation of flagellin monomers may yield some clues. A study of the phenomenon of 'biplicity' is also likely to be very relevant.

Forward propulsion

We have found mechanical models useful in considering qualitative aspects of propulsion by the mechanism we have discussed. A large-scale model demonstrating apparent rotation by a non-rotating helical structure is illustrated in Plates 10, 11. A clockwork boat running in a water tank with its screw replaced by a helically wound wire has also been useful in demonstrating several aspects of the problem whose mathematical treatment would be distinctly complex. We find that if the helix is made entirely rigid it will rotate in the manner shown in Fig. 6a but, depending on the parameters of the helix, may produce little or no forward propulsion. If, however, the helix is flexible (as is more likely to be the case *in vivo*), viscous forces change the motion as illustrated in Fig. 6b. The action is then much nearer to that of an Archimedean screw, and a propulsive force is produced.

Lastly, it is of interest to consider what happens when (as in some species) a large number of helical flagella form a closely associated bundle. It may easily be demonstrated with a pair of wire helices that entanglement of the flagella will prevent simultaneous rotation of all the helices if rotation is in one sense, but not if rotation is reversed. Flagella wound in left-handed spirals (Weibull, 1950, 1960) and rotating clockwise when viewed from the body, as illustrated in Fig. 6, will propel the body downwards in the diagram. Helical waves will then appear to travel down the flagella away from the body, and the flagella will point backwards from the moving bacterium. Under these conditions a point of entanglement of adjacent flagella will travel towards the free ends of the flagella, where the filaments will break free from each other. With rotation in the opposite sense, a point of entanglement will travel towards the bases of the flagella, and will then prevent further rotation. It is thus clear why bundles of flagella containing more than one turn of helix are observed to rotate only in one sense, with bundles pointing away from the direction of motion for clockwise rotation (Reichert, 1909). On the other hand, entanglement is much less likely to occur when the flagella have a larger pitch and contain only a short section of helix as is the case, for instance, in various species of *Spirillum*; here reversal is in fact observed (Metzner, 1920).

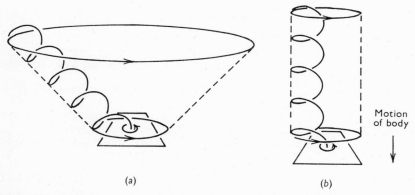

(a)   (b)

Fig. 6. *a*, Mode of rotation of a rigid helical rod, the rod being inserted at right angles to the plane of the base. In the model for flagellar motion being considered here there is no rotation of the rod relative to its base; the apparent motion results from the progressive transference of a small contraction from one large-scale subunit helix to the neighbouring ones. *b*, As *a* but with a flexible rod immersed in a viscous medium. Improved propulsion is obtained with this model.

CONCLUSION

It should be emphasized again that we cannot claim to have explained how flagella function. But we have shown that certain structural evidence favours a particular type of model. We believe that this type of model is inherently more plausible than models which postulate rotation of the flagellum relative to the body, or models assuming the existence of structural elements for which there is no evidence. Although some species have flagella showing structural features which suggest that they contain other components in addition to flagellin, in our model the flagellum needs to consist only of subunits of flagellin in order to function as a motor organelle.

We are grateful to Professor Sir John Randall for provision of facilities and for encouraging this research. We also want to thank Dr D. Abram, Mr J. N. Champness, Dr E. J. O'Brien and Professor B. A. D. Stocker for valuable suggestions and criticism, Professor S. C. Rittenberg for cultures of *Treponema zuelzerae* and Mr M. Jackson, Mr C. Dickson, Mr C. W. McCarthy, Miss M. Castle and Mr Z. Gabor for technical assistance.

This investigation was supported in part by a research grant (AM 06166-01) from the Institute of Arthritis and Metabolic Diseases, United States Public Health Service.

Since this work was completed, Dr A. Klug has kindly sent us the manuscript of a paper (*Symp. Soc. Int. Cell. Biol.* vol. 6, in Press) in which he discusses the formation of a large-scale helix from identical sub-units, and the way such a structure might propagate helical waves.

REFERENCES

ABRAM, D. & KOFFLER, H. (1964). *J. molec. Biol.* **9**, 168.
ABRAM, D., KOFFLER, H. & VATTER, A. E. (1965). *J. Bact.* **90**, 1337.
ABRAM, D., KOFFLER, H. & VATTER, A. E. (1966). *Abst. IInd Int. Biophys. Congr.*, Vienna, 1966, p. 45.
ABRAM, D., VATTER, A. E. & KOFFLER, H. (1964). *Abst. Biophys. Soc.* WC4.
ABRAM, D., VATTER, A. E. & KOFFLER, H. (1966). *J. Bact.* **91**, 2045.
ADA, G. L., NOSSAL, G. J. V., PYE, J. & ABBOT, A. (1963). *Nature, Lond.* **199**, 1257.
ASAKURA, S., EGUCHI, G. & IINO, T. (1966). *J. molec. Biol.* **16**, 302.
ASTBURY, W. T., BEIGHTON, E. & WEIBULL, C. (1955). *Symp. Soc. exp. Biol.* **9**, 282.
BARLOW, G. H. & BLUM, J. J. (1952). *Science, N.Y.* **116**, 572.
BLADEN, H. A. & HAMPP, E. G. (1964). *J. Bact.* **87**, 1180.
BÜTSCHLI, O. (1883). In *Klassen und Ordnungen des Thierreichs*, p. 851. Ed. H. G. Bronn. Leipzig: C. F. Winter.
CHAMPNESS, J. N. & LOWY, J. (1968). *Symposium on Fibrous Proteins*, Canberra, 1967.
DOETSCH, R. N. (1966). *J. Theor. Biol.* **11**, 411.
GIBBONS, I. R. & ROWE, A. J. (1965). *Science, N.Y.* **149**, 424.
GLAUERT, A. M., KERRIDGE, D. & HORNE, R. W. (1963). *J. Cell Biol.* **18**, 327.
HATANO, H., TOTSUKA, T. & OOSAWA, F. (1967). *Biochim. biophys. Acta* **140**, 109.
HODGE, A. J. (1949). *Aust. J. Sci.* **11**, 115.
HOLWILL, M. E. J. (1966). *Physiol. Rev.* **46**, 696.
HOLWILL, M. E. J. & BURGE, R. E. (1963). *Archs Biochem. Biophys.* **101**, 249.
IINO, T. (1962). *J. gen. Microbiol.* **27**, 167.
JAROSCH, R. (1964). In *Primitive Motile Systems in Cell Biology*, p. 599. Ed. R. D. Allen and N. Kamiya. New York: Academic Press.
KERRIDGE, D., HORNE, R. W. & GLAUERT, A. M. (1962). *J. molec. Biol.* **4**, 227.
LEIFSON, E. (1960). *Atlas of Bacterial Flagellation.* New York: Academic Press.
LEIFSON, E., CARHART, S. R. & FULTON, M. (1955). *J. Bact.* **69**, 73.
LOEWY, A. G. (1952). *J. cell. comp. Physiol.* **40**, 127.
LOWY, J. (1965). *J. molec. Biol.* **14**, 297.
LOWY, J. & HANSON, J. (1965). *J. molec. Biol.* **11**, 293.
LOWY, J. & MCDONOUGH, M. W. (1964). *Nature, Lond.* **204**, 125.
MARTINEZ, R. J., BROWN, D. M. & GLAZER, A. N. (1967). *J. molec. Biol.* **28**, 45.
MARX, R. & HEUMANN, W. (1963). *Zeiss Mitt. Fortschr. tech. Opt.* **3**, 110.
MCDONOUGH, M. W. (1965). *J. molec. Biol.* **12**, 342.
METZNER, P. (1920). *Jb. Wiss. Bot.* **59**, 325.
MITANI, M. & IINO, T. (1965). *J. Bact.* **90**, 1096.
NEWTON, B. A. & KERRIDGE, D. (1965). *Symp. Soc. gen. Microbiol.* **15**, 220.
PIJPER, A., NESER, M. L. & ABRAHAM, G. (1956). *J. gen. Microbiol.* **14**, 371.
REICHERT, K. (1909). *Zentbl. Bakt., Parasitkde*, Abt. 1, Orig. 51, p. 14.
ROBERTIS, E. DE & FRANCHI, C. M. (1951). *Expl Cell Res.* **2**, 295.

STOCKER, B. A. D. (1956). *Symp. Soc. gen. Microbiol.* **6**, 19.
WEIBULL, C. (1950). *Acta chem. scand.* **4**, 268.
WEIBULL, C. (1951). *Nature, Lond.* **167**, 511.
WEIBULL, C. (1960). In *The Bacteria*, vol. 1. Ed. I. C. Gunsalus and R. Y. Stanier. New York: Academic Press.
WOLPERT, L. (1965). *Symp. Soc. gen. Microbiol.* **15**, 270.

EXPLANATION OF PLATES

The flagella were negatively stained either with 1 % uranyl acetate (pH about 4·5), or with 1 % potassium phosphotungstate (pH adjusted to about 7) using methods described by Lowy & Hanson (1965).

PLATE 1

Flagella of *Salmonella typhimurium* negatively stained with uranyl acetate. Arrows point to zones where globular units are arranged along rows which make an oblique angle with the flagellar axis. × 125,000.

PLATE 2

Flagella of *Salmonella typhimurium* negatively stained with potassium phosphotungstate. Arrows marked *a* point to oblique rows of subunits. Arrows marked *b* point to short pieces of flagella which show structural polarization in that one end looks different from the other. Arrows marked *c* point to regions where the stain has penetrated into the 'core' of the flagellum. × 133,000.

PLATE 3

Flagella of *Pseudomonas fluorescens* negatively stained with uranyl acetate. Arrows point to oblique rows of subunits. × 166,000.

PLATE 4

Flagella of *Pseudomonas fluorescens* negatively stained with potassium phosphotungstate. × 200,000.

PLATE 5

Flagella of *Treponema zuelzerae* negatively stained with uranyl acetate. (*a*) Beaded structure of flagella; one emerges from its banded sheath which is partially disintegrating. × 200,000. (*b*) Relatively intact banded sheath with a short length of flagellum emerging at one end. × 250,000.

PLATES 6–8

Unidentified organism present in cultures enriched for *Sphaerotilus natans*. In all preparations uranyl acetate was used as the contrasting agent.

PLATE 6

Whole organism showing single polar flagellum surrounded by a banded sheath. × 50,000.

PLATE 7

Shows lined structure of the flagellum where it emerges from its broken banded sheath. × 133,000.

PLATE 8

Banded sheath which does not contain a flagellum. × 83,000.

PLATE 9

Flagella of *Pseudomonas fluorescens* placed across holes (in a collodion film) filled with uranyl acetate. × 250 000. Part of the sheet of stain over the hole is broken and due to the resulting distortions the flagella diameter is not uniform. In such preparations the separation of line-shifts is between 700 and 800Å. This periodicity is indicated by arrows. In preparations where the flagellum lies across holes in unbroken sheets of stain the flagellar diameter is more uniform and the periodicity is about 1000Å.

PLATE 10

General view of a mechanical model illustrating apparent rotation of a flexible helix. It consists of a large number of rings, each drilled with ten holes making an angle of 3° with the axis. Steel wires under tension join the rings together, with springs as spacers. The wires are terminated at the top on the circumference of a circular plate inclined to the horizontal, the highest point of the circle being transferred progressively round the rim of the plate by a motor-driven arm.

PLATE 11

A close-up of part of the model. It illustrates the fact that the wires run round the rod, making a small angle with its axis.

PLATE I

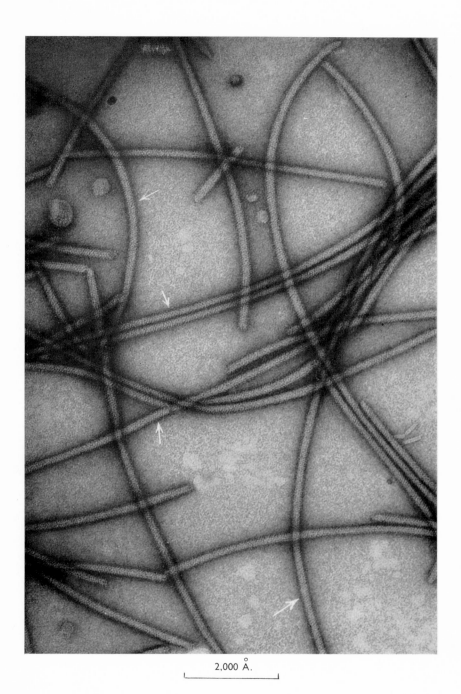

2,000 Å.

For explanation to Plates 1–11 see pp. 235–6

PLATE 2

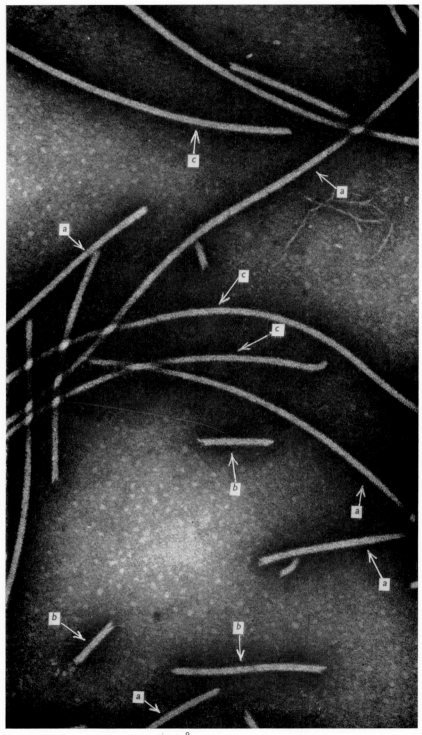

2,000 Å

PLATE 3

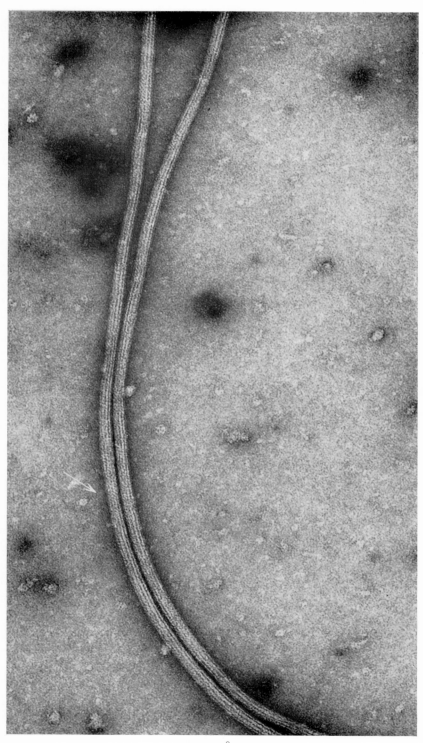

2,000 Å.

PLATE 4

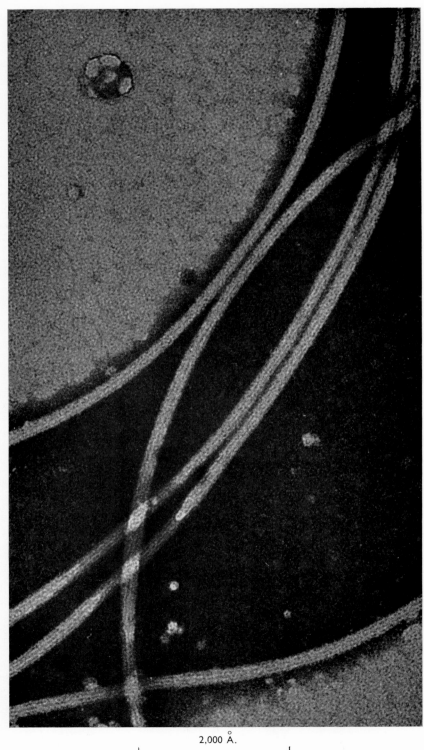

2,000 Å.

PLATE 5

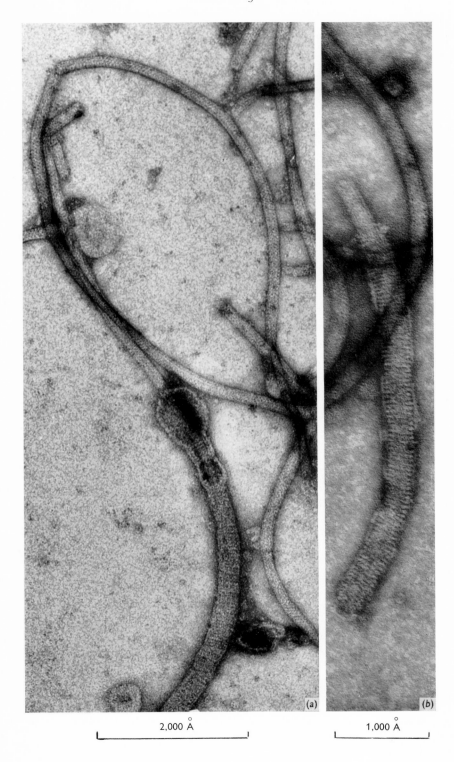

(a)

(b)

2,000 Å

1,000 Å

PLATE 6

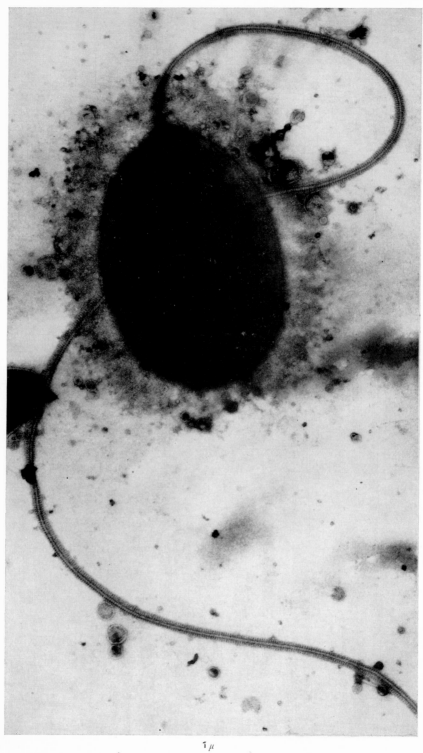

1 μ

PLATE 7

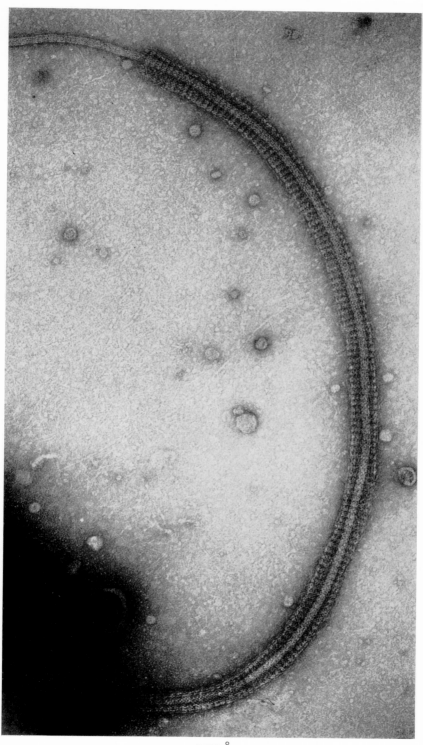

2,000 Å.

PLATE 8

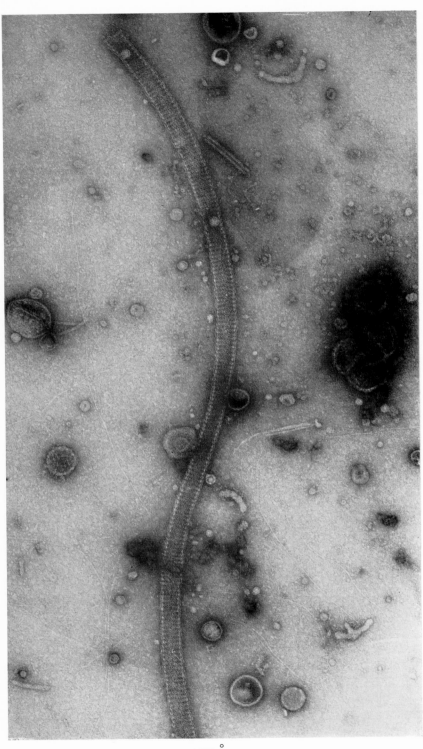

4,000 Å.

PLATE 9

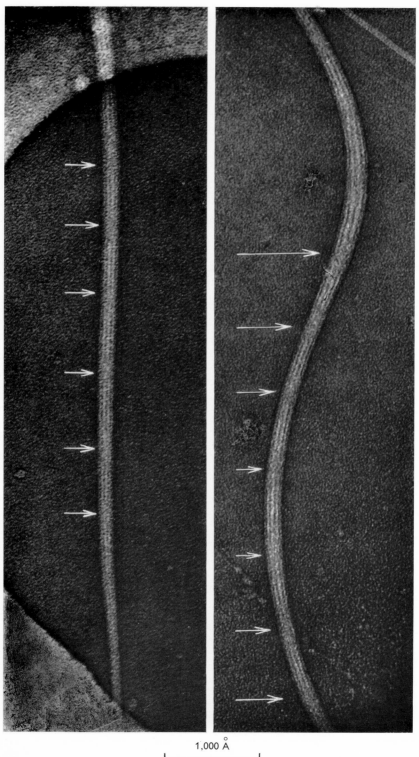

1,000 Å

PLATE 10

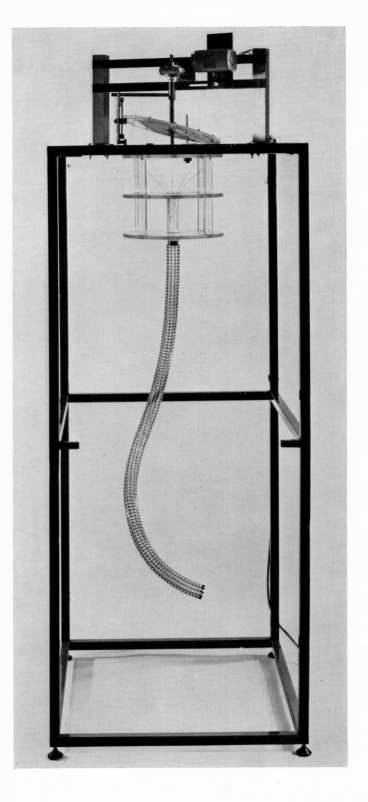

PLATE II

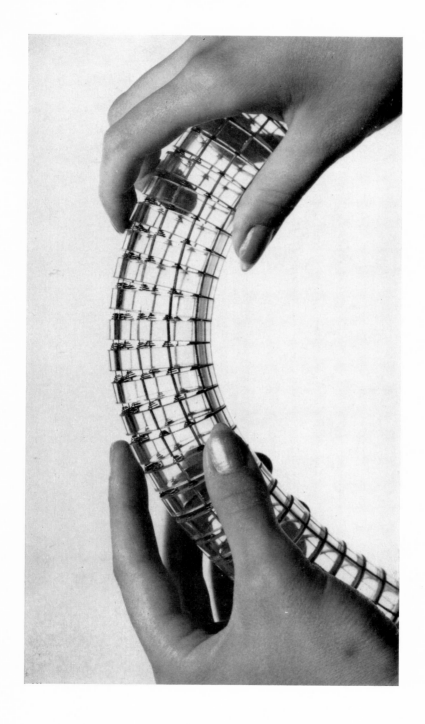

ELECTRICAL PHENOMENA ASSOCIATED WITH CELL MOVEMENTS

By E. J. AMBROSE and J. A. FORRESTER

Chester Beatty Research Institute, Fulham Road, London, S.W.3

INTRODUCTION

Our interest in problems of cell movements has been concerned mainly with their relationship to the behaviour of cell membranes, particularly those of mammalian cells in tissue culture. It is obvious from the fact that

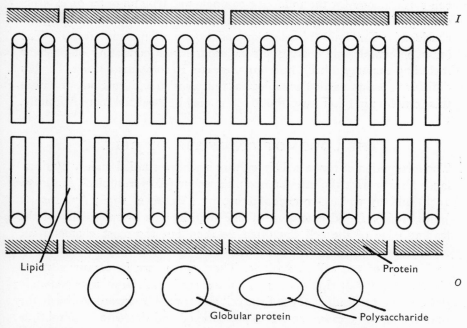

Lipid

Protein

Globular protein

Polysaccharide

Fig. 1. Model for cell membrane based on Danielli's lamellar structure. *I*, Inner surface with associated layer of enzymes, microfibrils, microtubules, etc. *O*, Outer surface of protein, mucoprotein and mucopolysaccharide.

the cell membrane is the organelle which makes immediate contact with the external environment that it must play some role in cell movements. The main question to be decided is whether the membrane plays a passive or an active role. Mammalian cells in culture are able to move on solid surfaces while remaining very firmly attached to them. This is shown by the fact that it is almost impossible to remove cells from glass by mechanical means alone without causing cell rupture. The adhesive forces responsible for this attachment must be connected with the characteristic properties of the cell surface and will be discussed in this article. Whether the membrane plays an active role in transforming chemical energy into work so that the cell is able to move and break its adhesion to the solid surface is still an open question. The main purpose of this paper will be to present evidence relating to this latter question. Of particular importance in this respect are the electrical properties of the membrane; that is, the surface or zeta potential and the transmembrane potential. When considering the role of the cell membrane in cell locomotion it may be better to refer to a 'cell surface complex' rather than a membrane. Referring to the model for the cell membrane (Danielli, 1938) shown in Fig. 1, we will include in the cell surface complex the following components. (i) The outer or external coating of the cell consisting of protein, mucoprotein and mucopolysaccharide. (ii) The lipid (bimolecular leaflet or micellar structure). (iii) The inner or cytoplasmic coating and adjacent layers consisting of proteins including enzymes, fibrils, microtubules, etc. In some cases it may be very difficult to assign particular biological functions to a given element within this complex; in other cases the function may be localized more definitely.

THE LOCOMOTION OF TISSUE CELLS

The locomotion of tissue cells in culture has been studied mainly by time-lapse filming with the interference microscope (Abercrombie & Ambrose, 1958) and by surface-contact microscopy (Ambrose, 1956; Ambrose & Jones, 1961). Rapid extension of fine pseudopodia or microvilli on the leading edge of the cell can often be seen but the most characteristic movement seen both with fibroblasts and epithelial cells is ruffling or undulation of the cell membrane. These waves are in certain respects similar to waves or ripples seen on a water surface. A large wave generally develops on the leading edge of the cell and travels backwards towards the nucleus. In some cases the waves are damped and decrease in amplitude very rapidly. In this case there is little co-ordination between the separate peaks of the waves. In other cases where the cell is moving rapidly these undulations may be well co-ordinated and look remarkably like a surface ripple as they travel back from the leading edge of the cell. Holtfreter (1948) also mentioned that he had seen peristaltic waves on the borders of moving fibroblasts. With the help of the surface-contact microscope (Ambrose, 1956) it is possible to see that these membrane undulations are taking place over the whole of the surface of the cell which is in contact with the glass or other substrate. The microscope is shown in Fig. 2. It produces an image similar to a dark-field microscope, utilizing light which is internally reflected within a glass prism. Light enters the prism to strike the surface at an angle slightly greater than the contact angle glass/water. But for those regions of the cell which are in contact with the glass the contact angle glass/cell membrane material is not reached. The regions of the cell which are in close contact with the glass are therefore illuminated whereas the regions not in contact are dark. This microscope shows that

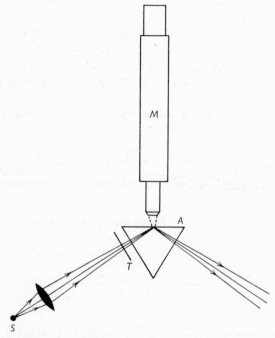

Fig. 2. Surface-contact microscope. S, Intense light source; T, slit; A, glass prism; M, microscope.

these regions of contact are forming and breaking continuously as a tissue cell moves on glass. The general conclusion from the studies with interference and surface contact microscopy is summarized in Fig. 3. It was suggested on the basis of these observations (Ambrose, 1961) that these membrane undulations might provide the locomotory mechanism for tissue cells. The membrane undulations would be generated by a combination of a Rayleigh transverse wave at the surface and a compressional wave. (The instantaneous points of contact between the cell and the solid substrate should be nodes in the wave motion, not antinodes as I originally proposed.) This would give rise to intermittent breaking and making of contacts between the cell and the substrate in small *local* areas as the cell moved forwards. Such peristaltic waves are known to provide the locomotory mechanism in earthworms. In this case the whole process occurs on a much larger scale, being due to co-ordinated contractions of groups of muscle cells. In the case of the tissue culture cells the motion is generated by a single cell surface complex.

The earlier optical studies had provided good evidence in favour of this theory of tissue-cell locomotion but we have now been able to demonstrate the existence of those intermittent contacts between cell and substrate using the Stereoscan electron microscope. This microscope gives a direct image of an object seen as a whole, by utilizing the secondary electrons emitted from the surface. The cells were fixed by freeze-substitution; the cultured cells were washed in synthetic medium at 37° C. and then dropped immediately into liquid nitrogen at −180° C. They were then freeze-substituted.

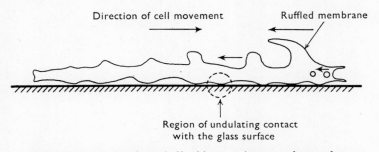

Fig. 3. Cross-section through fibroblast moving on a glass surface.

By comparisons of cell structure in fresh cells and after freeze-substitution by observation under Anopteral phase-contrast, it had already been shown that freeze-substitution produced very little change of cellular morphology. In Plate 1a a Stereoscan picture of a fibroblast (BHK21) moving on a glass surface is shown. The specimen has been inclined at 60° to the horizontal plane so that the contacts between the cell and the glass can be seen. In Plate 1b a high-power picture of the region of contact is shown. A ruffled membrane which is making close contact with the glass can be clearly seen while the remainder of the cell is not in contact. Locomotion by continuous making and breaking of contacts in this way clearly involves the overcoming of the very strong attractive forces between the cell and the glass surface. The only reason this can take place, when application of an external force will not pull the cell off the glass, is because only a small fraction of the cell surface is involved in breaking contact at any given moment. Even so these movements are not always successful in breaking all contact with the glass. In Fig. 4b remains of microvilli which have broken away from the cell and remain left behind on the glass can be clearly seen.

CELL SURFACE ADHESIONS

It may be as well now to consider the nature of these adhesive forces which operate at the cell surface. The shape and movement of tissue cells in culture is determined by a balance between the adhesions to the solid substrate and intercellular adhesions, whereas in amoeboid movement the problem of cell–cell attachment does not generally arise. I do not propose to go into details about the problems of intercellular contacts, contact

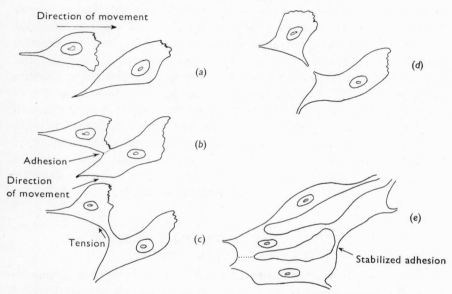

Fig. 4. Movements of fibroblasts on a glass surface. a–d, time sequence of making and breaking a cell–cell contact.

inhibition, etc., but merely to point out that the forces involved in cell–cell adhesion and cell–substrate adhesion are not necessarily the same. In Fig. 4 some tracings made from an actual time-lapse film of moving fibroblasts seen in the interference microscope are shown. The sequence shows the approach of a fibroblast to another cell, followed by the breaking of the contact. These intercellular adhesions are very stable and are not made and broken rapidly. The cell is only able to rupture them as a result of a very active membrane movement on the solid substrate in a region of the cell which is not attached to another cell. Considerable distortion of the whole shape of the cell occurs in the region of contact before rupture takes place (Fig. 4c). Epithelial cells show even stronger intercellular adhesions. They

16

form a sheet in which cells are in continuous contact with their neighbours. But these sheets can migrate as a whole across a glass surface. Undulations of their membranes across the whole surface of the sheet, similar to those shown in Plate 1 *b*, can be seen in the surface-contact microscope.

Intercellular adhesive forces must clearly depend on a balance between repulsive and attractive forces. The repulsive forces are mainly due to the repulsion between the negative charges on the cell surface as is the case with simple colloidal particles. If the attractive forces are unchanged there should be an inverse correlation between negative surface charge and intercellular adhesiveness. Cell surface charge can be measured by cell electrophoresis in which a suspension of cells is placed in an electric field. The velocity of the cells is measured microscopically. Non-adhesive cells such as red blood cells and ascites tumour cells always show a high mobility and high negative surface change. The attractive forces between cells are more complex and depend on short-range interactions between protein molecules. Calcium bridges—$COO^- + Ca^+ {}^- OOC$—are almost certainly involved. Even if cells carry a low surface charge they may not be able to adhere unless the cell surface groups are so placed that they can form close attachments to other surfaces. This applies particularly when we examine adhesion to other surfaces such as glass. The adhesion of a cell to a solid substrate is of a different type from its adhesion to another cell because it is a dynamic phenomenon as the following experiments show clearly.

EFFECTS OF SUBSTRATE TEXTURE
ON CELL MOVEMENTS

So far we have been considering the locomotion of tissue cells on smooth glass. We have examined the locomotion of two types of cell; BHK 21 fibroblasts and similar cells (PyY cells) after transformation to tumour cells with polyoma virus. The untransformed cells on glass show contact inhibition and alignment of the cells in close monolayers. The transformed cells show a more random type of growth indicating reduced intercellular adhesion. When examined on surfaces of differing texture an unexpected type of behaviour is observed. This is summarized in Table 1. The transformed cells are able to attach and spread out on all the surfaces examined but the untransformed cells pass through a minimum adhesiveness, depending on the textures of the surface. When they form colonies, the colonies may become quite large, with a compact mass of cells up to 1,000,000 per aggregate.

These studies demonstrate clearly a difference between the nature of intercellular and cell substrate adhesion because the two cell types behave

Table 1

S: Cells spread on the substrate to form a monolayer. C: Cells do not attach to substrate but aggregate to form compact colonies

	Cell types	
Substrate texture	BHK 21 ^{13}C fibroblasts	PyY transformed cells
Smooth glass	S	S
Smooth cellulose acetate*	S	S
Fine sintered glass	C	S
Fine millipore, 0·4 μ pore size	C	S
Medium-grade sintered glass	S, C	S
Medium-grade, millipore 0·6 μ pore size	S, C	S
Coarse sintered glass	S	S
Coarse millipore, 0·8 μ pore size	S	S

* Millipore material dissolved in ethyl acetate and cast on glass.

quite differently. But they are most interesting because they throw further light on the nature of the locomotory mechanism. In Plate 2a a Stereoscan picture of a BHK 21 colony on fine millipore is shown. In Plate 2b a PyY cell spread out on fine millipore is shown. In Plate 3a the underside of a BHK 21 cell on fine millipore is shown. It is producing fine microvilli which are not able to bridge the gap between the irregularities in the millipore texture. The PyY cells which produce more irregular membrane undulations appear to be able to bridge this gap as shown in Plate 3b. Once the BHK 21 cell gets on to a rougher surface it is again able to attach to the larger areas of uneven texture. We might liken these effects to an attempt by a man to walk up a ladder with narrow rungs. Once the tread has been widened it again becomes possible to make progress. The fact that similar effects are observed on sintered glass shows that we are dealing with a surface texture effect and not a change due to the chemical constitution of a surface.

EFFECTS OF ELECTRICAL CHARGE ON MEMBRANE DIMENSIONS

We have already considered the role of electrical surface charge in intercellular adhesions. The question now to be considered is whether this charge can play a role in the generation of the membrane undulations responsible for locomotion in tissue cells. Shape changes, sometimes occurring extremely rapidly, are frequently observed in living cells. The microvilli seen in the Stereoscan picture of Plate 3a have already been mentioned. Another striking example can be observed when cells are maintained under low oxygen tension. Rapid bubbling of the surface takes place, somewhat like formation of microvilli but on a much larger scale. Treatment of cells with anaesthetics (Goldacre, 1952) or with antiserum + complement (Easty & Ambrose, 1957) also gives rise to a rapid increase in membrane surface area. There appear to be three possible ways in which such changes could occur: (a) by an elastic or plastic deformation of the actual membrane structure; (b) by the unfolding of a highly convoluted surface; (c) by the incorporation of additional membrane material into the surface either in the form of small vacuoles surrounded by membrane or by the addition of phospholipid micelles lying near the cell surface complex. Method (c) is the mechanism that fits most readily into the known properties of phospholipids; for example, their readiness to form myelin tubes, etc. But for the purposes of the present discussion any of mechanisms (a), (b) or (c) would be suitable.

Let us now consider a simple experiment to illustrate how a change in cell surface charge can bring about a shape change in a membrane complex. It is possible to make such studies on whole living cells but in this case a local change in a particular region of the cell must be brought about. This is because the delicate osmotic balance precludes large volume changes. For this reason the basic studies we have carried out have been made with undamaged isolated nuclei of *Amoeba proteus*. The nuclei were isolated by applying just sufficient pressure under a microscope slide to an amoeba to burst the cell. The undamaged nucleus was then released (Korohoda, Forrester, Moreman & Ambrose, 1968). In this case the large membrane pores provide a free passage for ions and prevent osmotic effects from complicating observations of surface shape changes. The results of treatment with various positive and negative ions introduced into the medium are shown in Table 2. The swelling and shrinking of the whole nucleus under these conditions is quite different from the behaviour of nucleoprotein (Ambrose & Butler, 1953). Nucleoprotein, for example, shrinks markedly in the presence of calcium ions whereas the whole nucleus is unaffected except on adding a polyanion in addition to calcium (Plate 4).

Table 2

Surrounding medium	Behaviour of nucleus
0·05 % polylysine	Contraction
0·2 % protamine	Contraction
0·2 % sodium polyglutamate	Slight expansion
0·1 % heparin	Expansion
$MgCl_2$ or $CaCl_2$ alone	No effect
0·1 % heparin + 1 mM-$MgCl_2$	Contraction
1 mM ATP + 1 mM-$MgCl_2$	Contraction
1 mM EDTA + 1 mM-$MgCl_2$	Contraction

All changes are referred to the original size of the nucleus in 0·14 M-NaCl alone.

The changes described in Table 2 are reversible, it being possible to take the nucleus through numerous cycles of contraction and expansion simply by changing the medium. The results of these experiments may be summarized briefly as follows. (*a*) Addition of a polycation (polylysine) reduces the net negative charge of the cell surface complex and gives rise to contraction. (*b*) Addition of a polyanion (polyglutamic acid or heparin) restores the negative charge of the membrane complex and produces expansion. (*c*) Addition of the bivalent cations Ca^{2+} or Mg^{2+} alone is without effect. (*d*) Addition of ATP or a polyanion plus Ca^{2+} or Mg^{2+} causes contraction. This can be readily explained if the bivalent ion forms bridges between these molecules and the cell surface:

$$ATP^{-+}Ca^{+}- \quad \text{or} \quad Heparin^{-+}Ca^{+}-.$$

Studies of the effects of the more local application of factors which may be expected to alter the electrical charge of the cell surface complex in intact cells have led to rather similar results. Introduction of a pH gradient in a culture of fibroblasts led to contraction of the membrane on the high pH side and expansion on the low pH side (Taylor, 1962). We have made some rather similar observations by applying polylysine to a culture of fibroblasts. Addition of polylysine caused withdrawal of extended pseudopodia.

THE RELATIONSHIP BETWEEN ELECTRICAL PROPERTIES OF CELL MEMBRANES AND CELL MOVEMENT

A direct examination of the relationship between the electrical properties of membranes and cell movements in tissue cells is extremely difficult because the ruffles are very small and transient. Some studies made with amoeba have helped to provide some evidence which may also relate to the behaviour of other membranes.

Forrester, Gingell & Korohoda (1967) have observed a suspension of streaming *Neglaeria* in a cell electrophoresis apparatus. They have found that these cells are polarized. They behave like dipoles in the applied external field, with the expanding leading edge of the amoeba showing a higher surface negative charge than the tail. Gingell (private communication) has shown that the local application of polylysine to the tip of the advancing pseudopodium of *Amoeba proteus* causes an immediate local contraction of the surface region. The endoplasm then begins to stream backwards within the pseudopodium and the direction of locomotion is reversed at least in this region of the amoeba.

Evidence for differences in the trans-membrane potential when measured between the head and tail of *Amoeba proteus* was also reported by Bingley & Thompson (1962). The behaviour of the undulating membranes seen in tissue cells is different from the behaviour of *Amoeba proteus*. The former comprises extremely local and transient changes. But studies of the behaviour of water-surface waves show that there is a local expansion of the surface during their generation. This is accompanied by a circular motion of protoplasm in the neighbourhood of the wave (Fig. 5). In the case of *Amoeba proteus*, at least according to some theories, there is a more generalized local expansion of the membrane complex over the whole leading edge of the cell.

So the difference between the amoeboid behaviour and the movement of tissue cells may be one of degree rather than of kind. A simple model which illustrates how it would be possible for electrical potentials to generate

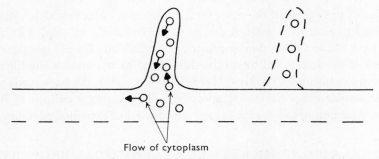

Fig. 5. Possible direction of cytoplasmic flow during the motion of an undulating membrane.

protoplasmic streaming is illustrated in Fig. 6. The sealed glass ring contains glass wool in its shorter arm. It is fitted with reversible silver/silver chloride electrodes. On applying a potential gradient of a few volts per centimetre the physiological saline in the closed tube streams in a circular path. This is due to asymmetry in the structure and can be brought about either by having unequal arms or by providing a large surface area on the fine glass fibres to give rise to electro-osmosis.

It is reasonable to suppose that the chemical source for the motive force in moving cells is derived from sources similar to those utilized in other processes which require energy, the direct source of energy being ATP, etc. The experiments described in this paper illustrate how a hypothesis based on interactions between ATP, calcium or magnesium ions and the cell surface complex might explain the generation of the membrane expansion–contraction sequence and the undulations described. Morales (1959) and Katchalsky (1964) have described how the conversion of chemical energy into work can be brought about by a change in the net charge on polymer molecules. A high charge gives rise to repulsion between the ionized groups and hence to expansion, whereas a low charge gives rise to contraction. The components which are necessary to give rise to a transformation of chemical energy into mechanical work by such a process are evidently present within the cell surface complex. Changes in surface charge give rise to expansion or contraction in cell surface area. These changes are most likely to give rise also to changes in transmembrane potential. Local changes in membrane potential *along* the membrane surface complex would be expected to provide the ideal conditions for electro–osmotic flow of cytoplasm within the microfibril–microtubule complex.

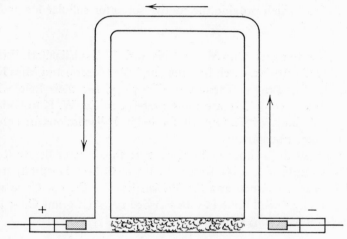

Fig. 6. Model to produce circular streaming of liquid by electro-osmosis.

Other possibilities ought to be considered (e.g. Jones, 1966) and it would be unwise at the present stage to specify possible mechanisms in more precise terms. But the attractive feature of such a system would be that it would be expected to be capable of feedback mechanism and could be self-propagating, like the action potential generated at the surface of the nerve fibre.

SUMMARY

Studies of the locomotion of mammalian fibroblasts and epithelial cells have shown that the main locomotory mechanism depends on undulations of the cell membrane and not on large-scale expansions of the leading edge of the moving cell. This has been established by three independent methods:

(i) By interference and phase-contrast microscopy.

(ii) By surface contrast microscopy which reveals the regions of contact between the cell and the solid substrate.

(iii) By Stereoscan electron microscopy which makes possible a direct examination of these membrane undulations adjacent to the surface on which the cell is moving.

These transient changes in the cell surface involve changes in cell surface area. Evidence is presented from studies on living cells and with isolated cell membranes to show that cell surface area can be changed reversibly by changing the net negative surface charge density of the cell surface complex. Increase in negative charge causes expansion. Reduction of charge causes contraction. These dimensional changes associated with electrical charge may provide the initiation of other biochemical processes below the cell surface which provide the motive force for cellular locomotion in tissue cells.

We should like to thank Miss Morag Ellison and Miss Elizabeth Wilkinson of the Chester Beatty Research Institute, and Mr Gordon and Miss Killingworth of the Cambridge Instrument Company, for their help with the Stereoscan microscopy. We are most grateful to Dr W. Korohoda, Professor Wolpert and Mr D. Gingell for helpful discussions in connexion with cell surface phenomena.

This work has been supported by grants to the Chester Beatty Research Institute (Institute of Cancer Research, Royal Cancer Hospital) from the Medical Research Council and the British Empire Cancer Campaign for Research, and by U.S. Public Health Service research grant CA-03188-08 from the National Cancer Institute.

REFERENCES

ABERCROMBIE, M. & AMBROSE, E. J. (1958). Expl Cell Res. 15, 332.
AMBROSE, E. J. (1956). Nature, Lond. 178, 1194.
AMBROSE, E. J. (1961). Expl Cell Res. Suppl. 8, 54.
AMBROSE, E. J. & BUTLER, J. A. V. (1953). Faraday Soc. Discuss. 13, 261.
AMBROSE, E. J. & JONES, P. C. T. (1961). Med. biol. Illust. 11, 109.
BINGLEY, M. S. & THOMSON, C. M. (1962). J. Theor. Biol. 2, 16.
DANIELLI, J. (1938). Cold Spring Harb. Symp. quant. Biol. 6, 190.
EASTY, G. C. & AMBROSE, E. J. (1957). Br. J. Cancer 11, 287.
FORRESTER, J. A., GINGELL, D. & KOROHODA, W. (1967). Nature, Lond. 215, 1409.
GOLDACRE, P. J. (1952). Symp. Soc. exp. Biol. 6, 128.
HOLTFRETER, J. (1948). Ann. N.Y. Acad. Sci. 49, 709.
JONES, BRYN W. (1966). Nature, Lond. 212, 362.
KATCHALSKY, A. (1964). Biophys. J. 4, 9.
KOROHODA, W., FORRESTER, J. A., MOREMAN, K. G. & AMBROSE, E. J. (1968). Nature, Lond. 217, 615.
MORALES, M. F. (1959). Rev. mod. Phys. 31, 426.

PLATE I

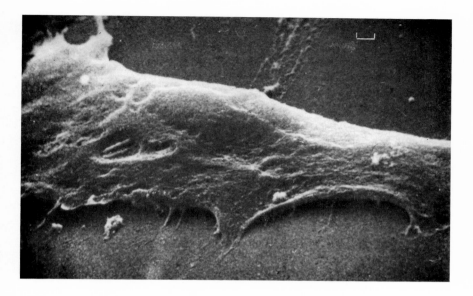

(a)

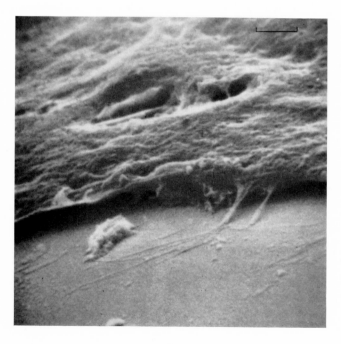

(b)

(a) Fibroblast migrating on a glass surface. Showing contacts between underside of the cell and the glass. Freeze-substituted. Stereoscan electron micrograph. Scale represents 2 μ; 60° inclination to horizontal. (b) The same at higher magnification, showing undulating membrane making local contact with the glass. Scale represents 2 μ; 72° inclination.

PLATE 2

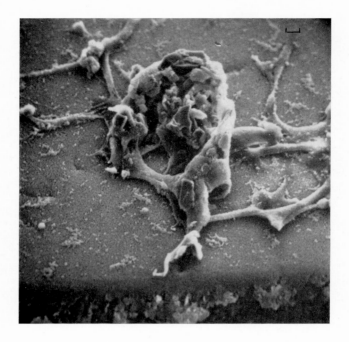

(a)

(b)

(a) BHK 21 fibroblasts growing on fine G.S. grade millipore, showing early stage of colony formation. Glutaraldehyde-fixed; scale represents 20 μ; 60° inclination. (b) Transformed cell (PyY) on fine G.S. millipore, spreading on surface without colony formation. Glutaraldehyde-fixed; scale represents 2 μ; 60° inclination.

PLATE 3

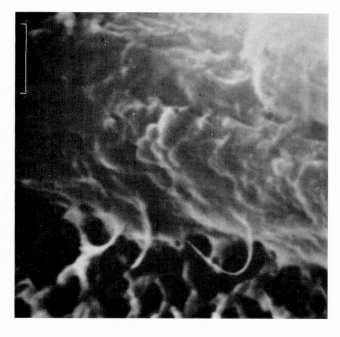

(a)

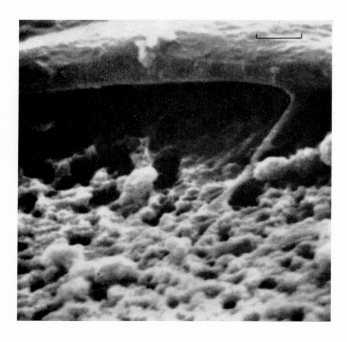

(b)

(a) Contacts between BHK 21 cell and millipore; scale represents 2 μ; 75° inclination.
(b) Transformed cell (PyY), showing undulating membrane in close contact with fine
millipore (G.S.). Scale represents 2 μ; 60° inclination.

PLATE 4

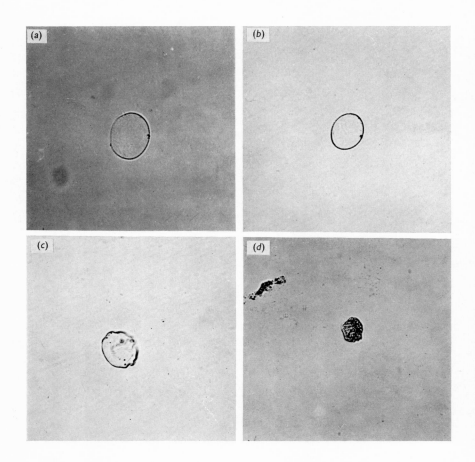

(*a*) Nucleus isolated in 0·14 M sodium chloride. (*b*) Nucleus in presence of 0·005 % poly-L-lysine. (*c*) Nucleus in presence of 0·05 % poly-L-lysine. (*d*) Nucleus in presence of 0·15 % poly-L-lysine.

ULTRASTRUCTURE AND DYNAMICS OF THE MOVING NUCLEUS

By MANFRED GIRBARDT

Institut für Mikrobiologie und experimentelle Therapie der Deutschen Akademie der Wissenschaften zu Berlin, Jena/DDR.

Movements of interphase nuclei are generally thought to be passive (Girbardt, 1962 a). Available information on this point is however scant as interest is mainly concentrated on the prometaphase and anaphase movement of chromosomes. Reports on nuclear rotation (Pomerat, 1953; Lehmann, 1959; Girbardt, 1958) and the presence of an activity centre, localized near or in the nuclear envelope (Girbardt, 1960), indicate that the nucleus may undertake movements independent of cytoplasmic streaming.

MATERIAL AND METHODS

Polystictus versicolor (L.) (= *Trametes versicolor* (L. ex Fr.)) was cultured in moist chambers at 24° C. on slides or coverslips, covered by agar or gelatine films (Girbardt, 1956). Twelve per cent malt-gelatine (n_D = 1,354) matches the refractive index of the cytoplasm in the nuclear region and allows a halo-free phase-contrast image (Barer & Joseph, 1954; Müller, 1956) to be obtained.

A special method (Girbardt, 1965) was used for combining phase-contrast pictures of the living cell, taken at the highest magnification, with electron micrographs. The observed cell area is selected in the block, mounted, trimmed and serial sections are examined in the electron microscope. By this method it is possible to divide a cell process (e.g. the movement of the nucleus) into static phases, provided that it is repeated in every cell, possesses morphological alterations and may be observed by light microscopy. By combining these static phases, dynamic events at the ultrastructural level may be reconstructed.

Cells were fixed at room temperature for 30 min. with 2% glutaraldehyde dissolved in 0·005 M phosphate buffer at pH 7·0. Fixation was followed by washing with buffer for 1 hr., 1% OsO_4 for 2 hr. and 0·5% uranyl acetate for 2 hr. Dehydration was performed by graded acetone and the material was embedded in Vestopal W. Sections were stained with lead citrate and were then examined in a Siemens Elmiskop I or SEM III (VEB Werk für Fernsehelektronik, Berlin).

An apparatus for continuous recording of the microscopical dark-field image, similar to that of Hürthle (1915) and Kamiya (1950), was used for studying 'shadow-imprints' of moving granules.

THE CELL

The tip-cell of the basidiomycete *Polystictus versicolor* is cylindrical, 5μ in diameter, 300–800μ long and elongates by apical growth at 5μ/min. This elongation is confined to a length of 5μ at the tip (Girbardt, 1955) and no secondary stretching occurs. All velocities measured within the cell therefore are absolute as the cell does not move as a whole when grown on solid media. The dikaryotic cell with two spindle-shaped nuclei was used, because a hook, the so-called clamp connexion, indicates the place and time of changes in the movement activity of nuclei. Comparison with mono-karyotic hyphae indicates that the behaviour of the moving single nucleus is the same as in dikaryotic hyphae.

LIGHT-MICROSCOPICAL OBSERVATIONS
ON THE MOVING NUCLEUS

Only *intra*-cellular movements of nuclei will be considered. The rapid transport of nuclei ('nuclear migration', 'nuclear streaming' (Dowding, 1958)) throughout the mycelium has been discussed by Dr Snider in this Symposium.

From many measurements of the nuclear movements it becomes evident that nuclei exhibit different motile activities during one cell generation. These may be divided into four phases (Fig. 1). For simplification of the diagram only one nucleus of the dicaryotic cells is considered since the second nucleus behaves in the same manner.

Phase I. The nucleus and most of the cell contents (granules, mito-chondria, vacuoles) move with about the same velocity as the growing tip. No indications of special cytoplasmic streaming or counter streaming are observable. The whole cell contents, including the nucleus, seem to be pushed forwards and the cell tip compensates for the internal pressure by extending. This extension generally is measured as 'hyphal tip growth'.

Phase I lasts 1–2 hr., depending on the temperature, the medium and unknown factors differing from cell to cell. No obvious activity of the nucleus may be observed by phase-contrast microscopy. Shadow imprinting, however, reveals incidental activity (saltatory movements (Rebhun, 1964)), as granules in the neighbourhood of the nucleus sporadically exhibit strongly accelerated movements against the direction of the nucleus and also in line with it. In the following, however, this minor activity will be neglected.

Phase II. Three to five minutes before the outgrowth of the clamp, the nuclear movement ceases, though the tip continues growing. At least part of the cytoplasm near the nucleus and the whole cell contents located before and behind it continue to move forwards. So the nucleus stops in spite of the continued cytoplasmic movement and frequently it may even move backwards for a short while. By this time the nucleus has reached its

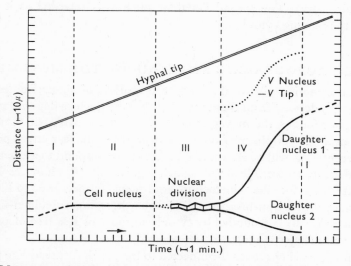

Fig. 1. Movements of the hyphal tip and one of the two nuclei of *Polystictus versicolor* during interphase and division. The curves represent middle values derived from measurements from 34 living cells. Active movements of the nucleus (independent of hyphal growth and cytoplasmic streaming) occur during phases II–IV. (From Girbardt, 1968.)

maximal size and is preparing for division. During the 10 min. duration of this phase the clamp is formed and one of the two nuclei enters the hook (Girbardt, 1961).

Phase III. The chromatin of the nucleus contracts and forms an entity enclosed by a membrane (Plate 1 *a*). The volume of the karyokinetic nucleus is about one-tenth of that of the interphase nucleus and the remainder, containing karyolymph and nucleolus, is dissolved in the cytoplasm. The small karyokinetic nucleus is bipolar, the poles being connected by a cord (*Zentralstrang*) (Plate 1 *a*). Frequently a complex of granules and mitochondria is seen outside the nucleus and apparently attached to it (Plate 1 *b*). About 2–3 min. after formation the karyokinetic nucleus exhibits oscillatory movements (Plate 1 *c*) independently of those steadily moving particles which are more than 10 μ distant from either pole. Particles less than 10 μ away are more or less included in these oscillations. By this manœuvre the nucleus is kept at a distinct locus in the cell which is represented by the central axis of the oscillations. After 2 min. the oscillations cease and within the next 2 min. the nucleus has divided.

Phase IV. One of the daughter nuclei moves rapidly forwards and later attains the velocity of the growing tip (phase I). The whole system seems to be so regulated that within about 30 min. the nucleus reaches a place in the cell which it would have attained had stopping and division not occurred (Girbardt, 1955). The second daughter nucleus is retarded as it moves against the moving cytoplasm.

CINÉ-MICROGRAPHIC ANALYSIS OF THE MOVEMENT

Time-lapse motion-picture films and the analysis of single frames (Girbardt, 1958) derived from them revealed that the nucleus does not move as a whole but follows the movement of an 'activity centre', which must be located near the periphery of the nucleus or at the nuclear envelope. This activity centre, as will be shown later, seems to correspond to a kinetochore rather than to a centriole or centriolar equivalent (Robinow & Marak, 1966). It is therefore the 'kinetochore equivalent' (abbreviated to KCE). It can be stained with iron-haematoxylin (Girbardt, 1960), is Feulgen-negative and is occasionally surrounded by cytoplasm more or less free of particles ('clear zone' (Bajer, 1958)).

The nucleolus behaves as if connected to the KCE. A thread-like pulling out of the nucleolar substance (Plate 2*a*) was interpreted (Girbardt, 1960) as a delayed response to the action of the KCE. During phase II the apparently stationary nucleus in reality exhibits the partly oscillatory motions of the KCE (Plate 2*b*). KCE-rotation through 180° is characteristic. After this rotation is completed, the KCE no longer lies at the end of the nucleus pointing in the direction of growth but at the opposite end. During this phase the nucleus is too large to follow as a whole the movements of the KCE and therefore it appears to be immobile.

ULTRASTRUCTURE OF THE MOVING NUCLEUS

Phase I. The nuclear envelope possesses pores about 0·1 μ in diameter. Outside the external membrane of the envelope, but always firmly attached to it, the KCE is located as a bipolar structure (Plate *c*2). It lacks the typical centriolar structure, never occurs as two independent units and is never found at any distance from the nuclear envelope.

The bipolar KCE always lies in an infolding of the nuclear envelope clearly seen in serial cross-sections. It is composed of a heavily stained, plate-like middle-part and two globular ends. The whole bipolar KCE is about 0·6–0·9 μ long and the diameters of the globules which are composed of granular or possibly fibrillar material are 0·3–0·4 μ. The nuclear envelope is often altered at the attachment area in that the cisternal and poral lumina are filled with material. This material is coherent with chromosomal material inside the nucleus. There is little doubt that the bipolar KCE represents the activity centre of the nucleus. However, it was not possible to demonstrate by electron microscopy its structural connexion with the nucleolus as predicted from observations of its behaviour in life. Its position is mainly at the end of the nucleus, which is in the direction of growth. When the nucleus rotates it may be found at this time located on one side of the nucleus.

Microtubules (MT) (diameter 20–30 nm.) are present in all parts of the cell. They do not show a specific arrangement but are scattered throughout the cytoplasm, preferentially orientated in the longitudinal axis of the cell. They are more frequent in the apical region. Only in exceptional cases do they meet the bipolar KCE (Plate 2c), possibly indicating the minor motile activities of the nucleus seen by shadow-imprinting during phase I.

The KCE is a persistent structure and is unipolar in the young daughter nucleus. The bipolar form is not derived from a division of the parental globule but by formation of a new bipolar entity at the base of the old one about 10–15 min. after division. Its formation starts with a small double granule (diameter about 0·5 μ) which seems to grow to its normal size within 5–10 min. It is not yet clear whether it is a condensation product of the unipolar KCE or a newly synthesized structure, generated under the influence of a special region of chromosomal material. At an early stage it is located outside the nuclear envelope but firmly attached to it.

Phase II. The most striking difference, as compared with the phase I nucleus, is the appearance of many microtubules which radiate from the globular parts of the bipolar KCE (Plate 3 a). They appear at the same time as active movement ('stopping') starts and may be found up to the end of phase IV. Their correlation with movement of the nucleus is further indicated by the positioning of the KCE at the point (compare Plate 2 a) where activity may be seen in the living cell.

It may be that MT are an aggregation or polymerization product of material derived from the two globular parts of the KCE. The young daughter nucleus, enclosed for a time in the clamp, loses all its MT and these are dissolved or transported away leaving the whole clamp free of MT after formation of the cross-wall. After fusion of the clamp the enclosed nucleus again starts to move and newly formed MT are seen radiating from the unipolar KCE. However we are not yet able to exclude the possibility that MT, synthesized in the cytoplasm, are only collected at the KCE during the active phase.

MT never enter the nucleus during phase II but always extend into the cytoplasm. Their orientation varies depending on the direction of movement. The endoplasmic reticulum (ER), formerly cisternal (*ERC*, Plate 2*c*) seems to be fragmented into vesicles or multivesicular bodies (*ERV*, *MvB*, Plate 3*a*). Connexions of the middle-part of the KCE with the nuclear envelope and the two globular parts are maintained (arrows, Plate 3*a*).

Phase III. At $\frac{1}{2}$–1 min. before the oscillations of this phase begin, the nuclear envelope breaks down, connexion with the KCE is lost and the bipolar KCE enters the condensing chromatin (*Chr.*, Plate 3*b*) inside the nucleus. *Within this period* (1 *min.*) *no MT are found in the cytoplasm.* The dense middle-part of the KCE is no longer present; instead of this a bundle of growing MT seems to push apart the globular poles, forming in this way the central cord (*Zentralstrang*) seen in the living cell (Plate 1*a*). In the course of these events, the axis of the KCE lies perpendicular to the direction which it exhibits later during division, i.e. the whole KCE rotates within or with the nucleus. No other movement of the karyokinetic nucleus is observable during this period (Plate 1*c*).

Within the next 20–30 sec., when all the condensing chromatin has been collected round the central cord, which now lies parallel to the longitudinal axis of the cell, and a new envelope is formed, *MT are again extending into the cytoplasm* (Plate 4). Both globular ends of the KCE, now lying at opposite poles of the karyokinetic nucleus, are mostly enclosed by a perforated cap of an ER-cisterna which is continuous with the nuclear envelope (arrows, Plate 4). The arrangement of ER-elements is better seen after permanganate fixation, which does not preserve the MT and the globular ends of the KCE (Plate 5*a*). As soon as this configuration has developed, oscillatory movements of the karyokinetic nucleus begin.

Microcinematography and continuous recording of granules by shadow-imprinting show that the karyokinetic nucleus does not oscillate alone but that a region, up to 10 μ from the poles (Plate 1*b*), is involved in this movement. This cytoplasmic area ('motility complex') is composed of ER-cisternae, mitochondria, granules (probably lysosomes) and ground cytoplasm (Plate 4). Granules near the poles of the KCE are strongly affected and exhibit the movement of the poles. Granules farther away are less influenced. Mitochondria and MT are bent or stretched according to the direction of movement.

At the end of phase III the two poles of the KCE move in opposite directions and the central cord is elongated. It is not clear if this elongation is performed by accumulation of new substance at the ends of MT or by fusion of existing ones. At any rate, intranuclear MT may double or triple in length until they are torn centrally. The envelope also tears in this region and immediately closes, surrounding the chromatin of the two daughter nuclei.

Phase IV. The young daughter nucleus shows no intranuclear MT, but many extend from the globular pole (half of the original KCE) through the ER-cap into the cytoplasm (Plate 5*b*). The ER-cap during this stage is frequently fragmented into multi-vesicular bodies. Connexion of the globular pole with the nuclear envelope is maintained, though it seems not to be very firm until the new bipolar KCE is formed. MT are found as long as the nucleus moves actively. This is not dependent only on time after division but also on other unknown conditions. The daughter nucleus, enclosed for about 20 min. in the clamp as already mentioned, rotates during the first 10 min. but then it rests and loses its MT. At the same time the daughter nucleus in the main hypha, which is derived from the same division, still moves and possesses MT. The formation of MT therefore seems also to be regulated by cytoplasmic factors.

DISCUSSION

Function and behaviour of the MT

Recent investigations show that MT are correlated with *intra*-cellular (Porter & Tilney, 1965) and chromosomal movements (Roth, 1967; Krishan & Buck, 1965). They are found in axopodia (Tilney & Porter, 1967) and sperm tails which are concerned with *cellular* movements. The data presented here strongly indicate that in *Polystictus versicolor* MT are formed not only during division of the nucleus but also during active movements in interphase, and a correlation between their appearance and active movements of the whole nucleus is evident.

MT seem not to act directly: for example, as contractile elements (Burton, 1966). This is indicated by their behaviour during the oscillatory movements when bundles of MT are bent against the direction of movement, indicating that they are passively dislocated as soon as movement is induced. The force therefore seems to originate in the cytoplasm. Nor do these observations suggest that MT act as cytoskeletal entities.

It is not yet clear if new MT are formed and dispersed within short intervals. A very rapid dispersal (within 30–60 sec.) seems to occur when KCE enters the nucleus, for it is improbable that the long MT present in the cytoplasm 30 sec. before this occurs break into short pieces and are arranged as the intranuclear central cord between the two globular ends of the KCE. It is more probable that under favourable conditions they may be formed within seconds by the aggregation of pre-existing subunits (Shelanski & Taylor, 1967).

The function of the intranuclear bundle of MT (*Zentralstrang*) during division is uncertain. From its origin it seems not to be analogous with the spindle of higher organisms. Intranuclear MT may possibly induce movements of the whole chromatinic material but not of individual chromosomes, each of which has to possess a kinetochore. It might be possible that the nucleus is composed of only one chromosome (Girbardt, 1962*b*) which starts dividing with the pushing apart of its KCE. During initiation of phase III, the central cord may act mainly as a stabilizing element to prevent tearing of the nucleus as long as the forces at the poles, working in opposite directions, are too weak to complete this tearing. MT of the central cord quickly disappear (within seconds) as soon as the central cord is torn.

Site of action of the forces producing movement

It was shown by microcinematography that forces producing movement do not affect the whole nucleus but act only on the KCE. It seemed possible that at the substructural level the forces primarily act on the MT, but the bending, mentioned above, excludes this possibility. The forces may act on the globular poles of the KCE. This is indicated by electron micrographs of cells fixed at the moment of reversal of direction during an oscillation, just after return has started (Plate 5*a*). In this case the KCE-pole which lies in the direction of movement is pulled (or pushed?) out of the nucleus and the pole at the opposite end is pulled (or pushed?) into it. This further indicates that the KCE, which is dumbbell-shaped during this stage, behaves as a unit. The connexion of its two globular ends by the central cord must be relatively stiff. One has the impression that the KCE as a whole could be pulled out of the karyokinetic nucleus if the ER-cap and forces at the opposite pole did not prevent this.

Pulling or pushing

If we assume that the forces act on the globular ends of the KCE during the oscillating phase, no decision can be reached as both alternatives are possible. Observations on the living material suggest that the KCE is pulled. This is most obvious during phase IV when the nucleus is monopolar (Plate 5*b*) and the globular end of the KCE always lies in the direction of movement. If, however, a pushing force of cytoplasmic origin is assumed, then it must be located *behind* the point of attack. In this case only a small amount of the cytoplasm could be effective since the nucleus at this time occupies $\frac{1}{2}$–$\frac{2}{3}$ of the cell diameter. This is of course not conclusive and further investigation is required.

Concluding remarks

It is obvious that the question of the nature of the working forces cannot be answered at this stage of the investigation. Some speculations may however be allowed.

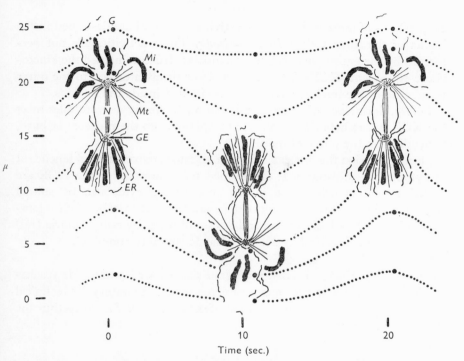

Fig. 2. Schematic representation of the behaviour of the nucleus during oscillations of phase III. *G*, Granules; *Mi*, mitochondria; *ER*, cisternal ER, *Mt*, microtubules; *Z*, *Zentralstrang*; *GE*, globular ends of the KCE; *N*, nucleus.

Electrical forces (membrane charges) seem to be ruled out as the distances between the KCE and membranous elements (ER, mitochondria) are too great for these forces to act.

The striking oscillations of the nucleus suggest that metabolic processes are responsible (Tager, Papa, Quagliariello & Slater, 1966). One may assume that membrane permeability (Pressman, 1965) is altered by the MT. This might induce an uptake or release of water and ions and lead to periodic swelling and contraction of mitochondria and possibly of ER

17

cisternae. These membranous organelles are always involved in the 'motility complex'. Variations in hydration of cytoplasm may thus occur, leading to a sol-gel transformation governed by the MT. The globular end of the KCE may be pulled into regions of gelled cytoplasm. On the other hand the aggregation of subunits into MT may release water (Tilney & Porter, 1967), making the cytoplasm more liquid and thus acting in the opposite manner.

SUMMARY

Four phases of more or less motile activities of nuclei are described in the hypha of the fungus *Polystictus versicolor*. These activities are not performed by the entire nucleus but by a bipolar structure named the kinetochore equivalent (KCE). The latter is either firmly attached to the outer membrane of the nuclear envelope or is situated inside the nucleus.

Before, during and after the division of nuclei, many microtubules meet the KCE and radiate either into the cytoplasm, into the nucleus, or both, depending on the phase of motility.

During division the nucleus exhibits oscillatory movements independent of cytoplasmic streaming. It is assumed that the poles of the KCE are pulled by forces originating in the surrounding cytoplasm by sol-gel transformations. These transformations are thought to arise from microtubule-induced periodic uptake and release of water by mitochondria and/or ER-cisternae involved in the cytoplasmic 'motility complex'.

I should like to thank Mrs Bähring, Mrs Fritsche, Mr Hädrich, Mr Wachsmuth and the team of the electron-microscopical laboratory for technical assistance. Thanks are also due to Professor R. Barer for correcting the English of the manuscript.

REFERENCES

BAJER, A. (1958). *Chromosoma* 9, 319.
BARER, R. & JOSEPH, S. (1954). *Q. Jl microsc. Sci.* 3rd ser., 95, 399.
BURTON, P. R. (1966). *J. Morph.* 120, 397.
DOWDING, E. S. (1958). *Can. J. Microbiol.* 4, 295.
GIRBARDT, M. (1955). *Flora* 142, 540.
GIRBARDT, M. (1956). *Z. wiss. Mikrosk.* 63, 16.
GIRBARDT, M. (1958). *Film T-HF*, 202.
GIRBARDT, M. (1960). *Planta* 55, 365.
GIRBARDT, M. (1961). *Expl Cell Res.* 23, 181.
GIRBARDT, M. (1962a). *Handb. PflPhysiol.* 17 (2), 920.
GIRBARDT, M. (1962b). *Planta* 58, 1.
GIRBARDT, M. (1965). *Mikroskopie* 20, 254.
GIRBARDT, M. (1968). In *Grundlagen der Cytologie*, ed. Hirsch, Ruska and Sitte. Jena: VEB Fischer-Verlag.

HÜRTHLE, K. (1915). *Pflügers Arch. ges. Physiol.* **162**, 422.

KAMIYA, N. (1950). *Cytologia* **15**, 189.

KRISHAN, A. & BUCK, R. C. (1965). *J. Cell Biol.* **24**, 433.

LEHMANN, F. E. (1959). *Expl Cell Res.* Suppl. 6, 1–16.

MÜLLER, R. (1956). *Mikroskopie* **11**, 36.

POMERAT, C. M. (1953). *Expl Cell Res.* **5**, 191.

PORTER, K. R. & TILNEY, L. G. (1965). *Science, N.Y.* **150**, 382.

PRESSMAN, B. C. (1965). *Proc. natn. Acad. Sci. U.S.A.* **13**, 1076.

REBHUN, L. J. (1964). In *Primitive Motile Systems in Cell Biology*, ed. Allen and Kamiya. New York, London: Academic Press.

ROBINOW, C. F. & MARAK, J. (1966). *J. Cell Biol.* **29**, 129.

ROTH, L. E. (1967). *J. Cell Biol.* **34**, 47.

SHELANSKI, M. L. & TAYLOR, E. W. (1967). *J. Cell Biol.* **34**, 549.

TILNEY, L. G. & PORTER, K. R. (1967). *J. Cell Biol.* **34**, 327.

TAGER, J. M., PAPA, S., QUAGLIARIELLO, E. & SLATER, E. C. (1966). *Regulation of Metabolic Processes in Mitochondria*, B.B.A. Library, vol. VII. Elsevier Publishing Co., Amsterdam, London, New York.

PLATE I

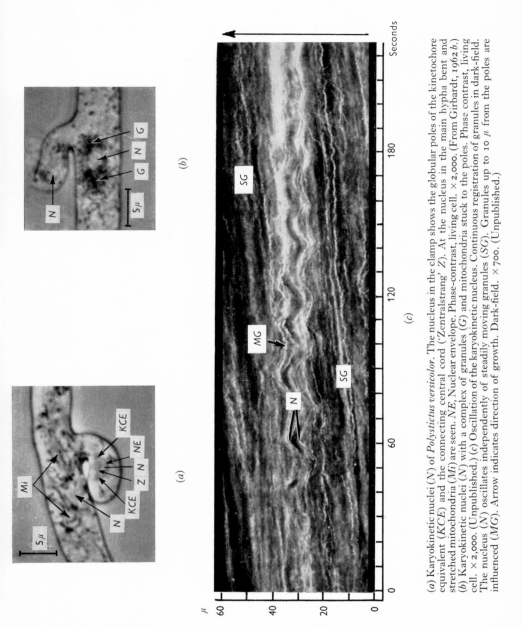

(a) Karyokinetic nuclei (N) of *Polystictus versicolor*. The nucleus in the clamp shows the globular poles of the kinetochore equivalent (*KCE*) and the connecting central cord ('Zentralstrang' *Z*). At the nucleus in the main hypha bent and stretched mitochondria (*Mi*) are seen. *NE*, Nuclear envelope. Phase-contrast, living cell. × 2,000. (From Girbardt, 1962 *b*.)
(b) Karyokinetic nuclei (N) with a complex of granules (*G*) and mitochondria stuck to the poles. Phase contrast, living cell. × 2,000. (Unpublished.) (c) Oscillation of the karyokinetic nucleus. Continuous registration of granules in dark-field. The nucleus (N) oscillates independently of steadily moving granules (*SG*). Granules up to 10 μ from the poles are influenced (*MG*). Arrow indicates direction of growth. Dark-field. × 700. (Unpublished.)

PLATE 2

(a)

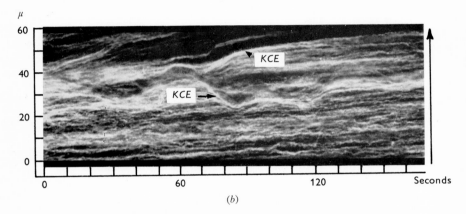

(b)

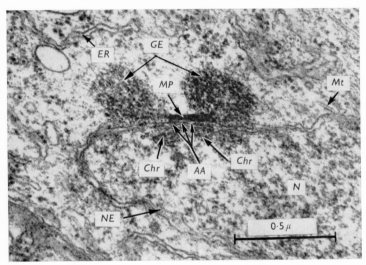

(c)

(a) Nuclei before entering division. Nucleoli (*Nu*) appear drop-like and their substance is pulled out (arrow). Kinetochore equivalents (*KCE*) are faintly seen at the end of the nuclei, opposite to the growing direction of the hypha. A 'clear zone' of cytoplasm surrounds them (from Girbardt, 1960). (b) Movements of kinetochore equivalents (*KCE*) of both nuclei before division. The upper KCE moves into the clamp and therefore is not registered along the whole diagram. The KCE below exhibits independent movements and weak oscillations. Dark field. × 700. (Unpublished.) (c) Kinetochore equivalent of the interphase nucleus (*N*) composed of a plate-like middle part (*MP*) and two globular ends (*GE*). It lies firmly attached to the nuclear envelope (*NE*), the attachment area (*AA*) of which is altered. Chromatin (*Chr*), Microtubule (*Mt*), Cisternae of the endoplasmic reticulum (*ER*). × 60,000. (Unpublished.)

PLATE 3

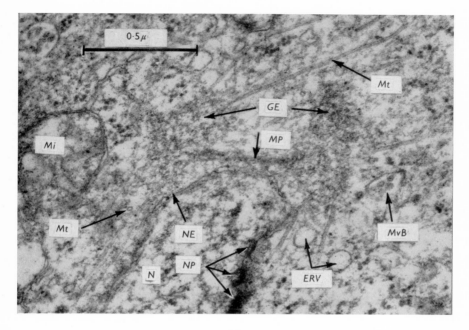

(a)

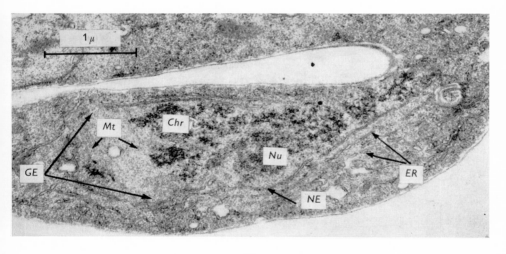

(b)

(a) Kinetochore equivalent of the nucleus (N) during phase II. Many microtubules (Mt) are radiating from the globular ends (GE) but none from the middle part (MP). Cisternal ER is fragmented into a vesicular form (ERV) or multi-vesicular bodies (MvB). Nuclear envelope (NE) with pores (NP); Mi, mitochondria. × 60,000. (Unpublished.) (b) Nucleus entering phase III. Chromatin (Chr) is condensing, rest of nucleolus (Nu) still present. Kinetochore equivalent comes into contact with chromatin by breakdown of the nuclear envelope (NE). Microtubules (Mt) bridge the gap between the two globular ends (GE). Shells of ER-cisternae (ER) round the nucleus. × 25,000. (Unpublished.)

PLATE 4

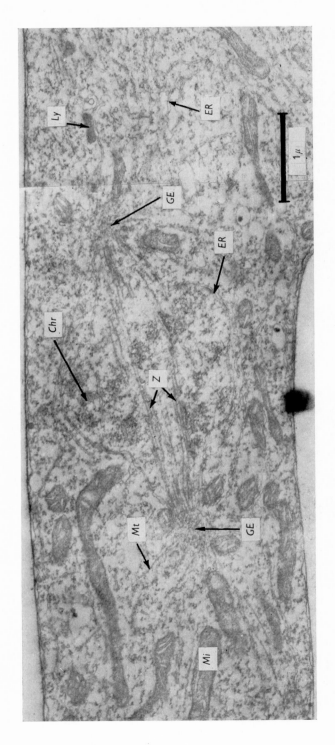

Nucleus during oscillatory movements of phase III. A bundle of microtubules ('Zentralstrang' *Z*) connects the globular ends (*GE*) of the KCE. Condensed chromatin (*Chr*) fills the nucleus, which is surrounded by several ER-cisternae (*ER*), Microtubules (*Mt*) are radiating into the cytoplasm. Mitochondria (*Mi*) and cisternal ER are arranged in typical fashion ('motility complex'). *Ly*, Lysosomal particle. × 25,000. (Unpublished.)

PLATE 5

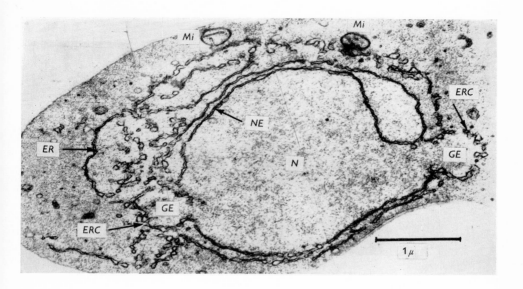

(a)

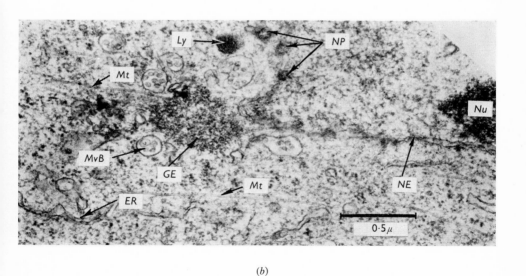

(b)

(a) Nucleus during oscillatory movements of phase III. Microtubules and KCE are not preserved by permanganate. The globular end (*GE*) lying in direction of movement is pulled out of the nucleus and both globular ends are covered by a perforated *ER*-cap (*ERC*). *Mi*, Mitochondria; *NE*, nuclear envelope; *N*, nucleus; *ER*, endoplasmic reticulum. (b) Globular end (*GE*) of the KCE during phase IV, surrounded by many multi-vesicular bodies (*MvB*) and in contact with the nuclear envelope (*NE*). *Nu*, Nucleolus; *NP*, pores in the nuclear envelope; *ER*, cisternal *ER*; *Mt*, microtubules; *Ly*, lysosomal particles. (Unpublished.)

NUCLEAR MOVEMENTS IN SCHIZOPHYLLUM

By PHILIP J. SNIDER

Department of Biology, University of Houston, Texas

INTRODUCTION

This paper deals mainly with nuclear migration, one of three translatory motions of nuclei known in the mycelium of the small mushroom *Schizophyllum commune*. One motion is associated with nuclear division, another with hyphal-tip growth. Compared to these two intracellular motions, nuclear migration is vastly long-range and rapid. The nuclei also display gyrations, undulations and other static motions, observable in the living state with phase-contrast illumination, but static motion will not be treated here. Translatory motions, which involve movement from point to point in a definite direction, are more accessible to measurement than the static motions. For the slower, intracellular motions, measurements of rate have been made by direct visual observation of living cells. All measures of nuclear migration were made indirectly, through procedures for detecting the migratory nuclei by differential genotypic selection.

Investigation of the mechanism for nuclear migration has focused upon the question (Snider, 1965): are the nuclei self-motile, or are they pushed by streaming protoplasm? In the simplest forms, the self-motile hypothesis implies that the immediate source of motive force is an apparatus inserted on the nucleus, but not on any extra-nuclear elements; the flow hypothesis implies an origin of motive force clearly external to and independent of the nucleus. Neither hypothesis seems to place narrow restrictions upon the nature of the molecular mechanism for motive force. While more complicated hypotheses can be imagined that would disallow these two as mutually exclusive alternatives, the approach has been the traditional one of postponing unnecessary assumptions. The progress of efforts to distinguish between the two simplest hypotheses favours passive motility.

Nuclear migration occurs as a natural part of the life-cycle in *Schizophyllum*. The mushroom, or fruit body, ejects haploid basidiospores into the air. These spores, the products of meiosis, germinate and grow into haploid, homokaryotic mycelia with one nucleus per cell and with cross-walls through which complex pores (Jersild, Mishkin & Niederpruem, 1967) connect adjacent cells. Hyphal fusion occurs within and between mycelia. If the fused mycelia are compatible, nuclear migration results in a reciprocal exchange of nuclei between mycelia, heterokaryosis of the dikaryotic type is established, and mushrooms can then develop on the dikaryotic mycelium. Dikaryotic cells contain a pair of compatible but unfused haploid nuclei and at each cross-wall there is a characteristic structure called a clamp connexion.

Each homokaryotic strain has a mating type, and sexual reproduction depends upon pairing homokaryons that are compatible for two series of mating-type factors, A and B. A pairing between $A1$ $B2$ and $A3$ $B6$, for instance, is compatible and can thus produce a dikaryotic mycelium and fruit bodies. The nuclei fuse in the basidial cells on the gills of the mushroom and the diploid nuclei so formed immediately undergo meiosis. With production of basidiospores, the life-cycle is complete.

For the work reported here, several specific mating types were used, but always in fully compatible combinations. Nuclear migration is controlled genetically, especially by the B factors, which prevent or greatly slow migration in pairings with identical B factors; but the most recent ideas are that migration is controlled by enzymic action altering the size of the pores in the cross-walls (Giesy & Day, 1965; Jersild *et al.* 1967; Wessels & Niederpruem, 1967) so that the control does not directly affect the motility mechanism of migratory nuclei. The mutants used include the non-leaky, biochemical mutations arginineless (*arg-2*), uracilless (*ura-1*) and nicotinic acidless (*nic-2*); the morphological mutant *puff* (*p*) distinctly alters hyphal morphology and this mutant has had special usefulness in research on nuclear migration. Strains with stock numbers preceded by 'R' are from the laboratory of Dr John R. Raper, Harvard University; stock numbers preceded by 'S' refer to strains of the author. The origin of the mutants is indicated in the papers by Raper & Miles (1958), a useful introduction to the genetics of *Schizophyllum*.

TWO INTRACELLULAR MOTIONS

A slow, steady, intracellular motion of the nucleus occurs in the cell at the tip of any elongating hypha. This motion is constantly in the same direction and at precisely the same linear rate as hyphal tip growth, except for periodic interruptions during the synchronized events of cross-wall formation and division of the nucleus (Fig. 1). The nuclei of cells other than the tip cell generally remain about mid-way along the cell and seldom display translatory motion until a lateral branch-hypha begins development. Then the nucleus in the cell producing the branch, but only this nucleus, resumes the intracellular motions, and thus the sequence depicted in Fig. 1 reoccurs in the new side-branch. When a hyphal tip ceases elongation, so also does the associated nuclear motion stop in the tip cell.

The imminent approach of the mechanically most active stages of nuclear division is anticipated in growing tip-cells as the nucleus in motion slows to a stop about 10 min. before the abruptly initiated separation of the daughter nuclei. These move straight away in opposite directions with

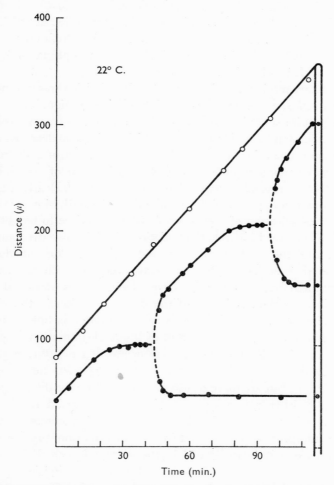

Fig. 1. Intracellular motions of nuclei. Nuclear motions (●) associated with nuclear division and with hyphal-tip growth (○) at 22° C. were measured at ×400 with a micrometer eyepiece, in bright field phase-contrast illumination. The positions of the hyphal tip and the nucleus in the tip cell at the beginning of the interval of observation are indicated at the left side of the graph; at the right a schematic representation of the same hypha (to scale, long dimension) when observation ended is given.

marked acceleration for a distance of about 50μ each, in 2–3 min. at 22° C. (Fig. 1). This translatory motion of the nucleus is undoubtedly associated with the operation of the microtubular apparatus for nuclear division.

While the intracellular motions were not studied in great detail, the data are sufficient to give a reasonable indication of comparative rates. The nuclear motion associated with tip elongation is about $2 \cdot 37 \, \mu$/min. at 22° C. (Fig. 1). Since the Q_{10} for the rate of hyphal-tip growth is known to be about $1 \cdot 7$ for the interval $22-32^\circ$ C. (Snider & Raper, 1958), this nuclear motion undoubtedly has a rate equivalent of $0 \cdot 24$ mm./hr. at 32° C. The temperature of 32° C. has been chosen as a standard reference for rate comparisons, as it is a suitable compromise between the optima for mycelial growth and nuclear migration.

The translatory motion associated with nuclear division was not measurable with the same accuracy as the other intracellular motion. The division movement is quite short in duration, and the nucleolus, more easily observed and accurately recorded than the position of the nuclear membrane in the average preparation, has the disconcerting action of suddenly becoming invisible moments before nuclear division and of remaining so during much of the crucial interval. The daughter nucleoli clearly reappear, however, enough in advance of the termination of the division movement to enable some indication of the slope of distance to time to be obtained. Extrapolation backward suggests the initiation of motion occurred not more than 1 min. after the nucleolus disappeared optically. The outside limit for the time differential is fixed, in any event, by the moments of disappearance and reappearance of the nucleoli. Slopes estimated either way give values for the maximum of the division motion in the vicinity of $10 \, \mu$/min. at 22° C. The Q_{10} for this nuclear motion is unknown. If it is near the likely value of $1 \cdot 7$, the rate of the nuclear motion associated with nuclear division could not be much in excess of 1 mm./hr. at 32° C.

The observations of the intracellular motions reported here apply to homokaryotic cells but are more or less similar to those for dikaryotic cells of *Polystictus* (Girbardt, 1955) and *Schizophyllum* (Jersild *et al.* 1967). The formation of clamp connexions in dikaryotic cells introduces what could possibly be interpreted as a separate translatory motion. As the clamp connexion develops, the two nuclei in the dikaryotic cell divide simultaneously. The nuclear motions for one of these nuclear divisions proceed as described. One daughter nucleus of the other division, however, moves into the incompleted clamp and is stopped there for about 15 min., until the growing tip of the clamp fuses with the cell temporarily containing only one daughter nucleus. The trapped nucleus resumes motion through the hole thus opened and moves to a position near the isolated nucleus, about mid-way along the cell. Direct observations with the electron microscope (Girbardt, this volume) have now excluded the simplest hypothesis, that this is part of the division movement. The division-apparatus fibres, no doubt crowded into the immature clamp, probably straighten out later through the fused pore into the next cell and then move the nucleus from the clamp toward the middle of the cell.

NUCLEAR MIGRATION

Description

Nuclear migration is intercellular motion which involves the rapid passage of nuclei from one mycelium into and throughout an established, spatially extensive mycelium of another fungal strain (Lehfeldt, 1923; Buller, 1931). The evidence that nuclei migrate is quite firm (Buller, 1931; Prévost, 1962; Snider, 1963). In *Schizophyllum* migration begins within a few hours after cellular fusion between homokaryotic strains with unlike B-factors. If both strains are homokaryotic, nuclear migration is reciprocal; that is, each mate acts as a donor and recipient. If one mate is dikaryotic, it acts only as donor (Snider, 1965). Why this is so is obscure, especially since dikaryons have unlike B-factors. Migratory nuclei proceed from cell to cell through the pores, which are structurally complex in the mushroom fungi (Moore & McAlear, 1962; Bracker & Butler, 1963, 1964). The B-factor genes seem to regulate migration at the pores by causing enzymes to dissolve the complex pores partially, thus facilitating nuclear passage (Giesy & Day, 1965), rather than possibly acting directly upon the motility mechanism. The rate of migration has been measured as being up to 20 times faster than hyphal tip growth, or 5 mm./hr. at 32° C., and the Q_{10} for migratory rate is 6·0 between 22° and 32° C. Since the nuclei have not been observed to divide much more frequently than once each hour, migration must often be independent of nuclear division. It is not known whether migratory nuclei stop and divide, as non-migratory nuclei do in tip cells. The pattern, rate and nuclear-population dynamics of the migratory process are influenced by the fabric texture of the recipient mycelium and by its general physiological state. These matters are taken into consideration in devising a way to measure nuclear migration.

Measurement

Two genetically dissimilar strains are grown separately for several days on agar media. Each is then macerated into a thick suspension of cells, which is inoculated evenly throughout a molten-agar minimal medium supplemented only for the strain introduced. These agar cultures, poured and gelled 3 mm. thick, are incubated for at least 40 hr., the time required at 32° C. to produce an entire mycelium by growth and hyphal fusion of numerous micro mycelia. Young mycelia, uniform in properties of age and physiological state, are thus fabricated in minimal time and are cut into any desired shape between 40 and 48 hr. after inoculation. In rate experiments rectangles of mycelia with dimensions of 20 × 100 mm. are cut to serve as recipients and they are implanted with a 2 × 20 mm. strip of the donor strain, placed across one narrow end of the recipient mycelium. The donor strains are pre-incubated for 8–10 hr. before implanting, as a fringe of new growth on the cut surfaces seems to facilitate the initiation of migration.

The distance of migration at any particular time is determined for a given recipient mycelium by cutting the entire 20 × 100 mm. rectangle into 2 × 20 mm. strips and transferring the fifty sampling strips so provided to minimal medium. This agar medium selects for growth only those strips containing donor nuclei, as a growth response here depends upon nutritional complementation between the non-allelic mutant genes in the genetically dissimilar strains. By the total analysis of separate recipients at intervals and in replicate sets, migratory distance can be related to time, and the rate of migration is thus determined.

Besides rate, migration involves another parameter of interest, an increasing population of donor nuclei distributed within a certain area of the recipient at any given time. The pattern of migration is measured by cutting whole recipients into 2 × 2 mm. squares and transferring all 500 cubes to the selective medium.

These procedures for measuring the distance and spatial pattern of migration were modified from earlier versions (Snider & Raper, 1958; Ellingboe, 1964) to improve the localization of donor nuclei within the recipient mycelium. This increased resolution of position was expected to aid in checking for the occurrence of two highly desired characteristics of the system: (1) consistent presence, and recovery, of donors in a linear, closely spaced series of sampling strips up to the boundary of the donor-populated territory most distal from the donor implant, and (2) a distal boundary for the migratory front that remains a straight line, at right angles to the long dimension of the recipient rectangle, for the entire period of nuclear migration. These characteristics would tend to increase confidence in the validity of the measurements. The first characteristic was virtually realized, except for an occasional blank strip in treatments with unusually fast migration or in treatments expected to have some adverse effect upon the viability of cells. The moving boundary, however, was mostly irregular, and the range of variation is illustrated in Fig. 2. In all cases the positive samples most distant from the implant were taken as the true indication of migratory distance.

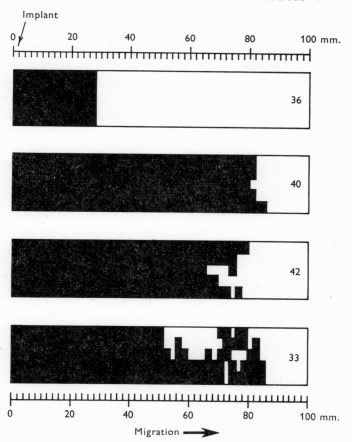

Fig. 2. Range of variation in boundary contour of the migratory front. Blackened areas represent demonstrated spatial extent of the population of donor nuclei in a typical recipient strip for each of four classes of variant boundaries in a total of 151 recipients: 36 strips, straight boundary, at right angles to direction of migration; 40 strips, boundary skewed 2–6 mm. in the direction of migration; 42 strips, skewed 8–18 mm.; 33 strips, skewed 20 mm. or more. Most of those in the straight-boundary class were in an early stage of migration, less than 20 mm. There was no suggestion of a correlation between treatments or experiments and the skewness of the boundary.

EXPERIMENTS ON INTERCELLULAR MOVEMENT

The results of several experiments done with *Schizophyllum* in the author's laboratory may bear upon the central question of whether the donor nuclei are self-motile or pushed during the rapid intercellular movement termed 'nuclear migration'. Evidence from other fungi and other laboratories is included in the discussion, where the conclusion reached is that passive motility is favoured, but not clearly demonstrated, in *Schizophyllum* and related fungi.

The direct visual approach

The most direct way to decide whether migratory nuclei are pushed or are propelled would obviously be to watch migration by phase-contrast micro-scopy. If the nuclei move independently of all other cellular components, the migrating nucleus must be self-motile. The authenticity of the observed motion would be reasonably assured if the migrating nucleus were recorded

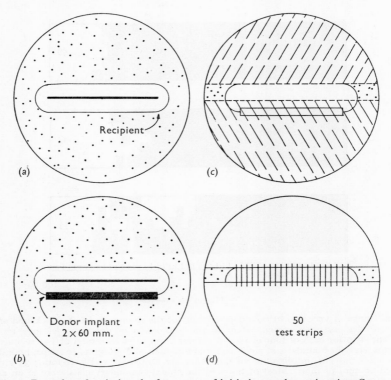

Fig. 3. Procedure for timing the frequency of initiating nuclear migration. See text.

visually at the known rates of migration, well in excess of the intracellular motions, through a number of consecutive cells. No intercellular motion of nuclei or cytoplasm sufficiently rapid and sustained to account for nuclear migration has been seen in *Schizophyllum* in this laboratory. If there are only a few widely separated hyphae involved in the most rapid interval of migration, the problem may be mainly that of visually locating an involved hypha at the proper time.

During the past year, considerable effort has been spent unsuccessfully in attempts to make the crucial direct observations in recipients of the *puff* (*p*) mutant. This mutation alters hyphal morphology quite strikingly and clearly signals the migration of p^+ donor nuclei into p precipient hyphae, by changing from *puff* to wild-type morphology (Snider, 1963). The difficulty is that the growth response is too delayed compared with the rate of migration. The change to wild-type morphology is not seen before 24 hr. after implantation of a p^+ donor, and by then p^+ nuclei have long since

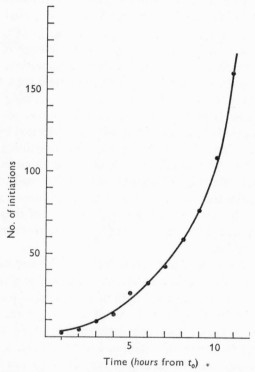

Fig. 4. Frequency for initiation of nuclear migration across a 2,000 mm. confrontation line. Initiation was measured in one direction only: donor, $A4\,B4$; recipient, $A2\,B2\,arg\text{-}2$.

completed migration through 30 mm. of *puff* hyphae, the longest stretch of individually traceable *puff* hyphae that could be grown to date. Efforts have continued with indirect methods of testing the hypotheses for nuclear migration.

Frequency of initiation

Evidence that the initiation of migration is infrequent has lent support to the possibility that a substantial part of the migratory process requires the involvement of relatively few recipient hyphae. The frequency of initiation was determined from the homokaryotic strain $A4\,B4$ (R672) as donor into the strain $A2\ B2\ arg-2$ (R667) as recipient. The procedure only allowed the detection of initiation in one direction across a linear contact between the strains. The contact line was extended to 2000 mm. by summing observations over a series of cultures with 60 mm. of confrontation line in each (Fig. 3). The $A2\ B2\ arg-2$ recipient was inoculated from a mycelial macerate about the consistency of tooth-paste by squeezing the macerate through a hypodermic needle to form a straight line of inoculum across the centre of each Petri dish containing migration-complete medium (Snider & Raper, 1958). After growth for 3 days at $32°$ C. (Fig. 3a) the recipient was implanted with donor strips, 2×60 mm., along one edge of the recipient mycelium (Fig. 3b). At 4, 12, and 24 hr. after implantation, the recipients were cut parallel to the implant, along a line exactly 2 mm. from the edge of the implant (Fig. 3c), so as to exclude from the remaining portion of the recipient any donor hyphae intermingled with those of the recipient mycelium. The unneeded sectors of the cultures, indicated by dashed lines in Fig. 3c, were removed and discarded. The remaining strip of the recipient was cut into fifty sampling segments, each 2 mm. wide (Fig. 3d), and these were transferred individually to selective medium. All of the 1,000 test strips from the 24 hr. treatment contained donor nuclei. Only a few positive test strips were found at 4 hr., and most of these were widely separated. The 12 hr. treatment, however, had numerous contiguous series of positive test samples.

By assuming that each band of consecutively positive test strips originated from the minimum of one initiation event, the probable time of initiation could be estimated by relating the length of each band of positive strips to the known rate of migration for this pair of strains, 3 mm./hr. (Snider & Raper, 1958, fig. 6, p. 544). This extrapolation of the data could be expressed as the accumulated frequency of initiation with time (Fig. 4), in which the interpreted frequency was, for example, very close to 100 initiations per 2,000 mm. of confrontation in 10 hr. at $32°$ C.; this amounts to a high probability for 1 initiation per 20 mm. of contact within 10 hr. after implantation. These considerations, incidentally, influenced the selection of 20 mm. for the width of the recipient rectangles used routinely in the current procedure for measuring the rate of nuclear migration (see Figs. 6–8). The possibility arises that a distinction can be made between hyphal fusions in general and effective fusions; that is, those through which nuclear migration is initiated. The results (Fig. 4) certainly suggest that the initiation of migration is an infrequent event relative to the number of apposed hyphal ends existing along a confrontation line between paired mycelia.

Specifically labelled cytoplasm

The presence of considerable amounts of donor cytoplasm in recipient hyphae is predicted by the flow hypothesis of nuclear migration. The definite presence of donor nuclei but absence of donor cytoplasm would be most consistent with the self-motility hypothesis. Two approaches have been tried to apply this indirect method of distinguishing between the hypotheses.

In the first, an experiment done in collaboration with Dr Clare Sun tested for translocation of the light-stimulated induction of fruiting. If dikaryotic cultures of *Schizophyllum* are grown for fruiting in the dark, only several in fifty cultures respond, the fruits appear late, and only one or two large fruit bodies are produced in each Petri dish. A strong stimulus of white light will greatly increase the number but decrease the average size of the fruit bodies. A white-light stimulus sufficient to induce about 500 fruit bodies per Petri dish was given to wild-type, dikaryotic donor implants. These were then implanted into *arg-2* recipient homokaryons kept in the dark. Samples removed to selective medium showed nuclear migration had occurred, as expected, to the limits of the *arg-2* recipients, but no fruit bodies were developed, except on the donor implant itself. The light-stimulus for fruiting was not translocated between donor and recipient mycelia.

If the receptor system for light-induced fruiting is in the cytoplasm, as assumed, the results are as expected if migratory nuclei are self-motile. Other probable interpretations are that the stimulus was translocated *and diluted* below the threshold concentration required to induce fruiting, that the light-receptor system is in the cell membrane or some other immobile structure, or that the receptor was in the cytoplasm but coagulated on exposure to light, and thus became immobile, as the first step toward fruiting. There are evidently too many probable interpretations to accept the results necessarily as evidence for nuclear self-motility in migration.

The other approach was to label the donor strain *A41 B41 ura-1* (S39) with a ^{14}C-labelled compound that should be taken up but not metabolized by the mycelium and to compare migration with translocation of the abelled compound. Inulin-^{14}C, immediately available, is not utilized as a sole carbon source by *Schizophyllum*, but it is metabolized adaptively in the presence of a good carbon source. The hope was that in a medium with 2% glucose and 1% inulin-^{14}C the utilization of inulin would remain repressed for long enough to do the experiment. A donor implant yielding 1100 counts/min. from the ^{14}C-inulin, compared to a background of 20–40 counts/min. (Packard Tricarb scintillation counter), was placed on a 10 × 50 mm. recipient of *A2 B38 arg-2* (S 35). In the time that donor nuclei migrated 30 mm., counts above background (73–356 counts/min.) were obtained from the 2 × 10 mm. sampling strips no further from the implant than occurred by diffusion in controls (8–12 mm.). There was no evidence for translocation of donor cytoplasm. The various hazards to interpreting the negative results weaken any desire to draw support for nuclear self-motility from these data. More research with this approach is indicated, but among the real difficulties is the small number of hyphae expected to be involved in migration.

Symmetry of reciprocal initiation

Two compatible mycelia act as donor and recipient on contact, but this reciprocity in the initiation of migration between mycelial masses leaves unclear whether the exchange can also be reciprocal through a single fusion of hyphae. The two hypotheses for migration have, in their simplest forms, unlike expectations here also. If the nuclei are self-motile, then there seems to be no reason why initiation could not be reciprocal at a single fusion between strains. If the nuclei are merely pushed, then nuclear migration would generate asymmetric patterns of invasion into the recipients. By the simplest assumption, the direction of such asymmetric initiation should be random.

The patterns generated during early migration were determined along sixty 2 mm. segments of contact line (total of 120 mm. linear contract) between strains *A41 B41 ura-1* (S 39) and *A2 B38 arg-2* (S 35), in an experiment done by Mr John Simon, one of my graduate students. The patterns observed were interpreted to indicate that a minimum of 18 initiation events occurred across the 60 linear segments (Fig. 5). The frequency in each direction of 9/120, or 1 initiation per 13 mm. contact line, within 10 hr., compares well with the frequency of 1 event per 20 mm. obtained with *different* strains in an experiment described in a preceding section (Fig. 4). If the direction of initiation was determined randomly, 9 events would be expected in each mycelium. The observed ratio of 11 into one to 7 into the other is a good fit to a 1:1 ratio ($P_{n=1} = 0.67$). The probability of initiation in any 2 mm. segment, in one direction, was about 9/60, or 0.15. Fourteen of the 18 patterns were clearly asymmetric, as there was no common boundary-segments between these 14 patterns along the contact line. What appeared to be 2 pairs of symmetric patterns could have been the occurrence by chance of matched, but independent, asymmetric patterns. One such pair would be expected at a probability of 0.15^2, which is 0.02. In 60 segments, 1 or 2 apparently symmetrical patterns are expected by chance alone. Two were observed, and one of these was a pair evidently unmatched as to the time of initiation. Mr Simon (1967) has proceeded to show, in work to be published in full elsewhere, that this experiment is reproducible. The results seem clearly consistent with the flow hypothesis for passive nuclear motility.

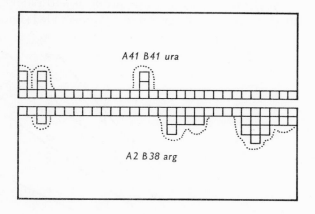

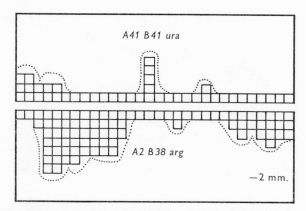

Fig. 5. Patterns of reciprocal nuclear migration 10 hr. after implantation. The recipients (large rectangles) have been slightly separated along the contact line. Squares indicate samples shown to contain donor nuclei. The dotted lines indicate the interpreted number of patterns, thus, the minimal number of initiations.

Oxygen requirement

Further efforts to distinguish between the hypotheses for the mode of nuclear migration have most recently concentrated upon comparing migration in *Schizophyllum* with protoplasmic streaming in the acellular slime moulds. Some similar properties may be expected for both processes if the mechanism of motive force should be the same for both.

The dependence upon oxygen is the only comparison, among several interesting possibilities, that has been made in any detail as yet. Direct measurements of the rate of streaming in *Physarum* have shown little change in pO_2 down to 1% O_2, a response proportional to pO_2 below 1% (Allen & Price, 1950), no response in 'pure' nitrogen, and a significant if low response in nitrogen after a small amount of CO_2 was added (Loewy, 1952).

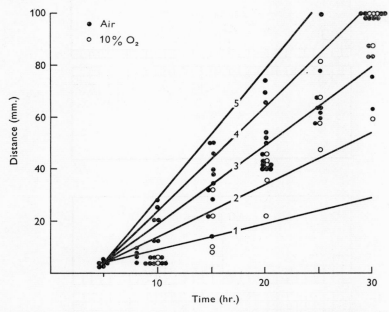

Fig. 6. Nuclear migration in air and in a mixture of 10% O_2 in pure N_2. Each point is one measurement: raw data are pooled from five experiments with air controls and two experiments with 10% O_2 treatments. The lines are theoretical, indicating where the data should plot if the rate of migration were 5, 4, ..., 1 mm./hr. from an entry time of about 4 hr. after implantation.

The general procedure for measuring the effect of gas mixtures was to implant recipients of strain *A2 B38 arg-2* with strain *A41 B41 ura-1*. Migration was allowed to begin, and then the cultures to be treated were placed into particular gas mixtures. The presence of an agar medium presented difficulties for the efficient and complete removal of pretreatment gases remaining dissolved in the medium. The oxygen, especially, had to be eliminated. This was accomplished (1) by two cycles of evacuation to a reduced gas pressure of 750 mm. of mercury and of flushing with a pre-purified grade of nitrogen (99.97% N_2 with not more than 20 p.p.m. of O_2, Matheson Gas Corp., La Porte Plant), followed by a third cycle in which the vacuum was held at 750 mm. Hg for 20–30 min. and, (2) by a continuous flow of 2–3 cu.ft./hr. of the treatment gas (after the third N_2 flush back to atmospheric pressure) for the duration of the experiment. The rate of gas flow was set to replace the gaseous content of the culture chambers every 45 min. The components of the apparatus were arranged in this manner: a compressed gas tank and attached double-valved gas regulator were connected through a flowmeter to a manifold, from which separate

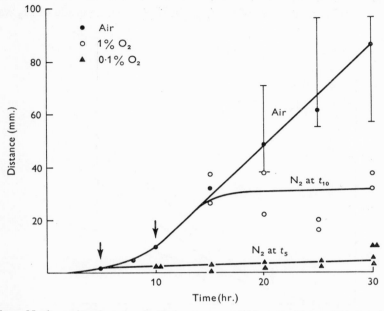

Fig. 7. Nuclear migration stops in N_2 (< 20 p.p.m. O_2 in $99 \cdot 97 \%$ pure N_2). Points for the air control here are the arithmetic means from the pooled raw data of air treatments in Fig. 6; the limits denote the *total range* of data in air. Points from N_2 treatments are raw data. Cultures were switched to N_2 at 5 and 10 hr. (arrows) after implantation in air.

connexions supplied gas to one of several glass desiccators. An inlet and outlet to each desiccator was arranged to provide good distribution of incoming gas. The flow rates into all the desiccators could be set equal with valves on the manifold. A branch connexion inserted between the flowmeter and manifold attached the system to a mercury-column pressure gauge and vacuum pump; this branch was closed off after the vacuum treatments. Leakage into the system under a vacuum was so slight that a reading of 750 mm. Hg was held for more than 10 min. after the pumping was stopped. This and the operation of the apparatus at a small positive pressure avoided any possibility of air contamination during an experiment. Controls showed that while the vacuum treatments had a temporarily inhibitory effect upon migration and seemed to reduce cell viability somewhat, as suggested by an increased number but scattered occurrence of blank sampling strips, there was no detectable reduction in the total distance or maximal, sustained rate of migration.

A measurement of the migration rate in air was included in each gas experiment. These controls, pooled from five separate experiments, have provided more data for establishing the standard response in air than any previous research. All the raw data from the air controls and from two experiments with treatments of 10% O_2 in N_2 (the same grade of N_2 was

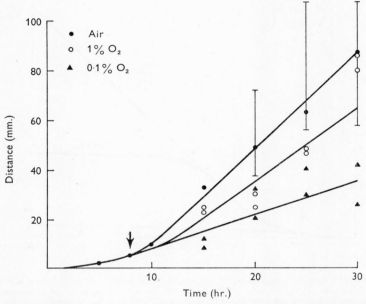

Fig. 8. Nuclear migration in 1 % and 0·1 % O_2. Data for the air control are repeated from Fig. 7. Raw data are given for the oxygen treatments.

used in all experiments) are presented together in Fig. 6 to illustrate several important points: (1) the data points show an obvious clustering at each time of sampling, except at 15 hr.; (2) the lack of homogeneity within and between groups, however, discourages any serious use of statistical tests of significance; (3) if there is a difference in rate, which is doubtful from inspection, migration in 10% O_2 was somewhat faster than in air; (4) several methods give estimates of migratory rates from 4–5 mm./hr. for both gas mixtures, (5) all the recipients in the 10% O_2 treatments were given the series of vacuum exposures, some at 5 hr. and some at 10 hr., and show indications of an extended lag phase for migration in samples taken during the first 20 hr. after implantation; (6) many of the recipients kept in air were also given the vacuum exposures, then returned to air, to serve as a control on the sole effects of vacuum exposure; but the air controls, with or without vacuum exposure, showed no evident difference in distribution, or, thus, in the distance of migration; and (7) the conclusion seems safe that there are probably several insufficiently controlled factors influencing the migratory process. Several other important results are evident, however, in spite of some obvious difficulties. Treatments in pure N_2 have established that migration slows to a complete stop when O_2

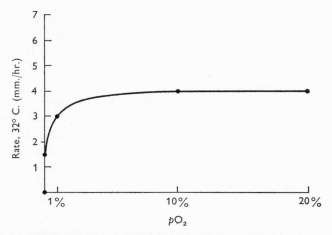

Fig. 9. Rate of nuclear migration as a function of pO_2 in pure N_2. The rates are interpreted from curves fitted to the data of Figs. 6–8 by inspection. The point at the origin relates to N_2 with less than 20 p.p.m. of O_2; the point at 1·5 mm./hr. relates to a pO_2 value of 0·1 %.

(as air) is rigorously removed and replaced with pure N_2 (Fig. 7). The possible stimulatory effect of a small amount of CO_2 in the N_2 will be tested, as soon as time permits, but there is a suggestion that negative results should be expected: the cultures were actively growing at the switch to N_2 and the *unusually* strong odour then generated implies increased fermentation (and release of metabolic CO_2).

Treatments at intermediate concentrations of O_2 in N_2 show the rate of migration decreasing in proportion to the partial pressure of O_2 (Fig. 8). The rate of 1·5 mm./hr. in 0·1 % O_2 is, without doubt, significantly different from that of 4 mm./hr. in the air controls, as almost all the raw data for the 0·1 % O_2 treatment are outside the limits for the distribution of all measurements in air. The rate in 1 % O_2 could hardly have been less than 3 mm./hr., though whether it is significantly different from the air control is plainly questionable. The relationship of oxygen concentration to the rate of nuclear migration is summarized in Fig. 9.

DISCUSSION

The important recognition that there can be several translatory motions of nuclei leads easily to the awareness that there may not necessarily be only one mechanism. The movement apart of daughter nuclei at nuclear division, including the escape of the one trapped in the clamp of a dikaryotic cell, is most probably analogous to the motion of chromosomes mediated by a spindle fibre, or microtubular, motility mechanism. The movement of the non-dividing nucleus in tip cells and in older, but newly branching, cells is most simply explained as a push by protoplasm flowing toward the hyphal tip at the same rate as the elongation of the tip. This does not imply, however, that there is a clear understanding of these intracellular nuclear movements.

For nuclear migration, which is a comparatively rapid, intercellular movement, the possible mechanisms of motility here considered, are protoplasmic streaming or autonomous nuclear movement. If it should involve streaming, then the possibility arises that both the nuclear movements in tip cells and in migration depend on a common mechanism localized in the cytoplasm; though, if this is so, the great difference in the rates of these two nuclear motions requires an explanation. Researchers on the mechanism for the motive force of streaming will undoubtedly consider models based upon contractile or microtubular elements in the cytoplasm. The possibility of autonomous nuclear movement would seem to imply consideration of models based upon analogies with amoeboid movement, flagellar propulsion, or contractility of cytoplasmic elements at least temporarily inserted upon the nucleus and with an origin on some relatively immobile component of the cell. Evidence is not yet available that definitely localizes the mechanism for the motive force of nuclear migration in the nucleus or in the cytoplasm.

There is, however, considerable indirect evidence. That which seems relevant to deciding between the pushed and propelled hypotheses will be discussed shortly in the context of a brief conceptual summary of the steps in the process of nuclear migration as now understood.

From the relative frequencies at which hyphal fusions between mycelia appear to be seen (Sicari & Ellingboe, 1967) and migration is initiated (Fig. 4), the likelihood is that many more fusions may occur between compatible mycelia than really participate in beginning long-range nuclear migration. Observations in several mushroom species (Lehfeldt, 1923) of killed and fixed mycelial pairings established that migratory nuclei move from cell to cell through holes in partially dissolved cross-walls (or through enlarged pores as Giesy & Day (1965) were able to interpret in their electron micrographs), that the first clamps often do not appear nearer than twenty or more cells from the fusion, that intercellular cross-walls can form behind migrating nuclei, and that the traversed cells are later observed to be empty of virtually all protoplasm. Dr George Bistis (personal communication) has recently confirmed and extended in great detail in yet another mushroom Lehfeldt's historic observations. Data given in the present paper show for the first time clear indications of a lag phase to nuclear migration. Intermingled but limited hyphal growth before fusion, slow generation of motive force, and migration through intact or slowly dissolved pores may all contribute to the characteristics of the lag phase, which usually lasts for 10–15 hr. at 32° C. The suspicion arises that numerous fusions initiate migration which soon terminates, seemingly prematurely, during the lag phase. This is a possible explanation for the asymmetric initiation of the deeply penetrating, rapid phase of migration observed in the symmetry-test experiment. This maximal rate phase, by whatever mechanism of nuclear motility, seems to proceed in only certain hyphae differentiated by at least the enlargement of the cross-wall pores. While the migratory nuclei may stop to divide on occasion, especially after moving into a side branch, the relative rates known for migration and nuclear division speak strongly for essentially an independence of migratory nuclei from the necessity or even the possibility of dividing in each cell passed through. Once migration has distributed nuclei throughout a recipient, dikaryosis becomes general in compatible matings and the capacity to serve as a recipient is lost in the dikaryotic state (Snider, 1965). The dikaryotic mycelium can proceed to fruit and it retains the ability to function as a donor (Buller, 1931).

Now to consider the mechanism of migration. Autonomous nuclear motility, for which no convincing precedent has been noted, has been forced into consideration (Snider, 1965) because no intercellular motion of nuclei or cytoplasm sufficiently rapid and sustained to account for nuclear migration has been seen in *Schizophyllum* in the laboratory.

A recent claim for self-motile nuclei in fungi related to *Schizophyllum* (Wilson & Aist, 1967) presents photos, taken of live cells in phase-contrast illumination, in which the centriole seems associated with an intracellular movement for 40–60 μ. No data on rate are mentioned, but the direction of movement was observed to be independent of the motion or lack of motion of surrounding organelles. The nucleoli are clearly visible in the photomicrographs, and the evidence presented seems to fit best the known properties of the later portion of nuclear-division movement. This possible interpretation must be clearly excluded before the evidence becomes strong for self-motility. Their observations imply a complicated model, involving an insertion near or on the centriole of a thin, cytoplasmic element that evidently stretches away from the nucleus in the direction of nuclear (division?) motion.

The most easily predicted property of self-motile models for nuclear migration is that donor nuclei should be expected to migrate into the recipient without being accompanied by large amounts of donor cytoplasm. The failures to show intermycelial transfer of the light stimulus for fruiting or of ^{14}C-inulin are consistent with autonomous nuclear motility, but the interpretation of these negative results involves considerable difficulties. The results of the symmetry test for initiating migration, on the other hand, tend to exclude the simplest form of the propelled-nuclei hypothesis.

There are thoroughly convincing precedents for rapid, long-range, generalized protoplasmic streaming in every major class of fungi. In the hyphal (walled) fungi such streaming is characteristically in one direction—from the older portions of the mycelium into the growing fringes. Passive motility of nuclei is either accepted or plausible in fungi exhibiting this generalized intercellular streaming (Snider, 1965). Most of the relevant indirect evidence in *Schizophyllum* and related fungi seems to support the push hypothesis.

One of the striking observations of Lehfeldt (1923) was the occurrence of cells empty of protoplasm in the hypha where migration had taken place between an intermycelial fusion and positions deeper in the recipient mycelium where the first clamps were found. Removal of the protoplasm by streaming or contraction in the direction of migration may be a sufficient explanation and fits the flow hypothesis. By analogy with fungi with observed generalized streaming, the internal appearance of cells with streaming and those without it are expected to be different. In the electron micrographs of Giesy & Day (1965) in which simple pores are interpreted to identify the hyphae of migratory routes, the interior of the cells appears rather similar to the characteristics expected of streaming cells, including the optically dense cytoplasm and the infrequency and smallness of vacuoles. More detailed comparisons of the cell types by electron microscopy should give strong indirect evidence if streaming is pushing migratory nuclei.

The asymmetrical patterns of initiation in the symmetry test provide about the best evidence to date consistent with the push hypothesis. Even if further research shows that the lag phase of migration can be reciprocal through a single fusion, the distances are expected to be slight, and the probability seems remote that the maximal rate phase could prove to be reciprocal through one fusion. This rapid phase most particularly is suggested to be motility by generalized protoplasmic streaming.

The high Q_{10} of migration has a simple interpretation consistent with the push hypothesis and can explain through one mechanism the difference in rates for the motion of tip-cell nuclei and migratory nuclei. Each arterial hypha for streaming and migration through the mycelial mass is assumed to branch into and supply flow to many growing tips. The quite dissimilar absolute rates of streaming in tip cells and in the arteries can thus be explained. As temperature is increased, furthermore, the rate in the artery will increase disproportionately to hyphal tip flow (and growth) if the changing temperature also increases the *frequency* of hyphal branching and if the rate of cross-wall dissolution increases. Several temperature-dependent factors could thus have a multiplied effect upon the increase in the rate of arterial streaming, and thus upon the rate of nuclear migration by the push hypothesis.

The main evidence seemingly against the flow hypothesis concerns the facts that nuclei can migrate from the edge into the middle of a growing, recipient mycelium (Buller, 1931), which is the direction opposite to that expected of any assumed streaming, and that nuclei can migrate at all through a reticulate mycelium (Snider & Raper, 1958; Snider, 1965). The difficulty here may lie more, however, with a too narrowly conceived model for the mechanism of protoplasmic streaming than with crucial evidence against the flow hypothesis. The hypothesis actually does not seem to place severe restrictions upon the mechanism for streaming; it merely assumes that streaming occurs and pushes nuclei. The realizations that hydrostatic pressure gradients are not the only possible means of streaming, that streaming patterns in unmolested cultures might be changed after fusion with another mycelium, and that streaming could possibly be generated entirely within the recipient mycelium (as is likely in a spore-to-mycelium initiation), together make the evidence against the push hypothesis equivocal. A basic similarity between protoplasmic streaming in slime moulds and nuclear migration in *Schizophyllum* seems compatible with the push hypothesis if hyphal (cell wall) growth is accepted as limiting some of the properties of the assumed streaming in *Schizophyllum*. Measurable growth as dry weight seems to occur in about as little oxygen (0·22%, Schwalb & Miles, 1967) as nuclear migration (0·1%, Fig. 8). The O_2 dependency curve for streaming in *Physarum* (Allen & Price, 1950) is similar to that for nuclear migration. That migration stops much sooner than streaming of *Physarum* in the absence of O_2 is understood as indicating that the assumed streaming in *Schizophyllum* is not sustainable without hyphal tip growth, clearly an anaerobic process. Further comparisons with specific inhibitors of respiration and fermentation should provide a thorough check of this interpretation, and biochemical studies (Niederpruem & Hackett, 1961; Niederpruem, 1964) have provided the necessary groundwork to make the contemplated experiments quite feasible.

While the possibility of nuclear self-motility cannot be firmly excluded at this writing, neither can the simplest and tempting conclusion that nuclear migration in all fungi with walls and cross-walls depends on generalized, intercellular protoplasmic streaming, yet be accepted. Whether the system in *Schizophyllum* is the material of choice for studying the mechanism of streaming in molecular terms should be considered with care, since it has obvious advantages when measurements of steady rates are desired for long distances and times.

SUMMARY

Three translatory motions of nuclei have been distinguished in the mycelium of the small mushroom *Schizophyllum commune*: a moderately fast, brief motion of daughter nuclei (rate equivalent to 1 mm./hr. for 2–3 min. at 32° C.), undoubtedly associated with the division apparatus of nuclear division; a slow, steady, intracellular motion (0·22 mm./hr. at 32° C.) associated with aspects of hyphal tip growth other than the immediate act of nuclear division; and a rapid, intercellular motion (1–5, or possibly more, mm./hr. at 32° C.), long-range in time and distance, associated with heterokaryon formation and sexual reproduction. This paper has dealt mainly with the intercellular motion, termed 'nuclear migration', which involves the rapid passage of nuclei from one mycelium into and throughout an established, spatially extensive mycelium of another fungal strain. Nuclear migration does not necessarily involve nuclear division. Investigation of the mechanism of migration was focused initially upon two questions: are the nuclei self-motile, or are they pushed by streaming protoplasm? A definite answer could locate the mechanism for nuclear motility on the nucleus or in the cytoplasm. Intercellular, generalized streaming of protoplasm is easily observed in a number of fungi, but autonomous nuclear motility, for which no convincing precedent is noted, has been forced into consideration because no intercellular motion of nuclei or cytoplasm sufficiently rapid and sustained to account for nuclear migration in *Schizophyllum* has been seen in this laboratory. Either this means there is no such streaming in *Schizophyllum*, or migration is so rare and rapid as to have little probability for visual detection. A few, widely separated hyphae, acting as major arteries for migration, may conceivably scatter migratory nuclei sufficiently well to account for all the facts about nuclear migration. Experiments and observations that bear at least indirectly upon distinguishing between the simplest forms of the hypotheses for autonomous and passive motility have given evidence interpreted as most consistent with passive nuclear motility. Current research has sought independent confirmation and further insight by comparing migration with streaming in slime moulds. If the properties of both are similar, so too may be their sources of motive force. The dependency of rate upon the partial pressure of O_2 is similar quantitatively for migration in *Schizophyllum* and streaming in *Physarum*. Nuclear migration stops completely within 5 hr., however, when O_2 is rigorously removed from cultures. While the possibility of self-motility cannot be firmly excluded at this writing, neither can the simplest and tempting conclusion that explaining nuclear migration is most likely the problem of understanding intercellular protoplasmic streaming in fungi with cell walls and cross-walls.

Acknowledgements are gratefully extended to Mr John Simon for collaborative efforts on the gas experiments and for permission to include here part of the research done for his M.A. thesis, to Dr Clare Sun for collaborative experimentation on the light effects, and to Mr Frederick Landa for preparing the illustrations. Portions of this research and travel to the symposium were supported by the National Science Foundation and by the University of Houston.

REFERENCES

ALLEN, P. J. & PRICE, W. C. (1950). *Physarum polycephalum. Am. J. Bot.* **37**, 393.

BRACKER, C. E. & BUTLER, E. E. (1963). *Mycologia* **55**, 35.

BRACKER, C. E. & BUTLER, E. E. (1964). *J. Cell Biol.* **21**, 152.

BULLER, A. H. R. (1931). *Researches on Fungi*, vol. IV. London: Longmans and Green.

ELLINGBOE, A. H. (1964). *Am. J. Bot.* **51**, 133.

GIESY, R. M. & DAY, P. R. (1965). *Am. J. Bot.* **52** (3), 287.

GIRBARDT, M. (1955). *Flora* **142**, 540.

JERSILD, R., MISCHKIN, S. & NIEDERPRUEM, D. (1967). *Arch. Mikrobiol.* **57**, 20.

LEHFELDT, W. (1923). *Hedwigia* **64**, 30.

LOEWY, A. G. (1952). *J. cell. comp. Physiol.* **40**, 127.

MOORE, R. T. & McALEAR, J. H. (1961). *Am. J. Bot.* **49**, 86.

NIEDERPRUEM, D. J. (1964). *J. Bact.* **88**, 210.

NIEDERPRUEM, D. J. & HACKETT, D. P. (1961). *Pl. Physiol.*, *Lancaster* **36**, 79.

PRÉVOST, G. (1962). Etude génétique d'un Basidiomycète: 'Coprinus radiatus' Fr. ex Bolt. Theses, Université de Paris.

RAPER, J. R. & MILES, P. G. (1958). *Genetics, Princeton* **43**, 530.

SCHWALB, B. & MILES, P. G. (1967). *Mycologia* **59**, 610.

SICARI, L. M. & ELLINGBOE, A. H. (1967). *Am. J. Bot.* **54** (4), 437.

SIMON, J. (1967). The mechanism of nuclear migration. Master's Thesis, University of Houston, Texas.

SNIDER, P. J. (1963). *Genetics, Princeton* **48**, 47.

SNIDER, P. J. (1965). In *Symposium on Incompatibility in Fungi*, ed. K. Esser and J. R. Raper. New York: Springer-Verlag.

SNIDER, P. J. & RAPER, J. R. (1958). *Am. J. Bot.* **45**, 538.

WESSELS, J. G. H. & NIEDERPRUEM, D. J. (1967). *J. Bact.* **94**, 1594.

WILSON, C. L. & AIST, J. R. (1967). *Phytopathology* **57**, 769.

CHROMOSOME MOVEMENT AND FINE STRUCTURE OF THE MITOTIC SPINDLE

By ANDREW BAJER

Department of Biology, University of Oregon,
Eugene, Oregon 97403

INTRODUCTION

Sooner or later one of the questions which everybody studying chromosome movement during mitosis and meiosis asks, is: what can be considered as the general and essential features of chromosome movements? Different authors will offer different answers to this question. A comparison of micro-cinematographic studies on cell division in various organisms—for example, plant endosperm (Bajer, 1966; Bajer & Molè-Bajer, 1963b), meiosis in crane fly (Dietz, 1956, 1958; Bauer, Dietz & Robbelen, 1961), grasshopper (Nicklas, 1961, 1963) and mitosis in animal tissue culture—leads the present author to conclude that one of the most important and generally occurring features of chromosome movement is the ability for highly individual movements during formation of the metaphase plate and *gradual* loss of independent movement during the progress of division up to the end of anaphase. However, some degree of independent movement is still retained up to late anaphase. It is hoped that the importance of this feature is generally appreciated. Some examples of such behaviour should clarify these points even further. It was reasoned that further understanding of such behaviour could be achieved by combining time-lapse studies with studies on fine structure of the spindle. This requires frequent analysis of structures seen, but not resolved, with the light microscope (LM) and questions arise as to what kind of conclusions can be drawn. Fortunately better understanding and interpretation of visible, but not resolved, structures in light microscopy have now become possible due to the recent and very elegant work of Beyer (1966). He has proved that if proper contrast relations exist between the object and background, an object up to 50 Å. thick is seen as a 'contrast swelling'. The dimension of the 'contrast swelling' is of the order of 0.2μ; that is, it is easily resolved by the LM. It is obvious that, although the object is seen, it is not possible to draw any conclusions about its real dimensions. However, details are easier to follow in large cells where areas of special interest are of considerable size and their observation is not obstructed by other organelles; for example, the endosperm of *Haemanthus*. Additional advantages of the endosperm are:

(1) Chromosome movements have been studied extensively in this species. It is possible to predict with great accuracy the behaviour of chromosomes in any given stage. The use of the Nomarski differential interference contrast system (Nomarski system hereafter) allows frequent observation of the activity of spindle fibres in the living state (Plate 1 a, b) (Bajer & Allen, 1966).

2. Cells divide under various mechanical conditions; that is, the resistance to the forces responsible for chromosome movements varies in different cells (late anaphase in Plates 15, 18 a). It is easy, if required, to select cells of exactly the same conditions.

3. Localization of the same cell and part of the cell (for example, selected chromosomes) with the LM and electron microscope (EM) is possible and permits one to correlate measurements of movements with fine structure.

Analysis of the fine structure has been performed during the whole cycle of division (Bajer, in preparation). In the present report, however, only features of the metaphase and anaphase spindle will be given, with a few remarks about prophase as background.

MATERIAL AND TECHNIQUE

The technique for light microscope studies *in vitro* of the endosperm of *Haemanthus katherinae* Bak. has been previously described (Molè-Bajer & Bajer, 1963). In this technique the endosperm cells were prepared on a thin layer of agar with dextrose (0·5% agar and 3·5% dextrose) and observed in a hanging drop. In the present studies this technique was modified and the endosperm cells were covered with a thin layer of gelatin-agar (0·75% gelatin, 0·75% agar, and 2·5% dextrose), making it possible to use a perfusion chamber. A dextrose solution of 3·7% was used to fill the perfusion chamber and the liquid could be easily changed to the fixative. The technique permits continuous observation of the same cell in the living state and during fixation and dehydration (up to 100% alcohol) (cf. Plates 4 a, 15 b, 20). A detailed description of the technique will be reported elsewhere (Molè-Bajer & Bajer, 1968). For fixation, most cells were perfused in 3·1% glutaraldehyde at pH 6·9 (phosphate buffer), washed with buffer, and post-fixed in 1% osmium tetroxide with phosphate buffer pH 6·9. Also, some cells were fixed in 6 and 18% glutaraldehyde and post-fixed with 2% and 4% osmium tetroxide at pH's between 6·5 and 7·1. Though all these variations preserve the microtubules (MT) well, MT seem best preserved at pH 6·9. At this pH with 3·1% glutaraldehyde and 1% osmium the endoplasmic reticulum is well preserved in many but not all cells. It remains unexplained why the endoplasmic reticulum is preserved to different degrees in different cells. No difference in the arrangement of MT was detected in cells irrespective of how well the endoplasmic reticulum had been preserved. Well-preserved endoplasmic reticulum obscures to some extent the visibility of the arrangement of MT. Periods of fixation in glutaraldehyde and osmium tetroxide of 10–45 min. each were tried. The cells were dehydrated with an ethanol series (35, 50, 75, 95 and 100%) and flat embedded in an Epon–Araldite mixture. For fixation, coverslips (number 1 or 2) were coated with a thin layer of carbon. Glass knives and an LKB ultramicrotome were used. Sections were collected on un-coated grids or on grids coated with formvar and reinforced with carbon; often the formvar–carbon layer was put on the sections after staining. Lead citrate and uranyl acetate were used as stains.

With the technique employed, one or more cells on the preparation have a full record from the living state up to dehydration. Before sectioning final microphotographs were taken of the cell in plastic, using a high dry or immersion lens. At the same time several other cells in plastic—there were often more than 100 cells dividing in a preparation—were photo-graphed without previous record in the living stage and each cell was always individualy sectioned. A photograph of the cell in plastic is given for all electron micrographs. Often a series of micrographs was taken of the same cell in plastic at different depths of focus. This made it easier to locate the same chromosome with the LM and EM, and the stage of the cell and plane of sectioning were then always known.

A great advantage of this technique is the possibility of fixing and select-ing cells in desired stages. This is important as the probability for observing stages lasting a few minutes—for example, breaking of the nuclear mem-brane or start of anaphase (Plate 10)—is very small when any other method is used. Therefore, the technique eliminates the problem of random sampling of material.

The fine structure of mitosis was studied from prophase to telophase. More than 50 cells were sectioned and often several serial sections of certain areas in the cell were studied. The results reported here are based on cells photographed previously *in vitro* and those photographed in plastic only.

RESULTS

A. *Summary of Chromosome Movements*

A general description of chromosome movements during mitosis has already been given (Bajer & Molè-Bajer, 1963*b*; Bajer, 1966) and only a summary of the most important features will be given here.

Extremely rarely kinetochores execute rapid movements inside the prophase nucleus before the breaking of the nuclear membrane (only a few cases in a few hundred cells were observed, cf. cell no. 8, Bajer & Molè-Bajer, 1962). They may, however, change their position slightly owing to the change of the shape of the nucleus. Kinetochore movements and consequently chromosome movements start after the nuclear membrane breaks. Formation of the metaphase plate is characterized by simultaneous movements inside the spindle in two opposite directions: (a) kinetochores move toward the equatorial plane and tend to arrange themselves in one plane; (b) acentric bodies such as small granules, chromosome fragments found after ionizing radiation, persistent nucleoli, etc., are transported toward the spindle poles with approximately the same speed irrespective of their size. Kinetochores do not always take the simplest or shortest route to their future position on the metaphase plate; for example, some may move slightly across the spindle or, more often, towards the pole and then back to the plate (cell No. 18, Bajer & Molè-Bajer, 1963 a). Spindle fibres co-operate with kinetochores from prometaphase to telophase. Using Schrader's (1953) nomenclature, this type of spindle fibre will be called 'chromosomal fibre'. Spindle fibres can co-operate for a short time, as a rule for only a few minutes, with other parts of the chromosome, and this results in abrupt bending or stretching of parts of the chromosomes. Such 'neocentric activity' has been analysed in detail (Östergren & Bajer, 1960; Bajer & Östergren, 1961).

The elimination of acentric bodies continues during all metaphase up to the beginning of anaphase. The behaviour of acentric bodies during anaphase was analysed previously (Bajer & Molè-Bajer, 1963; Bajer, 1967) and is of special importance in the present connexion. Granules which started to move toward the pole during metaphase—that is, that are between the spindle pole and kinetochore when anaphse starts—were analysed. If such granules are not too far from kinetochores (up to approximately half distance from the polar area) and are embedded in the spindle fibres, the distance between the granule and kinetochore does not change for a considerable part of anaphase (cf. also Fig. 3, p. 293, illustrating non-disjunction).

Anaphase is characterized by shortening of both half-spindles and elongation of the entire spindle. These two essential features of anaphase occur simultaneously. Some other features of anaphase will be discussed later.

During telophase the chromosomes contract, sister nuclei are formed, and the cell plate appears. In some ways movements within the phragmoplast resemble the movements within the prometaphase spindle. Acentric fragments are also eliminated from the equatorial region towards the sister nuclei (Bajer & Molè-Bajer, 1963 b). The phragmoplast grows towards both sides and a special mechanism, as yet unknown, results in a movement of the developing cell plate toward the side of the phragmoplast (Plate 20), which in turn produces 'lateral' movements (Bajer & Östergren 1963).

Individuality and, to a great extent, unsynchronized movements such as seen at prometaphase-metaphase are not visible during normal anaphase. During anaphase chromosomes usually move with the same speed and start and stop their movements almost exactly at the same time; therefore the question arises: what is the extent of unsynchronized individual movements during anaphase? This question seems pertinent to an understanding of the mechanism of anaphase. Observations on some disturbances and the course of anaphase in flattened cells provide the answer.

B. *Anaphase in flattened cells treated and untreated with chloral hydrate*

Endosperm cells do not have a cellulose wall and they can be flattened to a varying degree by controlling the thickness of the hanging drop (Molè-Bajer & Bajer, 1963a). The flattening process is performed slowly (20–45 min.); it does not interrupt the course of mitosis and observation of the cells in different mechanical conditions is possible (Plates 11a, 13, 15, 19). Flattened cells may be only 6–8μ thick with anaphase chromosomes more than 2μ thick. In flattened cells the chromosomes are often in one layer, and, therefore visibility of all the chromosomes is very clear. Only a few aspects of chromosome behaviour in such flattened cells will be discussed. Movements of kinetochores in a 'row' is of special interest and several examples of such groups are seen in Plate 11 (arrows). They occur in normal untreated cells (Fig. 1) as well as in cells treated with chemicals which partly disorganize the spindle. Such movements are very distinctive under the influence of chloral hydrate and one is illustrated in Plate 2 and Fig. 2.

An analysis of chromosome movements in cells treated with chloral hydrate is given by Molè-Bajer (1967). In general, under suitable concentrations of chloral hydrate, the arrangement of chromosomes at metaphase is exactly like that under the influence of colchicine but the chromosomes separate during anaphase (Plate 2; Fig. 2). The spindle is multipolar, or rather apolar, as no definite poles are seen. However, the chromosomes are bent at the kinetochore region and the kinetochores visibly lead the chromosomes during the anaphase movement, although the path is much shorter during normal anaphase. In normal and treated cells, due to lack of space, a few chromosomes (2–4) are often arranged exactly above one another perpendicular to the long axis of the spindle (cf. Figs. 1–2; Plate 2). It was previously noticed (Bajer & Molè-Bajer, 1956) that in such cases the kinetochores were arranged exactly on one line parallel to the long axis of

19

the spindle. Many cells with such chromosome arrangements were observed and this raises the question of whether all such chromosomes are connected to one chromosomal fibre. Birefringence of such a 'combined' chromosomal

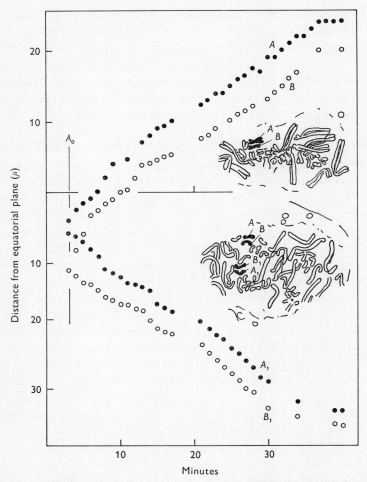

Fig. 1. Anaphase in flattened cells. Movement of two non-sister kinetochores moving in a 'row'. The distance of sister kinetochores (A–A and B–B) from the equatorial plane plotted toward two poles and also plotted against time. The distance between kinetochores does not change for a considerable time. A_0, The start of anaphase. Half schematic drawing of the cell at metaphase and anaphase in the inset.

fibre (as seen in LM) appeared stronger than that of a 'single' chromosomal fibre (detailed measurements have not yet been made) and EM observations show an intermingling of bundles of MT from different kinetochores. Although these observations do not prove that all kinetochores from the 'row' form one chromosomal fibre (at LM level), since the border between 'fusing' and 'joining' is never sharp, real fusing seems more probable (cf. also observations on cells treated with chloral hydrate). Detailed observations and measurements of such movements were performed repeatedly during anaphase (Bajer & Molè-Bajer, 1956) and it appeared that the movement always followed the same pattern: the distance between non-sister kinetochores does not change during a considerable period of anaphase or at the beginning of telophase when the chromosome closest to the

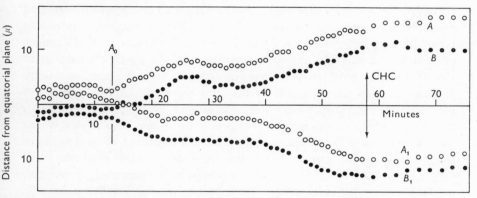

Fig. 2. Anaphase of chromosomes moving in a 'row' in a chloral hydrate-treated cell. Micrographs in Fig. 3. The distance of sister kinetochores from an arbitrarily chosen equatorial plane between them plotted against time. After chromosome separation at A_0 and a few microns movement, chromosomes do not move in a polar direction for about 15 min. They start to move again at the time which corresponds to the beginning of phragmoplast formation (time about 35 min.; cf. discussion p. 306). During all these movements the distance between kinetochores remains approximately constant until chromosomes begin to change at telophase. A_0, Start of anaphase; CHC, chromosome contraction which indicates the beginning of telophase changes; CPF, cell plate formation (from J. Molè-Bajer unpublished).

pole reaches the polar region. The other chromosomes of the row gradually approach the first one. These changes usually occur at the time when all the chromosomes begin to clump together during formation of the telophase nuclei. Chloral hydrate-treated cells (Fig. 2) also show a delay in anaphase movements after initial separation.

Conclusions. At anaphase chromosome movement proceeds at approximately the same speed over a considerable distance. That is why the anaphase chromosomes are transported in a row without mutually approaching one another. There are two possible explanations of such behaviour. (*a*) If the chromosomal fibres are really fused, then that part of the chromosomal fibre between the individual kinetochores and the pole does not change its length for a considerable part of anaphase; contraction does not occur along the whole length of the fibre but only at the poles. (*b*) If the chromosomal fibres are not really fused and act as independent units, they grow shorter at the same rate for a considerable part of anaphase. The decrease of distance between kinetochores occurring at late anaphase or the beginning of telophase is connected with the disorganization of the spindle and is of no importance in this connexion.

Another interesting type of chromosome behaviour is shown in Plate 3. As in the case of anaphase in flattened cells (movement in a row), a few chromosomes are parallel to each other and their kinetochores are arranged precisely above each other in a straight line. Such an arrangement is usually formed during prometaphase. After formation the whole 'group' changes position as one unit (cf. for example, movement before start of anaphase in Fig. 2). The change of position occurs in all directions, and is not necessarily perpendicular to the long axis of the chromosomes. This change is not illustrated by Fig. 2. Such a chromosome group may or may not split again into single chromosomes moving independently at anaphase. A case where they do not split is illustrated in Plate 3. During anaphase, chromosomes in the middle often do not move, while the ones on the outside of the group move only a little with slightly bent kinetochores (time 12 min. and 36 min., cf. discussion p. 304). This is typical of anaphase behaviour. Another behaviour pattern of such a group has been described earlier (cf. Plate 2; Fig. 2).

Conclusions. EM observations on normal mitosis where MT seem to connect two non-sister kinetochores (cf. Fig. 2, above) might also apply to the middle chromosomes of the group described above. If this is the case, then the fact that the middle chromosomes do not approach each other might indicate that chromosomal fibres do not contract during anaphase. The movement of the group as a single unit during prometaphase–metaphase indicates that chromosomal fibres of all kinetochores tend to behave as a single unit.

Apolar anaphases during chloral hydrate treatment indicate clearly that chromosomal fibres do not need to be fixed to any pole for anaphase separation to occur.

C. *Non-disjunction*

About 30 cases of non-disjunction were recorded with the time-lapse technique and a detailed analysis of their movements was made (Östergren & Bajer, in preparation). Cases where two sister kinetochores moved to one pole were observed after ionizing radiation, treatment with some chemicals (for example, acenaphtene and methanol) and uv microbeam irradiation. The typical course of non-disjunction proceeds as follows: a late pro-

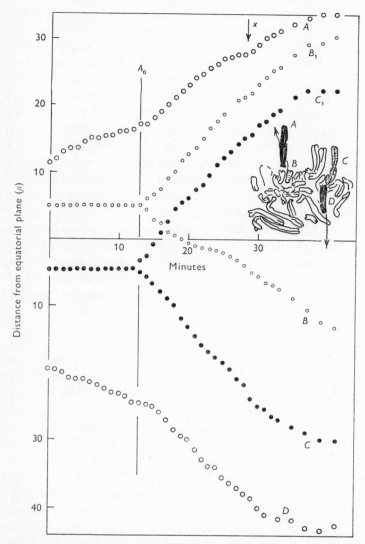

Fig. 3. Non-disjunction of kinetochores in an acenaphtene-treated cell. The distance from equatorial plane of non-disjunction (A, D) and the normal kinetochores (B–B, and C–C) close to them is plotted against time. The paths of non-disjunction chromosomes are in the inset drawing. At time (arrow x), chromosome A enters the cytoplasm and slows down. The slower speed of non-disjunction chromosomes (A, D) before the start of anaphase (A_0) is clearly seen.

metaphase or early metaphase chromosome starts to move slowly towards one pole. The speed is usually slower than the prometaphase movement from equator to pole and return. Figure 3 illustrates the movement for two chromosomes (the cell is under the influence of acenaphtene). Such a chromosome is often maloriented very clearly and its kinetochores face the sides, not the poles, of the spindle. If anaphase does not start soon after the movement begins, the chromosome reaches the pole. There are cases where anaphase starts when the non-disjunction chromosomes have moved half way or less from the equator toward the spindle pole. During anaphase either the speed of non-disjunction chromosomes does not change for a long time, or, simultaneously with the start of anaphase, they start to move faster and the distance between non-disjunction kinetochores and the others does not change for a considerable part of anaphase. In the latter case, the difference in distance may decrease from approximately the moment when non-disjunction chromosomes reach the polar area of the spindle. The two latter cases are illustrated in Fig. 3 (non-disjunction chromosomes A and D, respectively).

There seems to be little doubt that in certain situations chromosomal fibres from each kinetochore are directed towards both poles (Östergren, 1951). In some very elegant work on sea-urchin eggs Luykx (1965a) has found that connexions of MT from one kinetochore towards both poles occur in prometaphase but are not seen during later stages; that is, they break or disappear.

Conclusions

(a) The cause of malorientation may result from the attachment of two chromosomal fibres to each of the sister kinetochores toward both poles. Movement to the proper pole, if it occurs, might be interpreted partly as the result of disappearance of one chromosomal fibre. The fact that chromosomal fibres can be broken and not reformed was proved by microsurgical experiments (Nicklas & Staehly, 1967; Nicklas, 1967). The spontaneous breaking of chromosomal fibres has been demonstrated in films (doubly interlocked dicentric, cell no. 25, Bajer & Molè-Bajer, 1962) but it seems likely that continuous fibres play a role in this process (cf. discussion p. 305).

(b) The speed of an anaphase chromosome is influenced by the speed of its neighbours. When a chromosome moving rapidly approaches a slower one, the slower one may increase its speed. The last observation is important: a special case of sister-reunion bridges at anaphase which illustrates the contrary situation will be discussed in the next paragraph.

D. *Anaphase in cells with sister-reunion bridges*

Different types of bridges have been analysed (Bajer, 1964). In one type during stretching of the bridge, both or only one of the kinetochores slow down or may even stop until the bridge breaks (Plates 15, 17b; Bajer, 1964). Kinetochores of normal chromosomes that are distant from the kinetochores connected by the bridge show no retardation. However, kinetochores that are very close to the bridge often show some retardation, even though they themselves are not connected by the bridge. They again speed up the moment the bridge breaks. After the bridge breaks, all the chromosomes move at the same speed and the chromosomes which were retarded do *not* move faster than the others.

Conclusions. Kinetochores may be slowed down during anaphase due to the behaviour of their neighbours. After the resistance disappears, the chromosomes in question do not increase their speed and all chromosomes move with the same speed. This shows that during retardation, chromosomal fibres do not behave like elastic strings. This conclusion finds a good explanation on the basis of observations on fine structure.

Fine structure of the spindle

A. *Fine structure of the kinetochore*

The structure of the kinetochore as seen with the EM does not seem to change much between prometaphase (Plate 6) and late anaphase (Plates 15, 16). It is essentially a ball-shaped body entering deeply into the chromosomal body. Thus, the chromosome body forms a sort of 'cup' around the 'ball' (Plate 4). The first impression is that the central part absorbs electrons more. A closer examination reveals that the 'ball' is built from bands of lighter and denser material and MT are embedded into the lighter material (Plates 10, 11). The denser material seems to form protrusions tapering toward the kinetochore's surface. The 'ball' is between 500 and 600 mμ in diameter and is seldom seen in the living state, though the 'cup' is very clearly seen, especially at anaphase. In sections perpendicular to the long axis of the chromosome but parallel to the long axis of the spindle (Plates 11, 12), and in intermediate sections, it is observed that the sides of the 'ball' are exposed; that is, they are in contact with the spindle (Plate 5). This is seen even more clearly in sections through the kinetochore perpendicular to the long axis of the spindle (Plate 5). From sections parallel to the long axis of the chromosome (Plate 4b) it is evident that the edges of the chromosome protect the kinetochore only on two sides perpendicular to the long axis of the chromosome. During prometaphase–metaphase the 'ball' may be more or less stretched and protrudes towards the pole (Plates 6, 7).

The kinetochore structure in *Haemanthus* differs from that found in animal material. No spiral structures as described by Brinkley and Stubblefield (1966), double plate (Luykx, 1965 a, b) of denser material or a single plate (Harris, 1965) were found. In *Haemanthus* the protrusion of the whole 'ball' varies in size with different kinetochores during prometaphase and metaphase. It decreases during the progress of anaphase and is very unclear during late anaphase and early telophase (Plate 8). A comparison with living material leads one to the conclusion that the size of the protrusion depends on the relation of resistance to the pulling force of the chromosomal fibres. From early prometaphase, the chromosome is clearly divided in the kinetochore area and a 'hole' is seen between the kinetochores (Harris & Bajer, 1965). In a few cases one or two MT were seen in this 'hole'. However, as the serial sections were not complete, it cannot be stated with certainty that in these rare cases MT pass through two kinetochores. MT are primarily connected with the 'ball', but some also enter the 'grooves' on the sides of the kinetochores. In spite of considerable effort, no clear picture of how MT are connected was obtained. MT seem to be deeply embedded in the lighter material of the kinetochore and gradually fade, so that their ends are not distinct, although the ends of MT (if these are the ends) in some pictures appear to be slightly funnel-shaped.

No effort was made to count the number of MT connected with kinetochores at different stages of mitosis. It was previously reported (Harris & Bajer, 1965) that at metaphase the number is between 50 and 100. It is likely that the number varies with different cells and kinetochores in the same cell. Numbers between 70 and 150 were found for different kinetochores in middle anaphase.

During prometaphase some of the MT pass through, or are deeply embedded in, the chromosome body elsewhere than in the kinetochores. This is seen more often in the earlier stages than in the later ones. Some pictures of such MT were obtained during metaphase (Plate 4b) and anaphase. In most of these cases a very light area is seen around the MT (Plate 4b) while such an area is not seen in kinetochores. The light area not in kinetochores resembles that in descriptions by Behnke & Forer (1966) for similar cases. During all stages (prometaphase to anaphase) MT frequently pass through the outside layer of the chromosomal body. Usually these are the MT forming continuous fibres, but MT forming chromosomal fibres may also pass through the outside part of other chromosome arms. The picture of MT passing through the outside of chromosomes is obscured by chromosome contraction during dehydration in the alcohol series (cf. Plates 4a, 15b). Measurable contraction both in chromosome length and thickness begins in 75 % ethanol and reaches about 8 % in 95–100 % ethanol (Molè-Bajer & Bajer, 1968). The 'hairy' appearance of the chromosome surface is, at least to some extent, the result of dehydration.

B. *Prophase–metaphase*

The main aspects described here will be the changes in arrangement of MT at metaphase and anaphase. It is necessary, however, for an understanding of anaphase, to outline briefly the changes between prophase and metaphase.

During prophase the number of MT increases rapidly. Sometimes they are seen in bundles of 3–5 or more in a characteristic parallel arrangement. MT's form an irregular network around the nucleus and are straight or wavy. In the later stages of prophase they tend to be arranged slightly more regularly at the polar areas of the future spindle. Polarity and orientation of the spindle are not clear in all cells during prophase and thus it is not always possible to predict where the spindle poles will be.

After the breaking of the nuclear membrane the regular orientation of MT proceeds very rapidly. Within 5–10 min. there is a definite movement of MT into positions parallel to the long axis of the spindle, and a dense, rather regular, accumulation of the MT parallel to the long axis appears on the surface of the spindle. These MT form the mantle around the spindle and persist through late anaphase. However, connexions of MT to the kinetochores are already noticed at early pro-metaphase, but their formation has not been studied in detail. The evidence obtained so far seems to indicate that MT penetrating from the polar areas form the continuous fibres. This is followed quickly by the regular metaphase organization of the spindle during which only minor changes are seen for a considerable period. During metaphase MT are connected to both kinetochores of each chromosome and are straight or wavy. Also long continuous fibres are seen nearly connecting the two polar areas. As such long MT are seen on sections, it is most likely that MT do connect the two polar areas, although it is not clear how the bundles of MT's are seen with LM. Those bundles of MT's connected to the kinetochore will be called chromosomal fibres and those connecting the poles continuous fibres. How to classify MT's that are connected to the chromosomes but are not attached in the kinetochore region is an open question.

The bundles of MT forming chromosomal fibres may diverge slightly or not at all towards the pole during prometaphase (Plates 6, 9). The divergence of single chromosomal fibres increases during the progress of metaphase. However, during prometaphase (Plate 1) and metaphase, bundles of chromosomal fibres, as separate units, tend to converge towards the poles. This tendency is not very pronounced and was not noticed in flattened cells. The length of chromosomal fibres decreases from pro-metaphase to metaphase, but it is difficult to make any detailed measurements on the electron micrographs.

The problem of straightness and waviness of MT connected with kinetochores—that is, forming the chromosomal fibres—during prometaphase and metaphase has been studied in more detail. MT connected to two kinetochores of the same chromosome are either straight or wavy on both sides, the latter being very rare. More often the MT connected to one kinetochord are straight and those to the other, wavy (Plate 10). Waviness is rarely seen and, as a rule, MT connected with both kinetochores are straight. Waviness in the chromosomal fibres is, as a rule, seen only close to kinetochores (a few μ), and closer to the pole MT become gradually straight. Single chromosomes, which are seen between the pole and equator, and move toward the pole or equator as judged from their shape, were observed in several cases. From studies *in vitro* it is known that such chromosomes move temporarily towards the pole and then return during prometaphase. Such chromosomes had straight MT connected to both kinetochores; that is, both facing the pole and the other set the equator.

Waviness in chromosomal fibres has been observed only in the area near the equator, where a few chromosomes formed a close group and MT were close to the chromosome arm(s) orientated parallel to the long axis of the spindle.

Continuous fibres, as seen from cross-sections, are assembled in bundles or bands and often surround chromosomes. They intermingle and fuse with chromosomal fibres, the degree of intermingling varying from cell to cell apparently increasing as metaphase progresses. At prometaphase, continuous fibres sometimes run parallel and very close to chromosomal fibres, essentially forming one bundle (Plates 6, 7). Intermingling and fusing occur at different distances between the kinetochores and the pole, often leaving spaces of different sizes devoid of MT. Such spaces have also been seen with the LM (Nomarski system, Bajer, 1967). Because of intermingling, it is usually impossible to distinguish chromosomal and continuous fibres in the area some distance from the kinetochores, that is, about a quarter to a half of the length of the half-spindle. In a few cases, however, it is possible to follow continuous fibres close to polar areas.

In polar areas in cross-section the arrangement of MT is more or less uniform, and thus no areas with denser arrangements of MT exist. On sections parallel to the long axis of the spindle it is seen that, proceeding towards the pole, more MT are arranged askew or occasionally perpendicular to the long axis of the spindle. The process of disorganization of the polar areas increases during the progress of mitosis.

During metaphase and sometimes prometaphase, in the equatorial regions, continuous fibres begin to show bends in a very narrow area about 2–4 μ in length precisely at the level between two sister kinetochores. The bends are seen only if the metaphase plate is crowded; MT are straight if chromosomes are further apart. The evidence available at present indicates that the bends do not represent breaks in MT continuity. The MT of the continuous fibres also do not break at the start of anaphase (Plate 11).

Chromosomes are divided from early prometaphase in the kinetochore region and a hole develops between sister kinetochores (Plates 4b, 10). This is clearly seen at metaphase (Harris & Bajer, 1965).

C. *Anaphase*

Two main changes in the anaphase spindle are shortening of the half-spindles and simultaneous elongation of the entire spindle. The two half-spindles are the parts of the spindle apparatus between the kinetochores and the poles. The inter-zonal region is the area between the two groups of kinetochores. From studies on living cells it is clearly seen, especially on film, that the half-spindles are 'pushed' or 'move' through the surrounding cytoplasm and, at the same time, the interzonal region increases in length. This process is related to pronounced changes of the fine structure of the spindle.

During shortening of the half-spindle there is a rapid increase in the degree of intermingling of MT from the continuous and chromosomal fibres. Often, however, the MT run parallel for a long distance (Plate 12) and intermingling may be seen in serial sections only. Also, intermingling between MT from different chromosomal fibres increases. In spite of intermingling it can clearly be seen that chromosomal and continuous fibres are arranged in distinct bands and bundles (Plate 14). Increase in intermingling is partly due to an increase in divergence of single chromosomal fibres towards the pole during the progress of anaphase. There is some difference in the arrangement of MT in chromosomal fibres, depending on their position in the spindle, mechanical conditions, etc.; this is shown by a comparison of Plates 13 and 14. In exceptional cases this may lead to the situation shown in Plate 16, where short MT of chromosomal fibres are 'embedded' at right angles in another bundle.

An effort has been made to compare the divergence at different stages of anaphase in cells flattened to varying degrees. It was found that divergence during metaphase–anaphase is greater in more flattened cells. Also, during anaphase, divergence increases more in flattened cells than in less flattened cells. However, the tendency exists in all types of cells and, in late anaphase, MT connected with kinetochores may be arranged in a very wide angle (Plate 17). In spite of an increase in divergence of the bundle of MT within a single chromosomal fibre there is a pronounced tendency for separate chromosomal fibres to converge on the polar area. This tendency increases during the progress of anaphase, often resulting in a circular arrangement of kinetochores at early telophase. In flattened cells a few chromosomes often form a closer association. This may result in splitting of the polar area into two or more subunits and often leads to the formation of more than one nucleus at one pole after normal anaphase. During the progress of anaphase, it becomes increasingly difficult to distinguish the chromosomal and continuous fibres at the polar areas, and from mid-anaphase it usually becomes impossible. However, at the areas close to kinetochores, it is possible to distinguish these two types of fibres up to late anaphase. Polar areas of the spindle show an increasing number of MT arranged askew or even perpendicular to the long axis of the spindle (Plate 7).

Straight pieces of MT decrease in length during anaphase. However, a comparison of the arrangement in sections at different planes of the spindle leads to the conclusion that they decrease in length and do not break into shorter pieces. Also the density of the arrangement of MT in the polar areas does not seem to increase, as would occur if MT were breaking into shorter pieces. Shorter straight pieces are seen because of an increase in the degree of intermingling.

Important illustrations of the behaviour of MT during anaphase are provided by cells with very small amounts of cytoplasm, that is, division of nearly naked mitotic spindles which remind one of an isolated mitotic apparatus (Mazia, 1961). Such cells *in vitro* often show pointed tips at one or both spindle poles. These tips are formed by the pushing activity of the spindle and it has been found that MT in such a tip are arranged in parallel (Plate 18) and enter the protrusion. This important observation will be referred to in the discussion.

In the half-spindle MT are usually straight, or slightly wavy (Plate 16), and are not always of the same thickness. Although detailed studies have not been made, it seems that no simple correlation exists between position and thickness. Also, MT of different thicknesses are found throughout all stages of mitosis. However, the differences in thickness reported in prophase and later stages in *Psilotum* by Allen & Bowen (1966), probably do not exist in *Haemanthus*.

D. *Interzonal Region*

During anaphase the interzonal region and its fine structure undergo rapid changes. Short zones, or rather, more or less complete planes in cross-section, where MT of continuous fibres are strongly bent, are sometimes found between chromosome arms, always behind kinetochores advancing toward the poles. Analysis of the same region on a few planes of the same cell, and a comparison of such an area in several cells at different stages of anaphase, permit a better characterization of these zones. The zones may already be visible by early anaphase. There is one zone behind each kineto-chore group; and each is formed by continuous fibres. In some parts of the spindle only very slightly wavy, or in some cases even straight, MT are seen (Plate 11). This is most apparent in flattened cells where there is some distance between MT forming continuous fibres and the chromo-some arms. Bends and waves disappear at the end of anaphase when the whole structure of the spindle starts to become disorganized. Usually bends and waviness were not observed on the surface of the spindle, that is, in MT forming the outside coat on the spindle (Plate 9).

During anaphase, changes also occur in the interzonal region. This is the area which elongates faster during anaphase than the half-spindles shorten; consequently, the distance between the polar areas increases. In *Haemanthus*, the spindle elongates between early and late anaphase and MT are seen in the interzonal region from early anaphase. They are usually rather straight or show very gentle waves. It is not quite clear how they are related to the continuous fibres seen at metaphase: are they the same MT as in metaphase, or partly or completely formed *de novo*? Their location in relation to kinetochores indicates that they correspond closely to the con-tinuous fibres seen from prometaphase to metaphase. It is not known whether their number increases up to mid-anaphase.

It has been found from studies *in vitro* (Bajer, 1965) and confirmed by Bajer & Allen (1966) that the phragmoplast has begun to form by mid-anaphase. The phragmoplast is responsible for the formation of the cell plate and plays an important role in chromosome distribution (Bajer & Molè-Bajer, 1963b). Its development in later stages will not be discussed here. The early stages of phragmoplast formation overlap with elongation of the spindle. The number of MT increases rapidly and they often appear in bundles. Single MT in a bundle are often almost parallel, reminiscent of the arrangement seen at prophase (cf. Plate 19).

The only differences detected so far between MT in the clear zone and in the phragmoplast are the more regular arrangement of MT in the phrag-moplast and the lack of variation in their thickness.

DISCUSSION

Although several problems deserve closer attention, only some aspects of the fine structure of the mitotic spindle and how this fine structure contributes to the chromosome movements, especially at anaphase, will be discussed.

A. *Fine structure of the spindle*

Two questions arise about the structure of the spindle: (1) to what extent is spindle structure (arrangement of MT) affected by the technique employed, and (2) how typical is the structure in comparison to that of other objects? The problem of straightness and waviness of MT should also be mentioned.

Straight and/or wavy MT were described in a variety of objects (Behnke & Forer, 1966). In *Haemanthus* short 'waves' are likely to be dehydration artifacts although this may not apply elsewhere. The location of wavy MT in chromosomal fibres in relation to other kinetochores and chromosome arms (Plate 10) at prometaphase and anaphase seems to indicate that such chromosomes or chromosome arms are being pushed or squeezed. As chromosome arms contract during dehydration and the waviness in MT in the observed cases made up much less than 10% of the total MT length, this gives evidence that waviness of MT is caused by dehydration and does not exist in living cells. The 'gentle waves' that are seen in the central part of the interzonal region (e.g. some areas in Plate 12) remain an open question.

(1) In the technique employed, cells are removed from the ovule and flattened by surface tension. The degree of flattening is not uniform for all cells in the same preparation and it ranges from practically unflattened cells (Plate 18a) to cells where all chromosomes are arranged in one layer (Plate 19). Thus it is possible to select cells in exactly the same stages and with the same degree of flattening. A comparison of differently flattened cells was made for the different stages of mitosis, especially anaphase where more than 25 cells were studied. Unflattened, medium flattened and very flattened cells were studied for all stages. From these comparative studies the author concluded that flattening does not produce new effects, but exaggerates certain features of the fine structure instead. Thus intermingling and increases in the divergence of the chromosomal fibres during anaphase exist in all types of cells. They are more pronounced in very flattened cells and the irregular polar arrangement of MT (MT in different directions, even perpendicular to the spindle length) is seen further from the spindle pole. Straightness and waviness of MT of chromosomal and continuous fibres are seen in all types of cells. It is clear that there is no new mitotic mechanism in flattened cells and that increased resistance to chromosome movements seems to be the only factor modifying chromosome behaviour in them. This results, for example, in prolongation of all mitotic stages in the flattened cells. It is not clear why gentle undulations of MT in the interzonal region are more often found in flattened cells, while in unflattened cells the MT in this area tend to be straight.

(2) It is difficult to compare the structure of the spindle in *Haemanthus* with other objects as very little work has been done using similar techniques, although the work of Bloom (1960), Bloom & Özarslan (1965), and Robbins & Gonatas (1964) has offered such possibilities.

Some variations in the fine structure of the spindle are to be expected owing to the presence or absence of a centrosome and the size of the chromosomes. The role of the centrosome or centrosome-like structure during mitosis is not clear, although it might affect the organization of the mitotic spindle. However, in my opinion it is doubtful whether it affects chromosome movement. The work of Dietz (1959), who observed perfectly normal division in the same type of cells, with and without centrosomes, provides convincing support for this statement.

Chromosome size probably modifies some features of the spindle fine structure. Chromosomes of *Haemanthus* at metaphase are about 4μ thick and some of them are more than 25μ long. Other cells studied with the EM have chromosomes of less than 1μ (Allenspach & Roth, 1967; Daniels & Roth, 1964) or slightly longer (Harris, 1965; Luykx, 1965 a, b). The only comparable cells are those of insect spermatocytes (Krishan & Buck, 1965 a; Behnke & Forer, 1966). Some special features of the fine structure of the spindle in *Haemanthus* may therefore be expected, but it is not possible at present to state whether they exist and, if so, what they are.

The forces moving chromosomes differ considerably in different cells. There are only about 10 MT connected to the kinetochores of sea-urchin eggs (Harris, 1965) and less in amoebae (Roth 1967), while in *Haemanthus* there are around 100. In cells with large chromosomes many MT are attached to the kinetochores, for example, in *Lilium* (Dietrich 1966).

From pictures of other work it seems that the intermingling, as found in *Haemanthus*, is less pronounced in objects with chromosomes of smaller size and may not occur in cells with very small chromosomes. However, a parallel arrangement of chromosomal and continuous fibres is always seen from anaphase to metaphase, sometimes over a long distance (cf. Harris, 1962, plate 2 (sea urchin); Robbins & Gonatas, 1964, plate 1 (HeLa strain); Krishan & Buck, 1965 b (L strain fibroblasts); Roth, Wilson & Chakraborty, 1966, plate 1 (spermatocyte of insect); and Roth, 1967, plate 2 (amoeba)).

It is difficult to judge from the controversial work of Behnke & Forer (1966) how the structure of *Haemanthus* and that of the crane fly differ, since the stages of division and the location of areas in the spindle (polar–equatorial) are not always mentioned in their work. They do not report denser accumulations of MT forming chromosomal fibres and suggest that they might not exist in the crane fly. This, however, might require further confirmation before it is generally accepted. The fact that chromosomal fibres correspond to denser accumulations of MT is commonly accepted. Undoubtedly this also occurs in *Haemanthus* (Bajer, 1967), where similar results have been obtained on the same area using the Nomarski system, polarized light and EM.

The organization of the spindle pole seems to differ in cells with and without centrosomes. MT are arranged in different directions and pronounced convergence is not visible in the polar areas of *Haemanthus* (Plate 15) and the sea urchin (Harris, 1961, 1965; Fig. 3). MT converge on the centrosome in several examples, such as insect spermatocytes (Roth *et al.* 1966; Fig. 1) or in chick embryos (Allenspach & Roth, 1967; Figs. 4, 7). It is not possible to evaluate the meaning of convergence at present, but in some cases convergence of single MT may be correlated with the time of their disorganization; this results in the pushing activity (cf. Plate 20).

B. *Fine structure and chromosome movement*

Data on the fine structure of the spindle, combined with observations *in vitro* on *Haemanthus*, lead to conclusions about the properties of spindle fibres and their activity during mitosis. Although only anaphase will be discussed here, there is no reason to believe that different types of mechanisms are employed during the formation of the metaphase plate. A few properties of spindle fibres will be mentioned first.

(1) Spindle fibres are comparatively rigid structures as they are able to push the cell membrane (Plate 18*a, b*). Unfortunately it is impossible to state whether these are chromosomal or continuous fibres. However, MT of the phragmoplast but not of the spindle show the same property even more clearly (Plates 20, 21). There is no reason to think that a fundamental difference exists between the MT of these two structures. The fact that chromosomal fibres are rigid has also been confirmed by the microsurgical experiments of Nicklas (1967) and Nicklas & Staehly (1967) and it seems most likely that this is a general feature found in all cells.

(2) Chromosomal fibres either do not shorten for a considerable length between kinetochores and the pole, or they shorten at a uniform rate along their entire length. The author is inclined to support the former suggestion, although it is not possible at present to provide convincing evidence for either explanation. It is also doubtful whether the question can be answered before we know how MT in general are formed and disorganized, but this problem will not be discussed here. It should also be mentioned that the view that MT contract (Moor, 1966) does not seem to be generally accepted.

Rather convincing suggestions of how MT are able to shorten have been presented by Tilney & Porter (1967).

(3) Spindle fibres transport small granules toward the poles during prometaphase to metaphase. Granules within the half-spindles found at a certain distance from the pole travel for a considerable time at the speed of the anaphase chromosomes and the distance between the kinetochores and granules does not change (Bajer & Molè-Bajer, 1963; Bajer, 1967). The same mechanism is probably responsible for transport of the zone of reduced birefringence (ZRB) which forms after uv microbeam irradiation, and for acentric fragments, non-disjunction chromosomes, etc. (Inoué, 1964; Forer, 1965, 1966). The fine structure of the ZRB is not known and various interpretations are possible (Forer, 1966).

(4) Some time-lapse sequences with the Nomarski differential interference contrast system, and even with phase-contrast, suggest that a considerable portion of each chromosomal fibre moves to the pole during anaphase, but unfortunately no clear pictures have been obtained so far (Bajer, unpublished).

(5) Conspicuous movements within chromosomal fibres are seen in time-lapse films taken with the Nomarski system. The movements first found by Bajer & Allen (1966) were further analysed on larger material (Bajer, unpublished). The elements seen, but not resolved, with LM represent 'Kontrastschwelle' (Beyer, 1966) of a few or single MT or, more probably of points where they intersect. An important point in this connexion is that the intensity of these movements, as far as it was possible to estimate without precise measurements, does not change along the whole length of the chromosomal fibre and is the same throughout all of anaphase. Though further studies are necessary, this may provide evidence that no gradual changes, such as contraction, occur in the chromosomal fibres throughout their length.

(6) Retardation of some chromosomes may result in retardation of their neighbours, but laggards do not move faster than the others (see p. 295) when the cause of resistance is removed. Therefore, chromosomal fibres do not behave as elastic strings. The microsurgical experiments of Nicklas & Staehly (1967) on chromosome stretching and change of position also strongly support this statement. A related question is whether chromosomal fibres are anchored anywhere.

Studies with chloral hydrate indicate that chromosomal fibres are not anchored to the poles. On the basis of uv experiments, Forer (1966) concluded that about a third of the chromosomal fibres (measured from kinetochores) are needed for normal chromosome movements to occur. Nicklas & Staehly (1967) concluded that chromosomal fibres are anchored close to the pole. Therefore, the question of how and where chromosomal fibres are fixed can be explained by the intermingling of spindle fibres in the polar areas.

Whether it is possible to make any general interpretation of chromosome movement is questionable. However, the facts mentioned above can be understood if it is assumed that chromosomal fibres in *Haemanthus* (and in other objects) are transported towards the pole during anaphase (cf. also Bajer, 1961) and are disorganized during or after transport to the polar areas. The presence of dense accumulations of ribosomes known to participate in protein synthesis in the polar areas of the spindle may support this assumption. If polar areas are not well developed, as in the 'bare' mitotic spindle (see p. 300), MT may not be disorganized and may push out the cell membrane (Plate 18*a*, *b*). The transport of chromosomal fibres close to the pole would explain why the divergence of chromosomal fibres close to kinetochores increases during anaphase, and also why a gradual loss of regular arrangement of MT occurs in the polar areas. The contrary assumption that chromosomal fibres contract does not explain transport properties within the mitotic spindle. However, with the available data it is not possible to state how such transport is achieved. A very attractive hypothesis, but one needing further support, is that chromosomal fibres 'slide' on the continuous fibres which form the framework of the spindle (Bělař, 1929*a*, *b*). Such a mechanism could be responsible for movement during prometaphase and anaphase. A low degree of intermingling found during prometaphase and an increase during anaphase can be interpreted as the consequence of sliding. If such a mechanism exists, both chromosomal and continuous fibres would be found in all organisms. The only exceptions are the epithelial cells studied by Allenspach & Roth (1967), where very few continuous fibres were found during anaphase. Also Behnke & Forer (1966) failed to find chromosomal fibres on the fine structural level. Further studies on modified mitosis, especially the apolar type (cf. Molè-Bajer, 1967), should elucidate this problem. Thus, studies on the fine structure of chloral hydrate-treated cells should answer the question of whether continuous fibres are necessary for chromosome movement. In chloral hydrate some chromosomes move very slightly while others move a considerable distance. The movements often occur when the phragmoplast begins to form and when the number of continuous fibres in the interzonal region rapidly increases. This might indicate that chromosomal fibres get 'support' for movement. It is possible, however, that chromosomal fibres are formed here from the phragmoplast (Molè-Bajer, 1967) and there is a very short period in phragmoplast development when new properties arise. It coincides with the appearance of birefringence

(Bajer, unpublished) and the moment when acentric bodies (Bajer & Molè-Bajer, 1963) may move to the equator and again there is an increase in the number of MT in the interzonal region. This evidence would make the 'sliding' mechanism a possible explanation.

The problem of chromosome movement at anaphase should be discussed together with the elongation of the mitotic spindle. One of the more disturbing factors in studies of this process is the formation of the phragmoplast in plants and of the cleavage furrow in animals. The first sign of phragmoplast formation occurs at mid-anaphase when the spindle elongates, and here it is impossible to state whether new structures are elements contributing to spindle elongation only or are structural elements of the phragmoplast which contribute at the same time to spindle elongation. The author is inclined to support the latter view.

There is support for the assumption that elements of the phragmoplast in the first stage (and in later ones) exert a pushing action. Two facts are proved without doubt: (1) the number of MT in the phragmoplast increases rapidly—this has also been confirmed in other plant material (Allen & Bowen, 1966; Pickett-Heaps, 1967a, b; Pickett-Heaps & Northcote, 1966a, b); (2) MT of the phragmoplast exert a considerable pushing effect to the sides of the phragmoplast (Plates 20, 21) and are responsible for lateral movements (Bajer & Östergren, 1963). It is therefore possible that phragmoplast MT contribute to pushing the two half-spindles apart. These conclusions are supported by the occurrence of slight undulations of MT in the interzonal regions, frequently found in very flattened cells where resistance is increased, and the fact that MT are usually straight in this area in unflattened cells. The pushing activity of the interzonal region has been demonstrated in both plant and animal material by Bělař (1929a, b) and was the subject of endless discussions (cf. Schrader, 1953; Mazia, 1961).

It has already been stated that the 'sliding' hypothesis requires further support. One of the difficulties is that we do not know how chromosomal fibres are formed. It is sometimes assumed that they are formed by kinetochores and grow towards the poles. Specht (1961) came to this conclusion after very careful studies on the staining properties of the spindle. On the basis of uv microbeam work Forer (1965, 1966) concludes, however, that traction fibres coincide with birefringent fibres at anaphase, while in prometaphase they are different. This idea is difficult to understand.

According to the 'sliding' hypothesis, we have to assume that elongation of the spindle results from an increase in length of the MT forming the continuous fibres, probably at the polar regions. At the same time the MT of chromosomal fibres are disorganized. If these assumptions are correct, it is still not known whether both processes occur primarily at the spindle poles, or whether continuous fibres are organized in the interzonal region as observations on the fine structure of the first stages of phragmoplast formation seem to indicate.

Observations on chromosome movements and fine structure of the spindle at present seem to support the outlines of Bělař's (1929 a, b) hypothesis of the spindle structure and the mechanism of chromosome movements. They are also in full agreement with the interpretation of chromosome movements discussed in the 'molecular pump' hypothesis of Östergren, Molè-Bajer & Bajer (1960).

SUMMARY

Observations *in vitro* and with the electron microscope (EM) on the endosperm of *Haemanthus katherinae* Bak. are reported. The technique used permitted observation of the same cell with the light microscope (LM) in the living state, during fixation and dehydration, and in plastic before sectioning for observations with the EM. The stage and plane of sectioning were always known.

Some observations *in vitro* on anaphase in normal, chloral hydrate- and acenaphtene-treated cells were described. Under the influence of chloral hydrate, the spindle was partially disorganized and chromosome arrangement resembled that of c-mitosis. Kinetochores were active and multipolar anaphase followed. Behaviour of the chromosomes during non-disjunction of kinetochores (influence of acenaphtene) was also analysed. On the basis of the observations *in vitro* it can be concluded that a chromosome's movement is influenced by the behaviour of its neighbours. There is also some evidence that chromosomal fibres are transported towards the pole during anaphase.

Observations with the EM were concerned primarily with the change of arrangement of microtubules (MT) during metaphase–anaphase and with kinetochore structure. The kinetochore is essentially a 'ball' composed of electron-light and electron-dense material. MT are embedded in the lighter material. The number of MT connected with kinetochores varied, and between 70 and 150 were found in middle anaphase.

The number of MT in the clear zone increases during prophase, but the arrangement is irregular. After breaking of the nuclear membrane the metaphase organization of the spindle is quickly established and MT form a mantle around the spindle. Continuous and chromosomal fibres in the central part of the spindle are visible, with the spaces between them almost devoid of MT. It is estimated that between 5,000 and 10,000 MT are present in the mitotic spindle and may be straight or wavy or show both properties. Short bends and sharp waves are probably the result of dehydration during fixation.

MT of chromosomal and continuous fibres intermingle in the polar region of the spindle. Continuous fibres retain their continuity in the equatorial plane during anaphase and their number seems to increase at the middle of anaphase when the phragmoplast begins to form. Intermingling at the polar areas and divergence of single chromosomal fibres towards the pole increase during anaphase.

Chromosome behaviour is well understood if the following assumptions are made: (a) chromosomal fibres do not contract uniformly along their length during anaphase but, (b) they are transported ('slide') along continuous fibres and are disorganized at their polar ends during anaphase. At the same time, elongation of the continuous fibres is responsible for elongation of the spindle. A similar sliding mechanism might be responsible for prometaphase movements. This is considered to be a useful working hypothesis but further experiments are required before it is accepted as a theory.

The present studies were made possible by an N.I.H. Career Development Award to the author and a research grant GB 3335 from the National Science Foundation. The studies with chloral hydrate reported here are from the unpublished work of Dr J. Molè-Bajer and permission for the use of these data are greatly appreciated. The patient and skilful technical help of Miss Jean Ann Schacht during the whole course of the work, and of Mrs Trudy Cox during the final part of the work, is also gratefully acknowledged.

REFERENCES

ALLEN, R. D. & BOWEN, C. C. (1966). *Caryologia* 19, 299.
ALLENSPACH, A. L. & ROTH, L. E. (1967). *J. Cell Biol.* 33, C179–C196.
BAJER, A. (1964). *Chromosoma* 15, 630.
BAJER, A. (1965). *Expl Cell Res.* 37, 376.
BAJER, A. (1966). In *Probleme der biologischen Reduplikation*, p. 90. Ed. P. Sitte. New York: Springer-Verlag.
BAJER, A. (1967). *J. Cell Biol.* 33, 713.
BAJER, A. & ALLEN, R. D. (1966). *Science, N.Y.* 151, 572.
BAJER, A. & MOLÈ-BAJER, J. (1956). *Chromosoma* 7, 588.
BAJER, A. & MOLÈ-BAJER, J. (1962). *Mitosis in Endosperm.* IIIB. 16 mm film.
BAJER, A. & MOLÈ-BAJER, J. (1963a). *Mitosis and Mitotic Factors.* 16 mm film.
BAJER, A. & MOLÈ-BAJER, J. (1963b). In *Cinematography in Cell Biology*, p. 357. Ed. Geo. G. Rose. New York: Academic Press.
BAJER, A. & ÖSTERGREN, G. (1961). *Hereditas* 47, 563.
BAJER, A. & ÖSTERGREN, G. (1963). *Hereditas* 50, 179.

BAUER, H., DIETZ, R. & ROBBELEN, C. (1961). *Chromosoma* **12**, 116.

BEHNKE, O. & FORER, A. (1966). *C. r. Trav. Lab. Carlsberg* **35**, 437.

BĚLAŘ, K. (1929a). *Arch. EntwMech. Org.* **118**, 359.

BĚLAŘ, K. (1929b). *Z. Zellforsch. mikrosk. Anat.* **10**, 73.

BEYER, H. (1966). *Jenaer Jb.* p. 173.

BLOOM, W. (1960). *J. biophys. biochem. Cytol.* **7**, 191.

BLOOM, W. & ÖZARLSLAN, S. (1965). *Proc. natn. Acad. Sci. U.S.A.* **53**, 1294.

BRINKLEY, B. R. & STUBBLEFIELD, E. (1966). *Chromosoma* **19**, 28.

DANIELS, E. W. & ROTH, L. E. (1964). *J. Cell Biol.* **20**, 75.

DIETRICH, J. (1966). *C. r. hebd. Séanc. Acad. Sci., Paris* **262**, 1699.

DIETZ, R. (1956). *Chromosoma* **8**, 183.

DIETZ, R. (1958). *Chromosoma* **9**, 359.

DIETZ, R. (1959). *Z. Naturf.* B **14**, 749.

FORER, A. (1965). *J. Cell Biol.* **25**, 95.

FORER, A. (1966). *Chromosoma* **19**, 44.

HARRIS, P. (1961). *J. biophys. Biochem. Cytol.* **11**, 419.

HARRIS, P. (1962). *J. Cell Biol.* **14**, 475.

HARRIS, P. (1965). *J. Cell Biol.* **25**, 73.

HARRIS, P. & BAJER, A. (1965). *Chromosoma* **16**, 524.

INOUÉ, S. (1964). In *Primitive Motile Systems in Cell Biology*, p. 549. Ed. R. D. Allen and N. Kamiya. Academic Press.

KRISHAN, A. & BUCK, R. C. (1965a). *J. Ultrastruct. Res.* **13**, 444.

KRISHAN, A. & BUCK, R. C. (1965b). *J. Cell Biol.* **24**, 433.

LUYKX, P. (1965a). *Expl Cell Res.* **39**, 643.

LUYKX, P. (1965b). *Expl Cell Res.* **39**, 658.

MAZIA, D. (1961). In *The Cell*, vol. III, p. 77. New York: Academic Press.

MOLÈ-BAJER, J. (1967). *Chromosoma* **22**, 465.

MOLÈ-BAJER, J. & BAJER, A. (1963). *La Cellule* **63**, 399.

MOLÈ-BAJER, J. & BAJER, A. (1968). *La Cellule* (in the Press).

MOOR, H. (1966). Balzers High Vacuum Report **9**, 1.

NICKLAS, R. B. (1961). *Chromosoma* **12**, 97.

NICKLAS, R. B. (1963). *Chromosoma* **14**, 276.

NICKLAS, R. B. (1967). *Chromosoma* **21**, 17.

NICKLAS, R. B. & STAEHLY, C. A. (1967). *Chromosoma* **21**, 1.

ÖSTERGREN, G. (1951). *Hereditas* **37**, 85.

ÖSTERGREN, G. & BAJER, A. (1960). *Colloques int. Cent. natn. Rech. scient.* **88**, 199.

ÖSTERGREN, G., MOLÈ-BAJER, J. & BAJER, A. (1960). *Ann. N. Y. Acad. Sci.* **90**, 381.

PICKETT-HEAPS, J. D. (1967a). *Devl. Biol.* **15**, 206.

PICKETT-HEAPS, J. D. (1967b). *Aust. J. biol. Sci.* **20**, 539.

PICKETT-HEAPS, J. D. & NORTHCOTE, D. H. (1966a). *J. Cell Sci.* **1**, 121.

PICKETT-HEAPS, J. D. & NORTHCOTE, D. H. (1966b). *J. Cell Sci.* **1**, 109.

ROBBINS, E. & GONATAS, N. K. (1964). *J. Cell Biol.* **21**, 429.

ROTH, L. E. (1967). *J. Cell Biol.* **24**, 47.

ROTH, L. E., WILSON, H. J. & CHAKRABORTY, J. (1966). *J. Ultrastruct. Res.* **14**, 460.

SCHRADER, F. (1953). *Mitosis—The Movement of Chromosomes in Cell Division*, 2nd ed. Columbia University Press.

SPECHT, W. (1961). *Z. Anat. EntwGesch.* **122**, 266.

TILNEY, G. & PORTER, K. R. (1967). *J. Cell Biol.* **34**, 327.

PLATE I

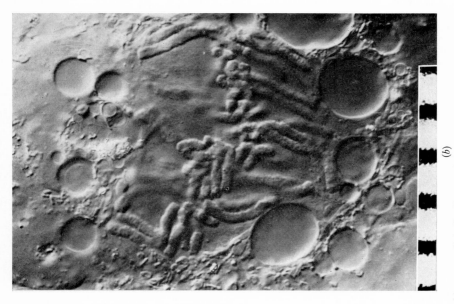

(b)

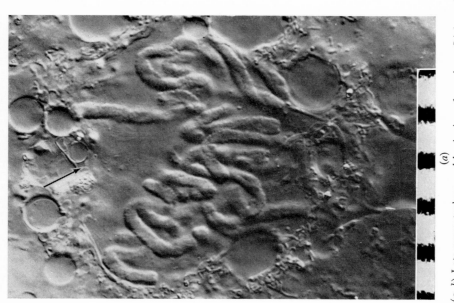

(a)

(a, b) Late prometaphase and beginning of anaphase. Living cell—Nomarski system. Spindle fibres and their intermingling in the polar area (a arrow) are visible, especially in the upper half-spindle. Notice uniform regular 'beaded' appearance of spindle fibres throughout the whole length of the fibre. Owing to an increase of intermingling the spindle has a more uniform structure at the beginning of anaphase. Intervals on the scale: 10 μ.

PLATE 2

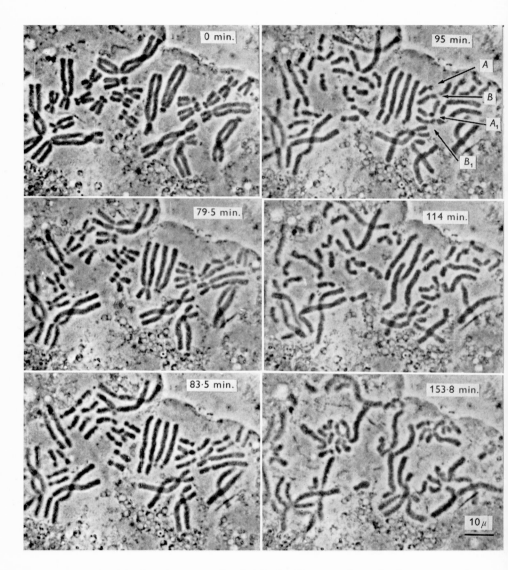

Anaphase in chloral hydrate-treated ceil (cf. also Plate 3 and graph of movements in Fig. 2). Chromosomes moving in a row marked by arrows. Arrangement of the chromosomes reminds one of c-mitosis. The spindle is 'split' into several smaller units composed of 1–4 chromosomes. A multipolar phragmoplast is formed. The time in minutes is given for each micrograph. Scale at the bottom, 10 μ.

PLATE 3

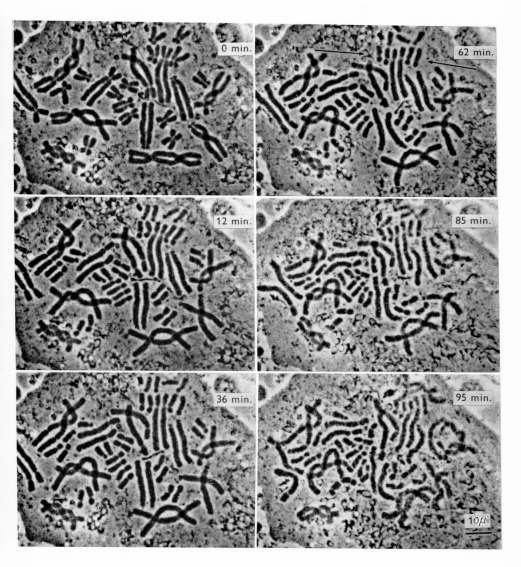

Movement of chromosomes in a chloral hydrate treated cell. Cf. Plate 2 and text for description. Time in minutes is given for each micrograph. Scale at the bottom: 10 μ.

PLATE 4

(a)

(b)

(a) Late prometaphase in flattened cell. Nomarski system after glutaraldehyde fixation (F), and in plastic (P). The arrow shows the approximate area seen in fig. (b). Intervals on the scale, 10 μ. (b) Late prometaphase. Four kinetochores with bundles of MT are seen. Arrows show MT entering chromosomes in areas different from kinetochores. Scale 1 μ.

PLATE 5

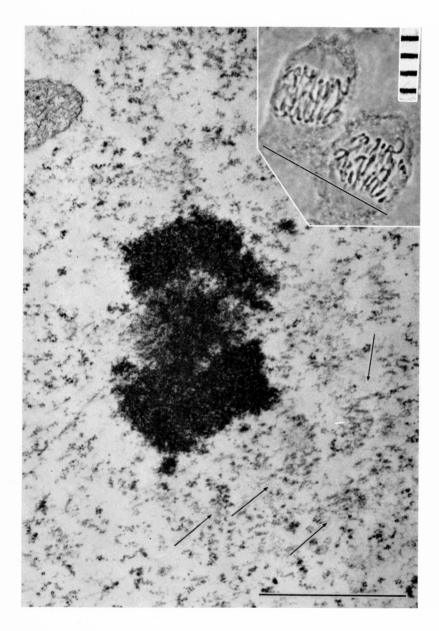

Kinetochore structure. A section approximately perpendicular to the long axis of the spindle. The plane of the sections is shown by a line on the inset. (The inset shows two cells in exactly the same stages.) No effort was made to find out to which of them the kinetochores belong. On the EM picture the lighter areas in which MT are embedded are seen in several places. The sides of the kinetochores are exposed. MT, sectioned under different angles, and forming 'bands' on the sides (arrows) are seen. Intervals on the scale for the LM picture, 10 μ, for the EM, 1 μ.

PLATE 6

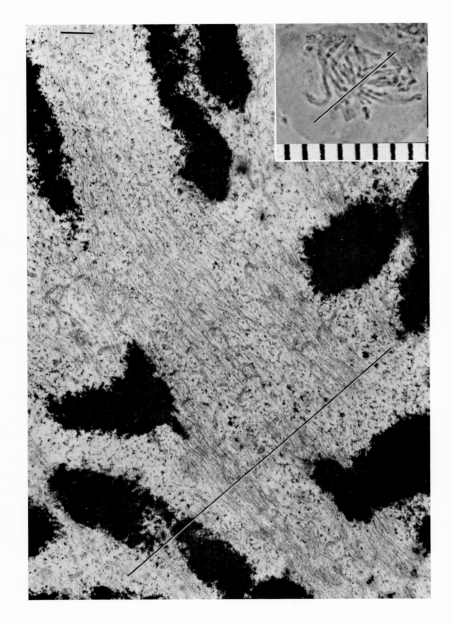

Prometaphase. Low EM magnification and LM micrograph of the cell in plastic. The long line indicates the approximate equatorial plane. Few kinetochores at different stages of stretching are seen. Intervals on the scale for the LM picture, 10 μ; for the electron micrographs, 1 μ.

PLATE 7

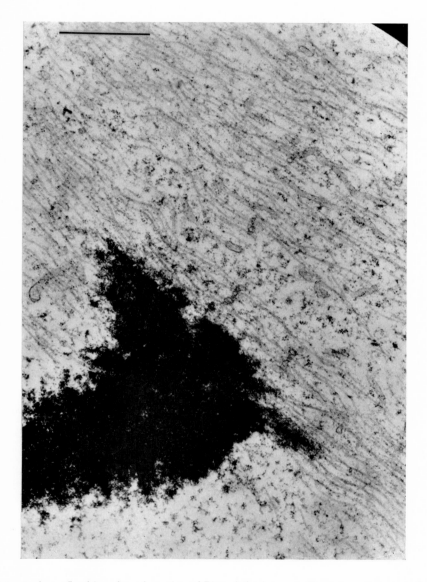

Prometaphase. In this enlarged portion of Plate 6 the intermingling of continuous and chromosomal MT is clearly visible. Two kinetochores at different stages of stretching are clearly visible. The scale represents 1 μ.

PLATE 8

Telophase. The arrow in the inset indicates the approximate area seen in the EM picture. Two kinetochores are seen (arrow *K*). There are still some MT connected with the upper one. The 'ball' of this kinetochore is not very clearly seen while the 'cup' is (cf. text). Pieces of the nuclear membrane (arrows *NM*) which have persisted from prophase are present. Scale on the EM picture (top) 1 μ.

PLATE 9

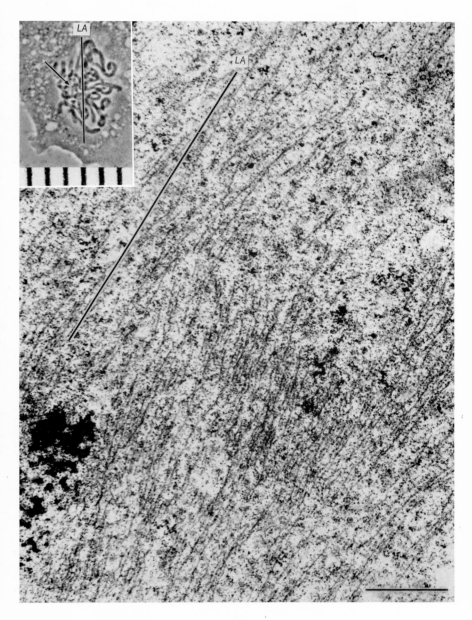

Early prometaphase. Dense, roughly parallel arrangement of MT on the surface of the spindle in the approximate area marked by the arrow. LA = long axis of the spindle. Intervals on the scale for the LM picture, 10 μ; for the EM picture, 1 μ.

PLATE 10

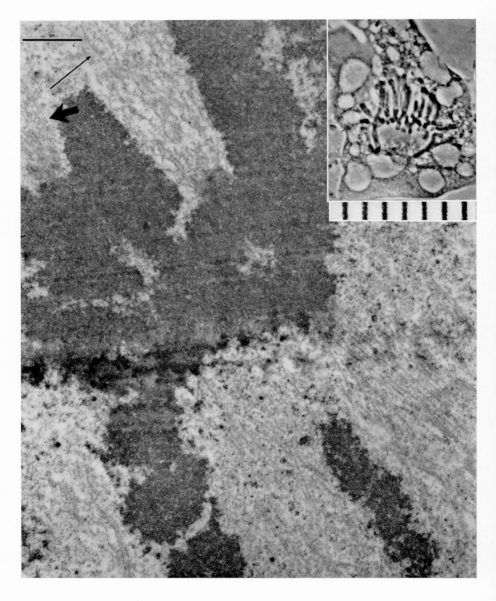

Wavy and straight MT connected to metaphase kinetochores. The kinetochores are divided. Wavy MT become straight again as soon as they are further from the chromosome arm. Only a small part of these straight MT is visible in this picture (arrow). The darker areas across the central part of the picture are knife scratches. Notice that MT (thick arrow) connected to neighbouring kinetochores are straight. Intervals on the scale for the LM picture, 10 μ; for the EM picture, 1 μ.

PLATE II

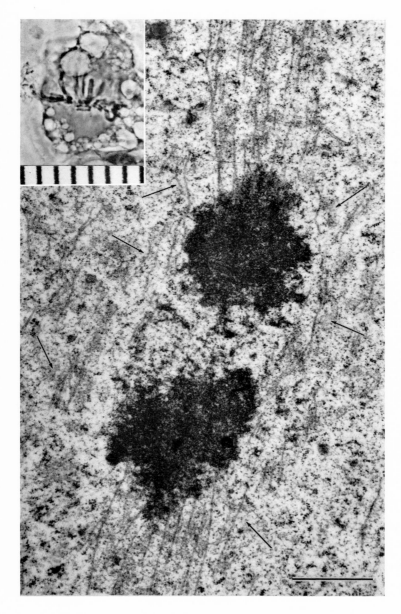

Start of anaphase. Kinetochores are sectioned parallel to the long axis of the spindle but perpendicular to the long axis of the chromosome. Several MT forming continuous fibres (as seen from other sections) are seen on the sides of the kinetochores. The continuous fibres are bent and wavy in the area where they are close to chromosomes (probably due to dehydration, cf. discussion p. 302) and straight where they are further away (arrows). Intervals on the scale for the LM picture, 10 μ; for the EM picture, 1 μ.

PLATE 12

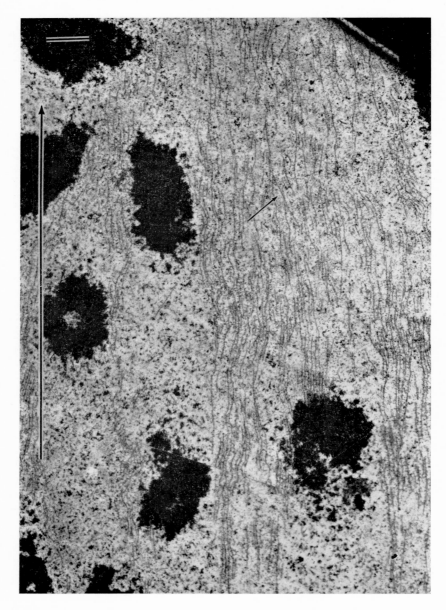

Middle anaphase-intermingling of MT. The long arrow indicates the direction of chromosome movement. Intermingling occurs both close to the kinetochore and close to the pole. Occasionally MT are skew (short arrow). Notice strong bends in the MT close to one of the chromosomes and the comparatively straight MT close to the other. Scale represents 1 μ.

PLATE 13

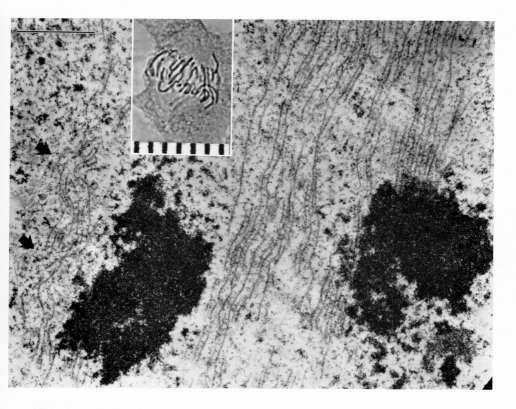

This is an enlarged portion of Plate 12. Intermingling occurs both close to the kinetochore and close to the pole (cf. discussion). This plate shows more clearly the strong bends in the MT close to one of the chromosomes (thick arrows) and the comparatively straight MT close to the other.

PLATE 14

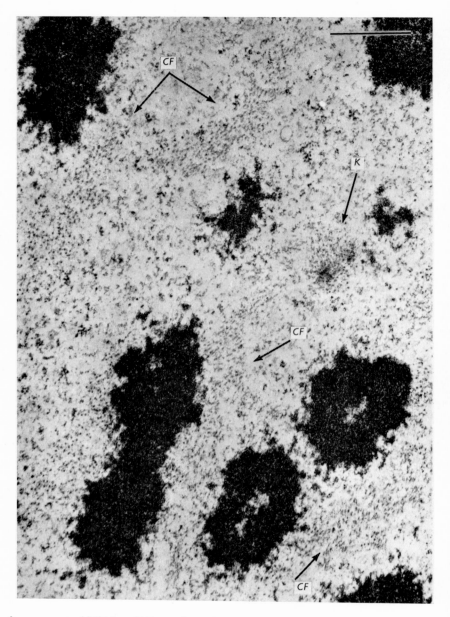

Arrangement of MT in middle anaphase. A section perpendicular to the long axis of the spindle, approximately at the kinetochore level. Arrow (K) points to a surface section through the kinetochore. Continuous fibres are arranged in 'bands' around chromosome arms (arrows CF). The LM micrograph of this cell is in Plate 5. Scale at the top, 1 μ.

PLATE 15

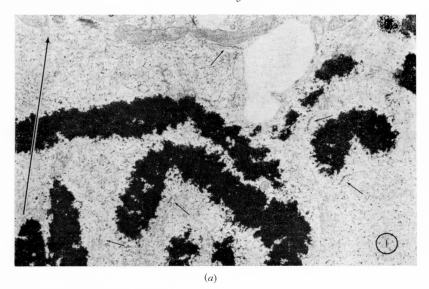

(a)

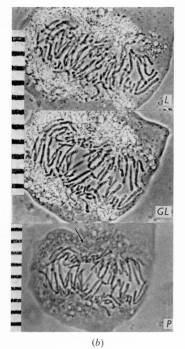

(b)

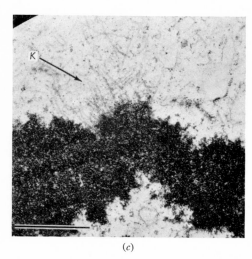

(c)

(a) The arrows point to pieces of the nuclear membrane which have persisted until ana-phase (cf. also Plates 8; and 16). The long arrow indicates the direction of chromosome movement. Scale in the circle, 1 μ. (b) Fixation and embedding. A comparison of the living cell (L) with the same cell fixed in 3·1 %, pH 6·9 glutaraldehyde (GL) for 30 min., and after embedding in plastic (P). The cell was fixed about 10 min. after the micrograph (L) was taken. Shrinkage is seen in the micrograph (P). The arrow indicates the area seen in fig. a and Plate 16. Intervals on the scale, 10 μ. Polar area of the spindle. LM micrograph is fig. b. Details are seen in fig. a and Plate 16. (c) Chromosomal fibres in late anaphase. This chromosome has reached the pole. The MT are arranged very irregularly and are rather short in comparison to the MT connected with other kinetochores of the same cell (Plates 16 and 17 c).

PLATE 16

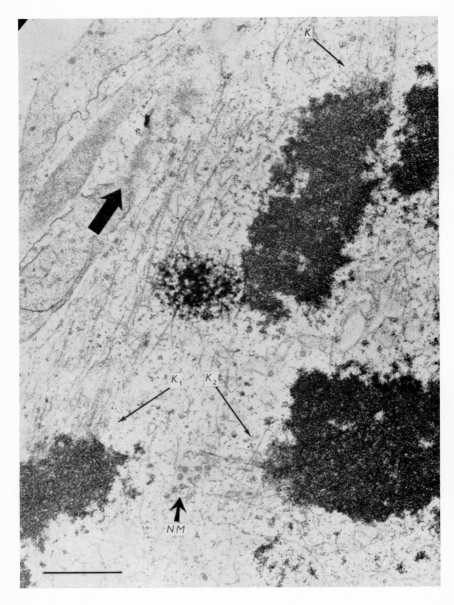

Chromosomal fibres at late anaphase. Direction of chromosome movement is marked by the thick arrow. LM micrograph of this cell is in Plate 15 *b* and low EM micrograph is in Plate 15 *a*. Three kinetochores (K, K_1, K_2) visible. MT of chromosomal fibres intermingle with long MT (upper left side of the picture) which most probably form the mantle on the spindle surface (cf. Plate 9). Kinetochore K_2 is arranged perpendicular to the direction of chromosome movement. This is a very exceptional phenomenon. The dark area in the centre of the field is stain. Scale 1 μ.

PLATE 17

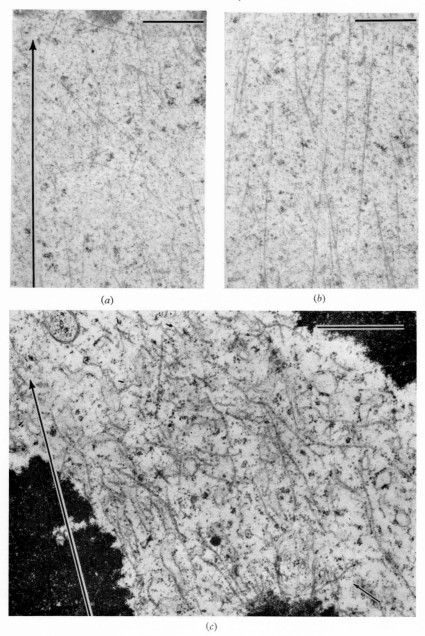

(a)

(b)

(c)

Arrangement of MT a few microns from the kinetochores (b) and in the polar area (a) of the same chromosomal fibre. The difference in regular arrangement is clear. The long arrow shows the direction of chromosome movement. LM micrograph of this cell is in Plate 19a. Scale at the bottom, 1 μ. (c) Chromosomal fibres at late anaphase. The direction of chromosome movement is marked by the long arrow. LM micrograph of this cell is in Plate 15b. The irregular arrangement of MT at the polar area is clearly seen. Some MT (small arrow) are nearly perpendicular to the surface of the kinetochores and to the direction of movement. Cf. also Plates 15a and 16. Scale 1 μ.

PLATE 18

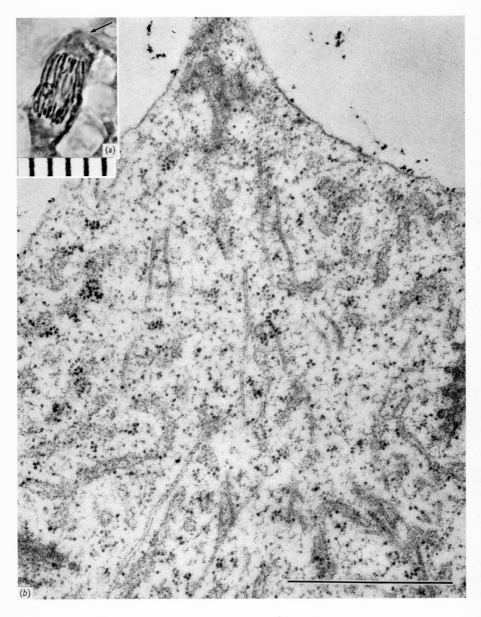

Late anaphase in a spindle without cytoplasm. The arrow in the LM micrograph (*a*) shows the area seen in the EM micrograph. (*b*). There is a general arrangement of MT and their roughly parallel arrangement in the protruding tip of the spindle is clearly visible (cf. text). Intervals on the scale for the LM micrograph, 1ɔ *μ*; for the EM micrograph, 1 *μ*.

PLATE 19

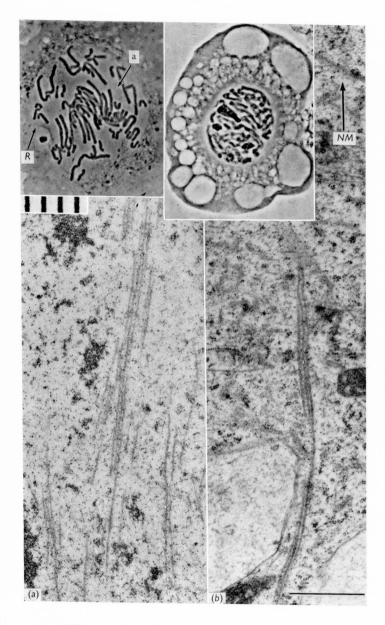

Comparison of MT in prophase (b) and in the interzonal region in late anaphase (a). The
approximate area seen in the EM micrograph is marked by the arrow in 19a. The region
seen in (b) has not been localized in the micrograph of the cell in plastic. NM, nuclear
membrane, skew section (b). The similarity between arrangement of some bundles of MT
in the interzonal region and in the clear zone is clearly evident. Intervals for LM micrographs, 10 μ; for EM (bottom), 1 μ.

PLATE 20

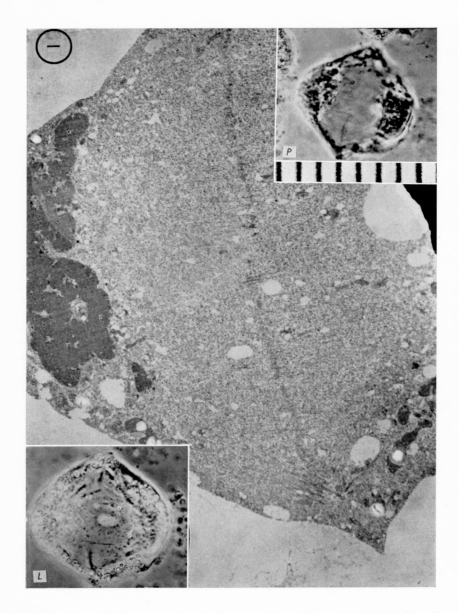

Pushing activity of the phragmoplast. During growth the phragmoplast expands laterally (Lateral movements, cf. Bajer & Östergren 1963). Converging bundles of MT penetrate the area. Serial section failed to show any MT passing across the cell plate. It is most likely that Plate 21 shows the actual ends of MT. A picture of the living cell (L) and the cell in plastic (P) are in the insets. Intervals for the LM scale, 10 μ; for the EM micrograph (inside the circle), 1 μ.

PLATE 21

For explanation see legend to Plate 20.

PLATE I

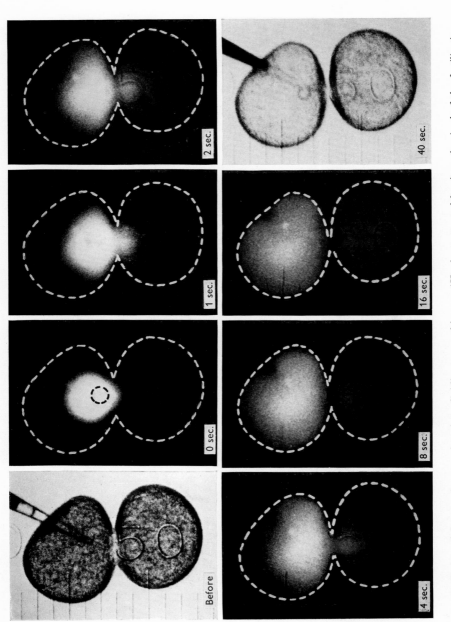

Diffusion of fluorescein potassium in a dividing sea urchin egg. (*Hemicentrotus pulcherrimus* deprived of the fertilization membrane and the hyaline layer at 19°C.)

The dye solution was microinjected into one of the incipient blastomeres. The site and approximate amount of the microinjection are indicated by a circle in the photograph taken at the end of the microinjection (0 sec.). The dye diffuses through the equatorial plane of the cell.

THE MECHANICS AND MECHANISM OF CLEAVAGE IN THE SEA-URCHIN EGG

By Y. HIRAMOTO

Misaki Marine Biological Station, Miura-shi, Kanagawa-ken, Japan

Since the last century a number of theories have been proposed by various investigators in order to explain cleavage on the basis of different mechanisms (for references, Swann & Mitchison, 1958; Wolpert, 1960; Mazia, 1961; Roberts, 1961). The aim of this paper is to describe some results of my recent experiments concerning the cleavage of the sea-urchin egg and to discuss the mechanism of cleavage in this material.

THE TYPE OF CLEAVAGE

It is well known that there are two entirely different modes of cleavage: one by a furrowing or constriction method, the other by the formation of a cell-plate. The first is characteristic of the amphiastral type of mitosis, the second of the anastral; but there are some exceptions and there are also certain conditions intermediate between the two types. Broadly speaking, cleavage by constriction is characteristic of mitosis in higher animals, and the cell-plate formation of higher plants.

In investigating the mechanism of cleavage in the sea-urchin egg it is important, first of all, to determine the type of cleavage in this material. Dan and his co-workers extensively investigated the behaviour of the cell surface during cleavage by observing the movement of particles attached to the surface. As a result, it was found that the surface at the equatorial region is stretched and is pulled into the furrow during cleavage in the sea-urchin egg (for references, Hiramoto, 1958). This result was corroborated by observations on pigment granules embedded in the cortical protoplasm (Dan, 1954b; Scott, 1960). These facts may imply that the cleavage in the sea-urchin egg is of the first type.

On the other hand, Motomura (1935) reported that in sea-urchin eggs which were allowed to cleave in normal sea water, the contact surfaces of the blastomeres of the two-cell stage lacked pigment granules which had been observed over the cortical region of the cell before the onset of cleavage. Later, he found special vacuoles at the equatorial plane in dividing sea-urchin eggs and suggested that they were the material of the new surface (Motomura, 1950). Selman & Waddington (1955) maintained, from their observations of the cortical movement, from measurements of the elastic properties of the cell surface and from cytological study of the subcortical morphology in dividing amphibian eggs, that the new cortex is first formed as a sheet of gel at the animal pole of the equatorial surface and that it grows downwards by a process involving gelation at its lower edge. Buck & Tisdale (1962) and Humphreys (1964) investigated by electron microscopy cleavage processes in mammalian somatic cells and in molluscan eggs respectively, and concluded that the cleavage furrow is formed by the fusion of vesicles which appear at the equatorial plane. Recently, Ashman, Kanno & Loewenstein (1964) reported that ion communication between the blastomeres of a dividing starfish egg, as determined electrically, progressively diminished during cleavage. They interpreted this result as a gradual increase in the resistance across the equatorial plane suggesting the formation of a new membrane which barred the passage of ions in this region. The results mentioned above imply that cleavage is of the second type in various animal cells including echinoderm eggs.

Tadano (1962) described that in nematodan eggs the cleavage furrow is first formed by constriction; the furrow then disappears and new membranes separating the blastomeres from each other are formed by fusion of vacuoles lining up at the equatorial plane. In other words, the processes characteristic of the two types of cleavage take place in succession in this material. Zotin (1964) maintained that the cleavage in sturgeon and amphibian eggs involves the furrowing by contraction of the equatorial surface and the formation of new membranes at the equatorial plane in the endoplasm.

If the cleavage is of the first type, the entire surfaces of the daughter cells should be derived from the surface of the cell existing at the beginning of cleavage, whereas if the cleavage is of the second type the surfaces of the daughter cells should partially be derived from the endoplasm before cleavage. Movements of the protoplasm during cleavage were followed by tracing the movements of granules or vacuoles existing in the cell, using time-lapse microcinematography. In this experiment, sea-urchin eggs deprived of the fertilization membranes and the hyaline layers were allowed to cleave in a Ca-free medium. Gross refraction effects at the cell surface were abolished by adding bovine plasma albumen to the medium to bring its refractive index close to the average value for the protoplasm. A typical result is shown in Fig. 1. Solid circles represent some granules embedded in the cortical protoplasm at the beginning and at the end of cleavage, and open circles represent some granules or vacuoles situated at the equatorial plane at the beginning of cleavage and their positions at the end of cleavage. It must be noted in this figure that the surfaces of the daughter cells are derived from the surface of the cell existing at the beginning of cleavage and not from the material at the equatorial plane of the cell.

In order to examine whether or not a barrier to diffusion of substances is formed at the equatorial plane of the dividing egg, a small amount of aqueous solution of fluorescein was micro-injected into one of the incipient blastomeres and the behaviour of the micro-injected dye was observed with a fluorescence microscope. The photographs taken before and at

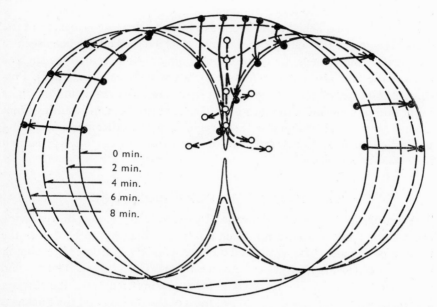

Fig. 1. Movements of the protoplasm during cleavage of a sea urchin egg. (*Clypeaster japonicus* deprived of the fertilization membrane and the hyaline layer at 24° C.). ●, Positions of granules embedded in the cortical protoplasm at the beginning of cleavage and at the end. ○, Positions of granules or vacuoles observed at the equatorial plane at the beginning of cleavage and their positions at the end.

various periods after the micro-injection are shown in Plate 1. As shown in this figure, the fluorescein freely diffused in the protoplasm, passing through the furrow stalk. This fact indicates that there is no structural barrier to diffusion corresponding to the future plasma membranes of the daughter cells at the equatorial plane.

The absence of a new membrane at the equatorial plane in the dividing egg was confirmed by my recent experiments in which an iron particle of several microns in diameter was readily moved through the furrow stalk by externally applied magnetic force. The details of this experiment will be mentioned later.

Scott (1946) and Rappaport (1966) observed a flow of the endoplasm through the furrow stalk which did not interfere with cleavage. Cleavage may take place when the equatorial plane is occupied by inanimate materials such as a micro-injected oil drop (Chambers, 1938; Hiramoto, 1965) or a large vacuole containing sea water (Hiramoto, 1965) or when the protoplasm at the equatorial plane is removed (Hiramoto, 1956). These facts may indicate that the surfaces of the daughter cells are not formed *de novo* in the endoplasm and that the cleavage is brought about by stretching the existing surface in the sea-urchin egg.

It has been established that the motive force of cleavage is located in the cortical region of the cell by experiments in which the cell has been seen to divide after the removal or destruction of endoplasmic structures such as the spindle and asters (for references, Swann & Mitchison, 1958). Presumably the cleavage is brought about by *active* contraction and/or *active* expansion of a region or regions of the cortical protoplasm resulting from intrinsic structural changes at these regions, while other parts including the endoplasm are *passively* stretched or compressed by the forces generated in the *active* regions.

THE INTRACELLULAR PRESSURE

The sea-urchin egg can be deformed by external force, and on removing the force it tends to round up. Such a return is believed to be due to the tension of the structure at the cell surface, which was termed 'tension at the surface' (Harvey, 1931) or 'surface force' (Cole, 1932). The tension at the surface, which is expressed as force per unit length of the surface, is considered to be the sum of the products of the tension and the thickness of the membranes or layers existing at the cell surface, such as the cortical gel, the cell membrane and the extraneous coats. If the endoplasm is assumed to be a liquid, the shape of the cell is governed by the equilibrium between the tension at the surface and the intracellular pressure, and therefore the tension at the surface is calculated from the intracellular pressure and the curvature of the cell surface.

The intracellular pressures of the sea-urchin egg before and during cleavage were determined as follows (cf. Fig. 2). An egg was compressed in the direction of the spindle axis between a rod (R in Fig. 2a) and a plate (G in Fig. 2a). The force applied to the egg was controlled by observing the displacement of the rod during the application of the force as a result of the bending of a fine glass needle (N in Fig. 2a) fixed to the rod (R) at the tip. The intracellular pressure of the compressed egg was calculated from the formula

$$P = F/\pi r^2, \tag{1}$$

in which P is the intracellular pressure, F is the applied force and r is the distance between the spindle axis and the point of the cell surface where the tangent is perpendicular to the axis (cf. Fig. $2b$). The intracellular pressures when the eggs were not deformed were determined from the intracellular pressures of the compressed egg calculated in this way,

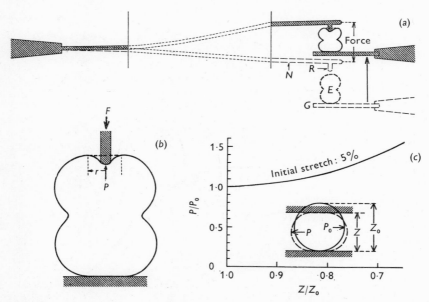

Fig. 2. Diagram showing the method for determining the intracellular pressure of the dividing cell. (*a*) The method for compressing the egg and determining the applied force. *E*, Egg; *N*, glass needle; *R*, glass rod fixed to the tip of the needle (*N*); *G*, glass plate. (*b*). A compressed egg showing the dimensions necessary to calculate the intracellular pressure. *F*, Applied force; *P*, intracellular pressure ($P = F/\pi r^2$); *r*, the distance between the spindle axis and the point of the cell surface where the tangent is perpendicular to the axis. (*c*) Relation between the deformation and the internal pressure in rubber balls filled with water when they are compressed between two parallel plates. The surface of the ball had been stretched by 5 % by applying internal pressure through a tubing connected to the ball before experimentation. The volume of the ball was fixed unchanged during compression. P/P_0; relative internal pressure. Z/Z_0: relative thickness of the ball.

correcting the increments of the pressure accompanying the deformation of the egg by using the relation between the internal pressure and the deformation obtained in a model experiment, in which a rubber ball filled with water was compressed between two parallel plates (cf. Fig. $2c$). The relative increment of the internal pressure depends not only on the degree of deformation but also on the 'initial stretch' of the surface membrane. The more the membrane has initially been stretched, the smaller the relative increment of the pressure is expected. The maximal possible initial stretch of the cell surface has been reported to be 9·7 % in the sea-urchin egg at anaphase

(Mitchison & Swann, 1955), while the surfaces of the rubber balls used in the model experiment had been stretched by 5% before experimentation. Although the model and the sea-urchin egg are not exactly similar to each other, the present determination may give approximate values for the intracellular pressures, because variations of the correction factor (P/P_0 in Fig. 2c) are small ($< 1·5$) in the present experimental condition.

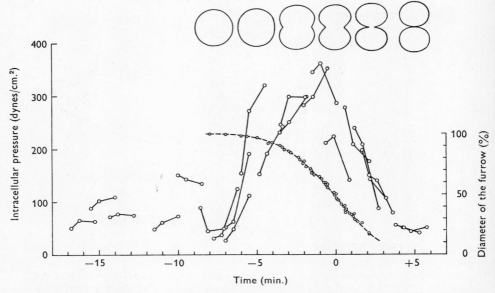

Fig. 3. Intracellular pressures of sea-urchin eggs. (*Temnopleurus toreumaticus* deprived of the fertilization membranes and the hyaline layers at 24° C.). Pressures were determined in different eggs at various stages before and during cleavage. Three circles connected in series represent the measurements taken in the same egg 30 sec., 1 min. and 2 min. after the application of a constant force (10^{-3} dynes). Small circles represent the diameters of the furrow of the eggs used in the present experiment.

Determinations of the intracellular pressure were carried out in different eggs at various stages before and during cleavage (cf. Fig. 3). In each egg, the pressures were determined three times, namely 30 sec., 1 min. and 2 min. after the application of a constant force (10^{-3} dyne in the case of determinations shown in Fig. 3). Groups of three circles connected in series in this figure represent these determinations. The diameters of the furrow in the eggs used in the present experiment are represented by small circles and approximate stages of cleavage are indicated on the top in this figure. The intracellular pressure gradually increases before cleavage, reaches a peak shortly before the onset of cleavage and then decreases. Simultaneously with the elongation of the cell at the beginning of cleavage, the pressure increases again and it reaches a peak during cleavage followed by a decrease during the second half of cleavage. The pressure increases by about tenfold during the first half of cleavage and decreases by a similar degree during the second half.

VISCO-ELASTICITY OF THE ENDOPLASM

An accurate and detailed knowledge of the mechanical properties of the protoplasm at different regions of the dividing cell is important in the study of the mechanics of cleavage. This is because any forces developed in the protoplasm during cleavage should be due to *active* contraction or *active* expansion resulting from intrinsic structural changes of the protoplasm and/or viscous and elastic stresses resulting from the *passive* deformation and flow of the protoplasm.

Heilbrunn and his co-workers extensively investigated the protoplasmic viscosity and its changes during mitosis in various marine eggs (for references, Heilbrunn, 1956). They maintained that the protoplasm can be regarded as a Newtonian fluid with a low viscosity; that the viscosity increases before the formation of the mitotic figure, and that it decreases at the time the spindle is forming reaching a minimum at metaphase. The interior of the protoplasm, however, is not homogeneous in microscopic appearance and it was shown by micromanipulation that gel and sol exist side by side in the dividing cell (cf. Chambers & Chambers, 1961). Therefore, the significance of the 'viscosity' determined by Heilbrunn and co-workers is problematical.

Recently, I devised a method for determining the visco-elasticity of the protoplasm at different regions of the sea-urchin egg. The basic principle of the method is to record the movement of a spherical iron particle which has been introduced into the cell when a magnetic force is applied. It was possible to determine the visco-elasticity of the protoplasm from the magnitude of the applied force, the character and the magnitude of the movement and the size of the particle.

An example from an egg shortly before the onset of cleavage is shown in Fig. 4. As shown in this figure, the rate of movement of the particle in the protoplasm gradually decreases during the application of a force which is practically constant (cf. *a*, *b* in Fig. 4) and the particle recoils after removal of the force. The recoil, however, is not complete. This fact may indicate that the protoplasm of the sea-urchin egg is visco-elastic. The rate of movement of the particle passing through the central region of the aster (*A* in Fig. 4) is smaller than its rate in the peripheral region of the aster (*B* in Fig. 4). The rate suddenly decreases when the particle approaches the cell surface (cf. *B* in Fig. 4). These facts indicate that the consistency of the protoplasm is high at the central region of the aster and at the cortical region of the cell while it is relatively low at the peripheral region of the aster.

An example from an egg during cleavage is shown in Fig. 5. In this case, a particle moves in parallel to the spindle axis from one of the incipient blastomeres to the other, passing through the furrow stalk. As in the egg before the onset of cleavage, shown in Fig. 4, the rate of movement of the particle is small at the cortical region of the cell (cf. *A* in Fig. 5) and at the centres of asters (*C* and *F* in Fig. 5), while the rate is relatively large at the

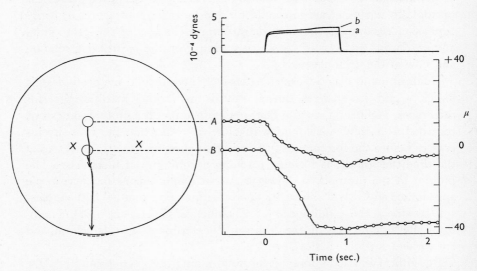

Fig. 4. Movements of an iron particle in the protoplasm of a sea-urchin egg. (*Temnopleurus reevesii* deprived of the fertilization membrane and the hyaline layer at 26·5° C.) Paths of the particle in the egg are indicated by arrows. Crosses represent the centres of the asters. The time courses of the applied forces, *a* and *b*, correspond to those of the movements *A* and *B* respectively.

peripheral region of the aster (cf. *A* in Fig. 5). It must be noted in this figure that the rate is very large at the region between the two centres of the asters, namely the interzonal region of the spindle (*D* and *E* in Fig. 5). This fact implies that the spindle has been completely isolated by this stage and that no rigid structure comparable to that at the cell surface is forming at the equatorial plane of the dividing egg.

The measurements of the sea-urchin egg by the magnetic particle method described above not only indicate qualitative differences of the visco-elasticity of the protoplasm at different regions of the cell but also make it possible to determine the values of the visco-elasticity. The behaviour of the particle in the protoplasm during and after application of a constant force as described above (cf. Figs. 4, 5) is explained by assuming that the visco-elasticity of the protoplasm is represented by the three-element visco-elastic model shown in Fig. 6 (i). The elasticity and viscosity values (γ_1, η_1, and η_2) are calculated from the following formulas,

$$\gamma_1 = F/6\pi a x_\infty, \tag{2}$$

$$\eta_1 = \tau\gamma_1, \tag{3}$$

$$\eta_2 = F/6\pi a v_\infty, \tag{4}$$

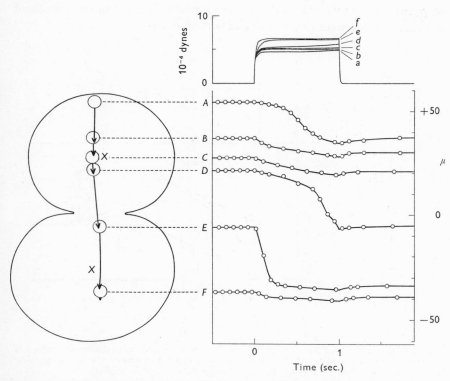

Fig. 5. Movements of an iron particle in the protoplasm of a dividing sea-urchin egg. (*Temnopleurus reevesii* deprived of the fertilization membrane and the hyaline layer at 26·5° C.). Paths of the particle in the egg are indicated by arrows. Crosses represent the centres of the asters. The time courses of the applied forces *a–f* correspond to those of the movements *A–F* respectively.

in which F is the applied force, a is the radius of the particle and x_∞, τ (retardation time) and v_∞ (curve inclination) are values determined from the record of the movement of the particle as shown in Fig. 6 (ii). Strictly speaking these formulas apply to the movement of a spherical particle in an unbounded medium represented by the three-element model shown in Fig. 6 (i), while the cell is of finite size and the protoplasm is not exactly represented by the three-element model. However, the present calculations may still give approximate values for the visco-elasticity of the protoplasm. As a result of a number of experiments on eggs of various sea urchins, the elasticity value (γ_1) and the viscosity values (η_1, η_2) at the peripheral regions of the aster were determined to be of the order of 10–100 dynes/cm.^{2} and 10–100 poises, respectively. The elasticity and viscosity values at the cortical region and at the central region of the aster were of the order of several hundred dynes/cm.^{2} and several hundred poises respectively. The viscosity values at the interzonal region of the spindle of the cleaving egg were of the order of several poises.

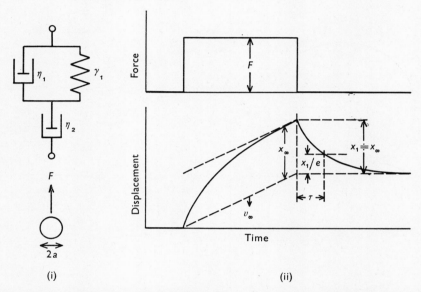

Fig. 6. Diagram showing the method for determining the elasticity and viscosity values of the protoplasm. (i) Equivalent visco-elastic model. (ii) Movement of a spherical particle in the protoplasm when a force with a rectangular time course is applied.

The viscosity values in the present determination are 100–10,000 times those obtained by Heilbrunn and his co-workers. This wide difference may be due to the existence of a framework (or fibrous) structure in the proto-plasm with meshes of 1 μ or so, as discussed elsewhere (Hiramoto, 1967). Presumably Heilbrunn determined the viscosity of the fluid phase of the protoplasm by measuring the rate of movement of granules smaller than 1 μ in size, while the visco-elasticity of the entire protoplasm including the framework structures was determined in the present experiment using iron particles of several microns in size.

THE STRESSES IN THE ENDOPLASM OF THE DIVIDING EGG

In determining the intracellular pressure mentioned above, it was assumed that the protoplasm is a liquid, i.e. that the pressure is uniform within the cell. The viscous and elastic forces due to the deformation and flow of the endoplasm, which were calculated from the values of visco-elasticity of the endoplasm and the observed deformation, were found to be, at most, a few per cent of the total forces applied to the egg in the present experiment. Therefore, it is unnecessary to consider the forces due to the deformation of the endoplasm.

The movements of the endoplasm during cleavage in the sea-urchin egg were described in detail by Hiramoto (1958). Using this result and the visco-elasticity of the endoplasm of the dividing egg at various regions, the shear stresses and the pressure differences at various regions of the dividing egg were calculated. As a result, it was found that the pressure differences within the cell were, at most, of the order of 1 dyne/cm.^{2}, which is far smaller than the intracellular pressures shown in Fig. 3 (30–400 dynes/cm.^{2}). This fact may indicate that the intracellular pressure is practically uniform within the dividing egg. In other words, the endoplasm can be regarded as a fluid of low viscosity, because the rate of movement of the protoplasm during cleavage is exceedingly small, in spite of the fact that the consistency of the entire endoplasm including the structures in it is far greater than the consistency determined by Heilbrunn and his co-workers (cf. Heilbrunn 1956).

THE TENSION AT THE SURFACE

The tensions at the surface are calculated from the intracellular pressure and the curvatures of the cell surface through the following formulas (cf. Fig. 7),

$$T_1 = P_0 r_2/2, \tag{5}$$
$$T_2 = [P_0 r_2(2 - r_2/r_1)]/2, \tag{6}$$

in which T_1 is the tension at the surface in the longitudinal direction (the direction joining pole to pole) and T_2 is that in the latitudinal direction (the direction at right angles to the former), P_0 is the intracellular pressure and r_1 and r_2 are the principal radii of curvature of the cell surface.

The tensions at the surface, which were calculated from the intracellular pressures shown in Fig. 3 and the curvatures of the surface determined in eggs at various stages of cleavage are shown in Fig. 8. T_1 and T_2 are the tensions in the longitudinal and latitudinal directions respectively at the furrow region (the region of the cell surface 5 μ from the equatorial plane) and T_p is the tension at the polar region, which is equal in all directions. The tensions gradually increase before the cleavage, reach peaks shortly before the onset of cleavage, increase during the first half of cleavage and decrease during the second half as shown in Fig. 8. These changes are, in general, parallel to the changes in the intracellular pressure (cf. Fig. 3).The tensional changes are similar over the entire surface before the onset of

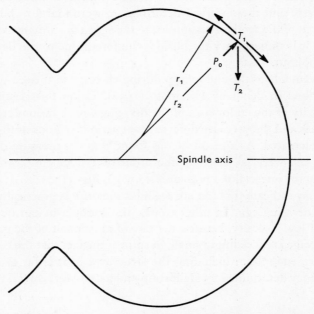

Fig. 7. Diagram showing dimensions necessary to calculate the tensions at the surface of the dividing cell. T_1, Tension at the surface in the longitudinal direction. T_2, Tension at the surface in the latitudinal direction. P_0; Intracellular pressure. r_1, r_2, Principal radii of curvature of the cell surface.

cleavage, whereas the tension at the furrow region in the latitudinal direction (T_2) is larger than either the tension at the polar region (T_p) or the tension at the furrow region in the longitudinal direction (T_1) during cleavage.

DISCUSSION

In discussing the mechanical changes of the protoplasm at the cell surface during cleavage, it is necessary to consider the changes in the configuration of the cell surface as well as the tensional changes. In Fig. 8, the expansion and contraction of the surface during cleavage, quoted from Hiramoto (1958), are shown by L_1, L_2 and L_p, which represent percentage linear changes of the furrow surface in the longitudinal and latitudinal directions, and of the polar surface, respectively. Broadly speaking, the furrow surface contracts in the latitudinal direction and expands in the longitudinal direction, while the polar surface expands in all directions during cleavage. Before the onset of cleavage, neither local contraction nor local expansion is observable, although the tension changes uniformly over the entire surface.

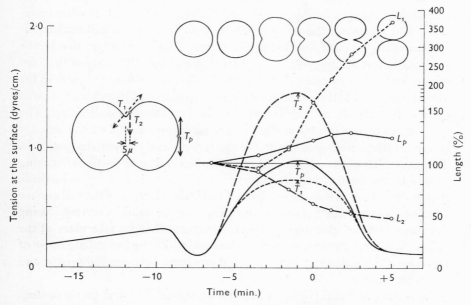

Fig. 8. Changes in the tension at the surface and the configuration of the surface in the sea-urchin egg (quoted from the data of Hiramoto (1958) in the eggs of *Clypeaster japonicus*). T_1, Tension at the surface in the longitudinal direction at the furrow region (the region of the cell surface 5 μ from the equatorial plane of the cell). T_2, Tension at the surface in the latitudinal direction at the furrow region. T_p, Tension at the surface at the polar region. L_1, Percentage linear change of the cell surface in the longitudinal direction at the furrow region. L_2, Percentage linear change of the surface in the latitudinal direction at the furrow region. L_p, Percentage linear change of the surface at the polar region. The tensions at the surface were calculated from the intracellular pressure shown in Fig. 3 and the curvatures of the surface of the dividing cell determined in the eggs of *Temnopleurus toreumaticus* deprived of the fertilization membranes and the hyaline layers.

During cleavage, the furrow surface contracts in the direction of the larger tension and expands in the direction of the smaller tension. This fact may indicate that these expansions and contractions of the furrow surface are not due to passive elastic deformation. The expansion of the polar surface continues until the stage shortly before the end of cleavage, while the tension at the polar surface is already decreasing at this stage. This non-parallelism between the tension and the length is not due to the retarded elasticity of the surface structure, assuming that the changes in the con-figuration of the polar surface is entirely passive, because the retardation time of the sea-urchin egg is of the order of several seconds (Hiramoto, unpublished) while the time interval between the maximal tension and the maximal area at the polar surface is several minutes, as shown in Fig. 8. Intrinsic structural changes must be considered both at the furrow region and at the polar region during cleavage.

From these facts, it is inferred that the structure of the protoplasm at the cell surface changes before and during cleavage as follows. During metaphase and anaphase, the tension of the protoplasm at the cell surface increases while the configuration of the surface does not change; that is, the surface 'isometrically contracts'. During telophase, the tension first decreases and then increases. At this stage the furrow surface contracts in the direction parallel to the equator, developing tension and stretching the polar surface. As a result, the egg is first elongated and then is constricted. The contraction of the furrow surface in the direction parallel to the equator continues thereafter, until finally the egg is completely constricted into two. The expansion of the polar surface is not merely due to passive stretching caused by the contraction of the furrow surface, but is also due to intrinsic structural change in this region. Even if the linear changes of the cell surface were suppressed, the tension at the polar surface would decrease during the second half of cleavage. In short, structural changes take place at the cell surface throughout mitosis and cleavage, while the immediate cause of cleavage is the difference in mechanical structure between the furrow and the polar regions.

According to Sakai (1960a, b; 1962a, b), the sulphhydryl group content and the contractility of protein extracted with concentrated KCl solution from the sea-urchin egg, especially from the cortical protoplasm, increase before cleavage, reach peaks shortly before the onset of cleavage and decrease during cleavage. These changes were recently confirmed by Kyono (personal communication) by a cytochemical method. The strength of the cortical birefringence of the sea-urchin egg generally increases before the onset of cleavage and decreases during cleavage (Monroy & Montalenti, 1947; Inoué & Dan, 1951; Mitchison & Swann, 1952; Dan, 1954a). Differences in the cortical birefringence appear between the polar region and the furrow region when cleavage is initiated (Mitchison & Swann, 1952; Dan, 1954a). These changes may indicate that chemical and structural changes take place in the cortical protoplasm before as well as during cleavage and that the cleavage is initiated when a structural difference develops between the furrow and the polar surfaces, supporting the conclusion of the present discussion.

Changes in the resistance to deformation (stiffness) of the cell before and during cleavage in sea-urchin eggs have been determined by various methods (Cole & Michaelis, 1932; Danielli, 1952; Mitchison & Swann, 1955; Wolpert, 1963, 1966; Hiramoto, 1963 a, b, 1967). The stiffness increases before cleavage and reaches a peak at or shortly before the onset of cleavage. In some eggs, the stiffness decreases thereafter until the end of cleavage, while in others, the stiffness again increases after a transient drop at the beginning of cleavage, reaches the second peak at the mid-point of cleavage, and decreases thereafter. Variations in the results may be due to the different experimental materials used (cf. Hiramoto, 1967). These stiffness changes may be mainly caused by structural changes in the proto-plasm at the cell surface since it is inferred from the results of the visco-elasticity measurements of the endoplasm in the present study that the force developed by the deformation of the endoplasm is very small com-pared with the force produced by the deformation of the cell surface.

Presumably the general changes in the structure of the protoplasm at the surface which accompany mitotic cycles are not directly controlled by the mitotic apparatus since the changes in sulphhydryl contents, the cortical birefringence and the stiffness persist when the formation of the mitotic apparatus is suppressed by irradiation of the egg with ultraviolet rays or by treatment with colchicine (Ikeda, 1965; Monroy & Montalenti, 1947; Swann & Mitchison, 1953). In contrast the development of the furrow-polar differentiation is directly controlled by the mitotic apparatus. Prob-ably the site and the direction of the high contractility at the furrow surface during cleavage are determined by a 'message' derived from the mitotic apparatus before the onset of cleavage.

SUMMARY

1. Movements of the protoplasm during cleavage in the sea-urchin egg were analysed by tracing the movements of granules and vacuoles in the protoplasm using time-lapse microcinematography. As a result it was con-cluded that cleavage is brought about by stretching the existing surface.

2. Aqueous fluorescein, when micro-injected into one of the incipient blastomeres of the dividing egg, freely diffused in the protoplasm passing through the furrow stalk. An iron particle which had been introduced into the egg was readily moved across the equatorial plane of the dividing egg by the application of a magnetic force. From these results the possibility of the formation of new membranes at the equatorial plane in the proto-plasm was ruled out.

3. The mechanical properties of the protoplasm of the dividing egg at various regions were determined from the movements of spherical particles which had been introduced into the cell when magnetic fields of controlled

magnitudes were applied by an electromagnet. The protoplasm of the sea-urchin egg was shown to be visco-elastic contrary to the results of previous investigators. The consistency of the protoplasm is relatively high at the central region of the aster and at the cortical region of the cell as compared with the consistencies at the peripheral region of the aster and at the inter-zonal region of the spindle. The absolute magnitudes of the 'viscosity' of the protoplasm are much higher than those of the protoplasmic viscosity previously reported, suggesting the existence of rigid structures embedded in fluid protoplasm.

4. Pressure differences at various regions of the dividing egg were estimated from the results of the visco-elasticity and of the movements of the protoplasm during cleavage. As a result, it was concluded that the intracellular pressure is practically uniform within the dividing egg.

5. The intracellular pressures at various stages before and during cleavage were determined from the relation between the deformation and force when the egg was deformed by a minute rod applied to the polar region of the egg. The intracellular pressure increases before cleavage, reaches a peak shortly before the onset of cleavage, decreases at the beginning of cleavage, increases during the early part of cleavage and decreases during the later part.

6. The tensions at the surface of the dividing egg were determined from the intracellular pressure and the curvatures of the cell surface. The tension at the surface changes before and during cleavage in parallel to the changes in the intracellular pressure. Before the onset of cleavage, the tension is almost uniform over the entire surface of the cell, whereas the tension is different at different regions of the cell and in different directions in reference to the equatorial plane during cleavage.

7. From the results of tensional changes and the changes in the configuration of the cell surface during cleavage, it was concluded that the structure of the cortical protoplasm changes before as well as during cleavage and that the immediate cause of cleavage is the difference in the structure of the cortical protoplasm between the polar region and the furrow region.

This investigation was partly supported by grant in aid for special project research on biophysics from the Ministry of Education.

REFERENCES

ASHMAN, R. F., KANNO, Y. & LOEWENSTEIN, W. R. (1964). *Science, N.Y.* **145**, 604.
BUCK, R. C. & TISDALE, J. M. (1962). *J. Cell Biol.* **13**, 117.
CHAMBERS, R. (1938). *J. cell. comp. Physiol.* **12**, 149.
CHAMBERS, R. & CHAMBERS, E. L. (1961). *Explorations into the Nature of the Living Cell.* Cambridge, Mass: Harvard University Press.
COLE, K. S. (1932). *J. cell. comp. Physiol.* **1**, 1.
COLE, K. S. & MICHAELIS, E. M. (1932). *J. cell. comp. Physiol.* **2**, 121.
DAN, K. (1954a). *Embryologia* **2**, 99.
DAN, K. (1954b). *Embryologia* **2**, 115.
DANIELLI, J. F. (1952). *Nature, Lond.* **170**, 496.
HARVEY, E. N. (1931). *Biol. Bull. mar. biol. Lab., Woods Hole* **61**, 273.
HEILBRUNN, L. V. (1956). *The Dynamics of Living Protoplasm.* New York and London: Academic Press.
HIRAMOTO, Y. (1956). *Expl Cell Res.* **11**, 630.
HIRAMOTO, Y. (1958). *J. exp. Biol.* **35**, 407.
HIRAMOTO, Y. (1963a). *Expl Cell Res.* **32**, 59.
HIRAMOTO, Y. (1963b). *Expl Cell Res.* **32**, 76.
HIRAMOTO, Y. (1965). *J. Cell Biol.* **25** (1-2), 161.
HIRAMOTO, Y. (1967). *J. cell. Physiol.* **69**, 219.
HUMPHREYS, W. J. (1964). *J. Ultrastruct. Res.* **10**, 244.
IKEDA, M. (1965). *Expl Cell Res.* **40**, 282.
INOUÉ, S. & DAN, K. (1951). *J. Morph.* **89**, 423.
MAZIA, D. (1961). *The Cell*, vol. **3**, p. 77. Ed. J. Brachet and A. E. Mirsky. New York and London: Academic Press.
MITCHISON, J. M. & SWANN, M. M. (1952). *J. exp. Biol.* **29**, 357.
MITCHISON, J. M. & SWANN, M. M. (1955). *J. exp. Biol.* **32**, 734.
MONROY, A. & MONTALENTI, G. (1947). *Biol. Bull. mar. biol. Lab., Woods Hole* **92**, 151.
MOTOMURA, I. (1935). *Sci. Rep. Tohoku Univ.* IV, **10**, 211.
MOTOMURA, I. (1950). *Sci. Rep. Tohoku Univ.* IV, **18**, 255.
RAPPAPORT, R. (1966). *J. exp. Zool.* **161**, 1.
ROBERTS, H. S. (1961). *Q. Rev. Biol.* **36**, 155.
SAKAI, H. (1960a). *J. biophys. biochem. Cytol.* **8**, 603.
SAKAI, H. (1960b). *J. biophys. biochem. Cytol.* **8**, 609.
SAKAI, H. (1962a). *J. gen. Physiol.* **45**, 411.
SAKAI, H. (1962b). *J. gen. Physiol.* **45**, 427.
SCOTT, A. (1946). *Biol. Bull. mar. biol. Lab., Woods Hole* **91**, 272.
SCOTT, A. (1960). *Biol. Bull. mar. biol. Lab., Woods Hole* **119**, 260.
SELMAN, G. G. & WADDINGTON, C. H. (1955). *J. exp. Biol.* **32**, 700.
SWANN, M. M. & MITCHISON, J. M. (1953). *J. exp. Biol.* **30**, 506.
SWANN, M. M. & MITCHISON, J. M. (1958). *Biol. Rev.* **33**, 103.
TADANO, Y. (1962). *Japan J. Zool.* **13**, 308.
WOLPERT, L. (1960). *Int. Rev. Cytol.* **10**, 163.
WOLPERT, L. (1963). *Cell Growth and Cell Division*, p. 277. New York and London: Academic Press.
WOLPERT, L. (1966). *Expl Cell Res.* **41**, 385.
ZOTIN, A. I. (1964). *J. Embryol. exp. Morph.* **12**, 247.

LIGHT AND CHLOROPLAST MOVEMENTS

By HEMMING I. VIRGIN

Department of Plant Physiology, University of Göteborg, Sweden

INTRODUCTION

It is an old observation that the chloroplasts in the cells of green plants can slowly change their positions (Fig. 1). The first worker to observe and describe the phenomenon caused largely by the direction and intensity of the incident light was J. A. Böhm (1863). Pioneer work on the phenomenon was performed by Stahl (1880) and Senn (1908) and their papers are still

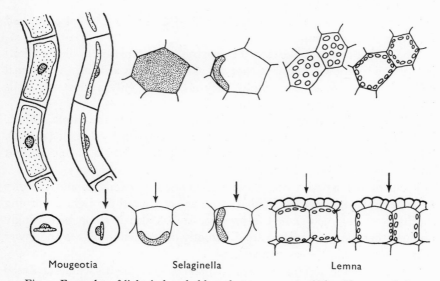

Mougeotia   Selaginella   Lemna

Fig. 1. Examples of light-induced chloroplast movements. (After Haupt, 1963.)

important sources for details on the process. These investigators distinguished different characteristic types of chloroplast positions, but they are nowadays of less interest as they represent a classification based, not on the physiological mechanisms behind the movements, but on plant types. At the present time the most interesting type is represented by algae with large plate-like chloroplasts such as *Mougeotia*, *Mesocarpus* and *Mesotaenium*. These algae have been used extensively during the last few years for making action spectra of the light-dependent movements.

The names for some characteristic types of stationary positions which the chloroplasts can assume in common chlorenchymatic tissue and in algae with many chloroplasts are listed below; these names are still used in modern literature.

A. *Diastrophy*. The chloroplasts in this position are separated into two groups lining the two cell walls nearest and furthermost from the light source. The position frequently occurs under weak light conditions and in some cases in darkness.

B. *Apostrophy*. The chloroplasts line the radial walls of the borderline cells.

C. *Parastrophy*. The chloroplasts line the cell walls which because of internal reflexions and refractions are most shaded. The position occurs in very strong light; that is, direct sunlight under natural conditions.

D. *Epistrophy*. The position occurs in cells of *Funaria* in diffuse light. The position is very similar to A.

The positions A–C are referable to cells of *Lemna*, but can also be used for other multi-plastid cells.

The main difference between the apostrophic and parastrophic positions is that the plastids in the first case are assembled towards all the internal cell walls whereas at parastrophy they are found only against the walls perpendicular to the surface of the leaf.

In the present paper no attempt will be made to cover the whole subject. For this, reference must be made to the monograph by Haupt (1959*a*). The main emphasis will be on newer investigations which have cast light on this extensively studied phenomenon.

From recent experiments where well-defined wavelengths and energies have been used, it is evident that there are at least three light-absorbing mechanisms (pigments) in the process. It has also become increasingly obvious that the mechanisms are differently developed in higher and lower plants—at least in the species studied.

In the following account the light-dependent movements will be analysed more closely, firstly in *Mougeotia*, *Mesotaenium* and other one-chloroplast-containing algae, and secondly in multichloroplast-containing cells.

The classical species for the study of chloroplast movements in multi-chloroplast-cells are duckweed (*Lemna* sp.) and mosses with thalli containing just one or only a few layers of cells, like species of *Funaria*. Most older studies have been performed on such plant material. Zurzycka's (1951) interpretation of the movements in cells of these plants is, however, complicated by the fact that the qualities of light which produce a chloroplast movement from apostrophy to epistrophy differ from those giving a change from epistrophy to parastrophy (Fig. 2). Also the response to different spectral ranges depends on the initial position of the chloroplasts in respect to the light falling upon them. Thus it has been shown that in red light no change in the position of the chloroplasts occurred if the initial position was apostrophic. But if the optical axis of the chloroplasts is parallel to the beam of light, complete or partial rearrangement to parastrophy is obtained—the degree depending upon the intensity. In blue

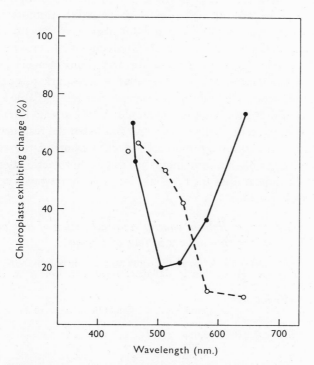

Fig. 2. Action spectra for the epistrophy → parastrophy reaction (●—●) and the reverse (○ – – ○) in *Funaria hygrometrica*. (After Zurzycka, 1951.)

light, however, it is possible to obtain reactions from both initial positions but it is evident that plastids starting in the parastrophic position undergo a more complete reaction than they do starting from the epistrophic position.

In earlier studies it is stated that red light and darkness give the same positions; that is, no light response would be obtained in red light (Frank, 1872; Senn, 1908; Stahl, 1880). But Zurzycka (1951) showed that in red light the chloroplasts of *Lemna* changed their position from the epistrophic to parastrophic 2·5 times faster than in darkness (experimental time 3 hr.).

HIGH- AND LOW-ENERGY REACTIONS

A characteristic feature of the movements of chloroplasts is that one can clearly distinguish between high- and low-energy reactions. In weak light only the short-wave radiations elicit movement in the chloroplasts and the reaction can be characterized as positive phototaxis (apostrophy → epistrophy), whereas in strong light, causing negative phototaxis (apostrophy/epistrophy → parastrophy), red light also seems to be involved. The influence of red light on this chloroplast movement has been thoroughly studied by Zurzycki (1962 a). Irradiation with long wavelength light gives a final chloroplast arrangement similar to the dark position (apostrophy), but the speed of the movement is greatly affected (Table 1). These findings are very interesting as they give clues to the many differences in earlier findings in respect to light effects, and show that the results obtained must be greatly influenced by the method of measuring the response. Therefore as red light has a photokinetic but not a phototactic effect, comparative reaction time studies for the long- and the short-wave regions are very difficult to perform.

Table 1. *The influence of light in causing an acceleration of displacement of the chloroplasts in cells of Lemna*

The figures denote the number of ergs and quanta necessary to reduce the reaction time to 35 min., i.e. half of that in darkness. Irradiation time 1 hr. (After Zurzycki, 1962 a.)

Wavelength (λ, nm.)	Ergs/cm.^{2}.sec.	Quanta/cm.^{2}.sec..10^{12}
558	4,400	1,235
622	1,600	500
682	290	137
715	8,900	3,200

The blue-light response mentioned above can be compared with spectra for phototropism and for the inducement of changes in protoplasmic viscosity (Thimann & Curry, 1961; Virgin, 1954). As yet the determinations of the action spectra for phototaxis do not allow any conclusions to be drawn about which pigment is involved at the primary light-absorbing process —except that it is yellow. In the red response, in some instances also coupled with a blue-light response, photosynthesis might be involved. However, experiments with algae (see below) suggest that in the movements of chloroplasts in cells of higher plants the phytochrome system may operate, but this has not been proved.

When light of long and short wavelength is given simultaneously to cells of *Lemna*, the long-wave light causes an effect only if it exceeds an intensity of several thousand ergs and if it is applied when the chloroplasts have reached a certain arrangement, regulated by blue light. An eventual effect of additional red light on the course of the phototactic displacement caused by blue light is completely disguised.

TEMPERATURE

It is very important that the temperature is kept constant during studies of plastid movements. The effects of temperature on the speed of regular plastid displacement from the epistrophic to the parastrophic state follows Van't Hoff's Law (coefficient 1·26). In darkness there is a lag phase, dependent on temperature, before leaves will change from the epistrophic to the apostrophic state. At 10° C. this lag phase lasts about 75 min., whereas at 20° C. it lasts only 30 min. After the lag the displacement starts rather quickly, the temperature coefficient for this displacement being 1·47 (Zurzycka & Zurzycki, 1950).

Still more complicated is the effect of temperature on the light response of the cells of *Mougeotia* which contain one plastid (Mugele, 1962). In these it is possible to distinguish between a low- (red sensitive) and a high- (blue sensitive) light-intensity response, resulting in a positive phototaxis and a negative phototaxis respectively. In the former the induction of the chloroplast movement is independent of temperature within the range of 2–30° C., whereas the speed of response is strongly temperature-dependent. A 10° difference results in a change in the speed of movement by a factor of about two. This means that the induction process as such is limited by the photochemical reaction, whereas the resulting movement is limited by chemical reactions. At low temperatures it is also possible to separate the induction from the response by several hours. A response to a given induction takes place as much as 9 hr. later, provided that the material is kept at low temperatures and that it is brought back to normal temperatures afterwards. In the latter response (the blue-light response) the speed of response is independent of temperature within the temperature range 10–20° C.

In contrast to the chloroplast movements in *Mougeotia* the induction of which in red light is more or less temperature-independent, that in *Lemna* is strongly dependent on temperature (Haupt & Weisenseel, 1966). A comparison between the response of *Lemna* (representative of a multi-plastid cell) and that of *Mougeotia* (one-plastid cell) gives data (Mugele, 1962) shown in Table 2.

From Table 2 it is obvious that the strong light- and weak light-induced movements have the following in common: (a) one temperature-*inde-pendent* movement induced by blue light, and (b) one temperature-*de-pendent* movement, induced by red as well as by blue light. The fact that

Table 2. *Comparison between the responses of Lemna and Mougeotia
chloroplasts to light and temperature*

	Light quality	Temp.	Light quality	Temp.
Lemna	Weak light Blue	movement independent	Strong light (Red and) blue	movement dependent
Mougeotia	Strong light Blue	movement independent	Weak light (Blue and) red	movement dependent

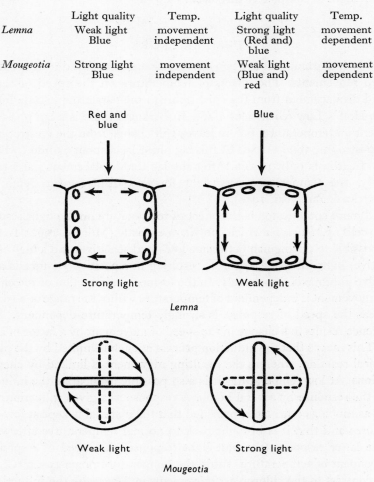

Fig. 3. Schematic comparison between the light responses in
Lemna and *Mougeotia*. (After Mugele, 1962.)

one kind of movement with the same characteristic pattern (red light and
temperature-dependence) is called strong-light movement in *Lemna* and
weak-light movement in *Mougeotia* could be explained by the fact that here
the response to white light is referred to, and also to the fact that in the
case of *Mougeotia* more consideration is taken of the orientation of the
chloroplast in respect to light than of the conditions for absorption within
the cell and plasma proper. Also in the movements in *Mougeotia* induced

by weak light the chloroplasts move away from the part of plasma which gets the strongest irradiation. This means that movements induced by weak light can correctly be interpreted as a negative phototaxis (Mugele, 1962). This is also justifiable since the light responsible for the movement is probably absorbed in the plasma and not by the chloroplasts (Bock & Haupt, 1961; Haupt, 1960). A comparison between the response of the two kinds of cells is given in Fig. 3.

THE LIGHT RESPONSE OF CELLS WITH ONE BIG CHLOROPLAST

While cells of higher plants seem to exhibit the strongest response to blue light, the conditions are quite different for cells containing one chloroplast such as the algae *Mougeotia* and *Mesotaenium*. Here the strongest response is to red light. It is interesting in this connexion that the red response is not confined to algae as such, as *Vaucheria*—containing many chloroplasts—only shows a blue response (Fischer-Arnold, 1963). It seems more to be determined by the kind of chloroplasts present in the cells.

Haupt (1958) was the first to study this response more closely, and the phenomenon has since been thoroughly investigated by him and his students. In the cells of *Mougeotia* and the related species the chloroplast can orientate itself towards incoming light by twisting around its own axis (Fig. 4). The two extreme positions are: (1) the rectangular-shaped surface of the chloroplast is orientated perpendicular to the beam of incident light (positive phototaxis); (2) the surface of the chloroplast is orientated parallel to the incident light (negative phototaxis). The question whether these are positive and negative responses in the true sense is closely connected with the problem of which part of the cell is the primary light absorber—in this case either the chloroplast itself or the surrounding cytoplasm (cf. above).

In pretreated cells, i.e. irradiated sidewards with weak light, causing one edge of the chloroplast to face the incident beam of the experimental light (perpendicular to the light used at the pretreatment), the chloroplast starts to twist if the cell gets light strong enough to produce a change in the character of the response. This twisting is finished after about 30–40 min. Then a more or less stationary condition is reached even if the irradiation itself has not lasted for more than 1 min. (Fig. 5).

The action spectrum for eliciting a twisting of the chloroplast—that is, to obtain a response of positive phototaxis—is seen in Fig. 6. It is obvious from this Figure that the reaction belongs to the large group of phenomena

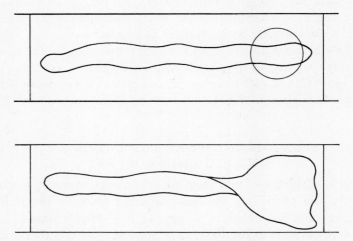

Fig. 4. Effect of a partial irradiation on the chloroplast in a cell of
Mougeotia. (After Bock & Haupt, 1961.)

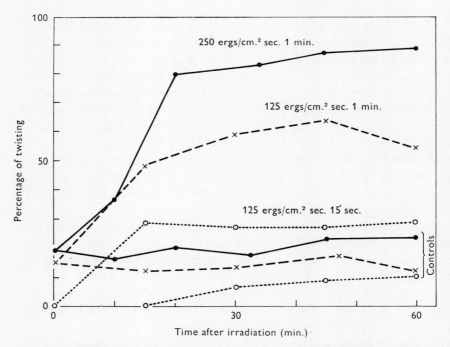

Fig. 5. Statistical course of the chloroplast movements in cells of *Mougeotia* in darkness
and after varying light treatments (679 nm.). (After Haupt, 1959*b*.)

which are governed by the pigment phytochrome. The reversibility between the action of red light (660 nm.) and far-red light (770 nm.) is characteristic of this group of responses. This can be interpreted as a reversible shifting of absorption maxima of the pigment from 660 nm. (P_{660}) to 730 nm. (P_{730}). From experiments where far-red light has been given after a pulse of red light (Fig. 7), it was shown that such a reversibility exists also

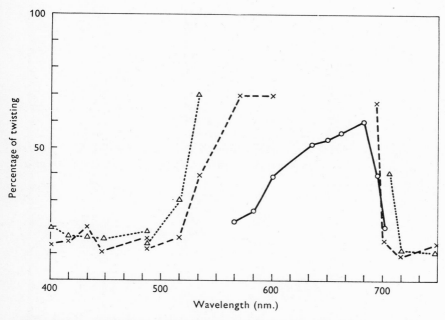

Fig. 6. Twisting of the chloroplast of *Mougeotia* in relation to wavelength of the incident light. Equal amount of quanta per time unit (679 nm. = 1000 ergs/cm.² sec.). Irradiation time: O—O, 10 sec.; × −− ×, 1 min.; △ -- △, 7 min. (After Haupt, 1959*b*.)

here. That this reversibility is completely repeatable is seen from Table 3, where results are shown from an experiment in which red and far-red light were alternatively administered for 1 min. with an interval of 15 sec. between them. The chloroplast positions were measured 45 min. after the onset of the first pulse of light.

The action spectrum presented here is for the weak-light response, causing positive phototaxis, and it is to be noted that the far-red light has no effect in itself; it only nullifies the effect of a previously given red-light stimulus. To obtain negative phototaxis, rather high intensities have to be used and the response seems to be strongest in blue light (Mosebach, 1958).

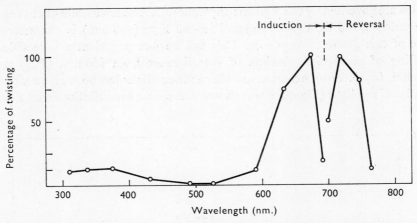

Fig. 7. Action spectrum for the induction and the reversal of chloroplast movements in *Mougeotia*. (After Haupt, 1959*b*.)

Table 3. *The effect of alternating irradiations with red (R) and far-red (FR) light on the chloroplast movements (twistings) in cells of Mougeotia*

R (679 nm.) = 350 ergs/cm.^{2}.sec. 1 min. FR (700 nm.) = 300 ergs/cm.^{2}.sec. 1 min. 15 min. of darkness between the light treatments. (After Haupt, 1959.)

Treatment	Twisted chloroplasts after 45 min. (%)
Darkness	22
R	77
R—FR	31
R—FR—R	75
R—FR—R—FR	34

THE LOCALIZATION OF THE PHOTORECEPTOR

By using polarized light it has been possible to get information on the localization of the light-absorbing agent which elicits the response (Haupt, 1960). If a filament of *Mougeotia* is irradiated with polarized light the response appears mainly in those cells which are localized in the parts of filaments more or less perpendicular to the plane of the light vibrations (Fig. 8). The effect of light of the same intensity but with the vibrating plane parallel to the filaments is more than 100 times weaker. From this the conclusion could be drawn that the photoreceptor molecules are anisotropically orientated. Similar experiments with far-red light gave the puzzling result that in this case the plane of vibration was of minor importance. Only small differences in response of light polarized in two opposite planes could be established. The explanation for this will be discussed further on.

The finding that the photoreceptors are anisotropically orientated leads to the question of where these receptors are localized. Haupt (1960) argued that if they were to be found in the chloroplasts themselves, one would expect quite different absorption conditions according to whether the plastids were irradiated perpendicularly or parallel to their surface. The same energies given to the edges and to the surfaces would not necessarily

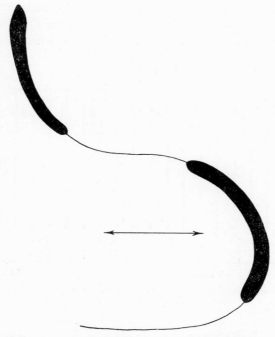

Fig. 8. Schematic picture of a *Mougeotia* filament after irradiation with linearly polarized light (u.v. 300–400 nm.) from above. The arrow indicates the plane of polarization. Thick lines: cells showing response (chloroplasts with their surfaces perpendicular to the incident light). Thin lines: cells showing no response (edges of chloroplasts towards the incident beam of light). (After Haupt, 1960).

be compensating. In cytoplasm lining the cell walls, however, one would expect the absorption conditions to be the same at any place round the filament of alga. Thus a gradient obtained by irradiating the edges should be nullified with the same energy given to the surface. Experiments performed to test these ideas showed that a considerable reduction of the induction took place, when, starting with edge irradiation, the surface was irradiated with energies half of that of the edge irradiation. Using one-eighth of these, the nullifying effect was small, however. The results point to a localization of the photoreceptors in the cytoplasm and not in the plastids.

Through a series of ingenious experiments, Haupt and his collaborators (Bock & Haupt, 1961; Haupt & Bock, 1962; Fischer, 1963) have finally succeeded in establishing that the photoreceptors are localized in the peripheral cytoplasm close to the cell wall, and that they are placed in a spiral pattern around the cell surface. The lines of this spiral form an angle about 45° with the cell axis. The definite proof of the orientation was obtained by irradiating the filaments with a small light spot of differently orientated planes of polarized light. The spot was small enough to allow irradiation of either the chloroplast only or parts of the cytoplasm free from the chloroplast. Some of the experiments are exemplified in Fig. 9.

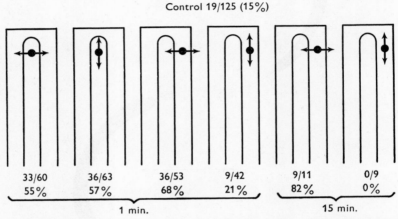

Fig. 9. Schematic picture of the effect on the *Mougeotia* cell of partial irradiation with a small point of light (cf. Fig. 6). The double arrow indicates the plane of the polarized light. The results are given in absolute figures and in percentage of irradiated cells. Denominator: amount of irradiated cells. Nominator: amount of cells showing response. (After Bock & Haupt, 1961).

THE RESPONSE IN RELATION TO THE
P_{730}-FORM OF THE PHYTOCHROME

While the experimental results described above give a more or less clear picture of the orientation of the red-absorbing form of the pigment system, active in eliciting positive phototaxis, the conditions are more puzzling in respect to the orientation of the far-red absorbing form of the pigment. This has clearly been shown by the experiments of Fischer (1963). If filaments of *Mougeotia* with chloroplasts facing the light are irradiated with high-intensity polarized light, vibrating parallel to the cell axes, a negative phototaxis is induced; that is, a twisting of the chloroplast from face to profile orientation. This response, which is also controlled by the phytochrome system, needs more light energy than the positive one, but even with saturating energies the response is never as great as the positive phototaxis. From earlier experiments it is clear that a light response in one or another direction is due to the absorption gradient obtained when the light penetrates the cell contents. In this case, the results suggest that the response which causes negative phototaxis is smaller than that needed to produce the positive reaction. This can be explained by the fact that since parallel vibrating light can be absorbed around the whole cell, there is a weaker absorption gradient (Fig. 10). It was found, however, that parallel vibrating light striking the cell obliquely to its axis was more effective in inducing a response than light falling perpendicular to the axis. The

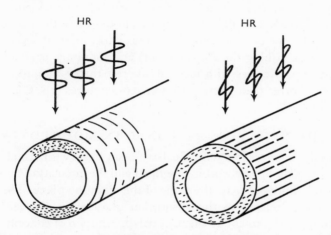

Fig. 10. Schematic picture of anticipated absorption conditions in a cell of *Mougeotia*. The thin lines on the cell surface represent the photoreceptors and the arrows above indicate the incident light and the planes of polarization. The intensity of absorption is denoted by points in the cross-sections. (After Haupt, 1960.)

question arises of how parallel vibrating light may lead to an absorption gradient. It could be proved that an absorption gradient must result if the phytochrome pigment (in red-absorbing form) is unevenly distributed around the cell surface at the beginning of the irradiation. Such uneven distribution can result from the pretreatments necessary to obtain the proper starting-position of the chloroplast. It can be cancelled if far-red light is given prior to the inducing red light. But as soon as the uneven distribution is re-established by proper pre-irradiations, parallel vibrating red light again becomes active. Also negative phototaxis will not always appear as a profile position; rather the chloroplast always turns through 90°. Thus it turns to profile position if starting from face position, but turns to face position if starting from profile position.

From these and other experiments Fischer (1963) could draw the conclusion that the far-red absorbing form is unequally distributed or can exist in two different states, only one of them being in a physiologically active form. However, this active form can quickly turn over to the in-active form. It is also possible that these results could be related to the results obtained by direct measurements of phytochrome concentrations in intact material. It has been found *in vivo* that newly formed far-red absorbing pigment is changed rather quickly into a form that shows no absorption, but probably still having a physiological action (Butler & Lane, 1965).

Further studies by Haupt (1966) have verified the existence of a trans-formation of active P_{730} into an inactive form. If the quick conversion of $P_{act.}$ to $P_{inact.}$ were a result of the response in question, the response must decrease with drastic shortening of the dark interval between pre-irradiation (establishing the P_{660} gradient) and inductive irradiation. This was shown to be the case with intervals shorter than $\frac{1}{2}$ min. at room tem-perature, or shorter than 3 min. at lower temperatures (10° C.).

THE NEGATIVE RESPONSE IN MOUGEOTIA

Hitherto only responses to red light have been dealt with. In all of these phytochrome is the light-absorbing pigment and the intensity of the response to polarized light depends on the angle of the vibrating plane. The reaction obtained is also related to the absorption gradient in the cell material penetrated by the light, and to the unequal distribution of concentrations of the absorbing agent.

A true negative phototaxis is produced in *Mougeotia* by light in the blue region within the wavelength range 400–510 nm. (Schönbohm, 1963),with a maximum between 450 and 480 nm. This response differs from the red-sensitive positive phototaxis in that it requires continuous irradiation during the whole course of the response for the twisting of the chloroplast to be completed. This is in contrast to the red-light response, where only a short-lasting impulse is necessary to start the reaction which is completed in the dark. It is in agreement with what should be expected for a system where the phytochrome is the light-absorbing pigment. The effect of light in such a system is only to convert P_{660} to P_{730}, which is a rapid photochemical reac-tion. As long as the pigment system is present as P_{730} it is physiologically active.

The negative response induced by blue light is also affected by far-red irradiation. If far-red light is administered after the blue-light response has been completed, the twisting back of the chloroplast is prevented for several hours. From this the conclusion can be drawn that the twisting back of the chloroplast into face orientation is due to an after-effect brought about by the irradiation and which must be identical with the normal positive phototaxis following a short irradiation (Schönbohm, 1963). As has been shown above, such an induction can be cancelled by far-red light. Further evidence supporting this assumption is provided by the fact that this after-effect is more effective if the negative phototaxis has been in-

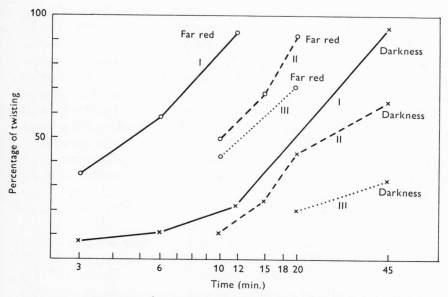

Fig. 11. Sensitizing action of a far-red light impulse given at different times between the end of the pre-treatment (irradiation for obtaining all chloroplasts in the same position) and the following induction. O—O, ×—×, 42,000 ergs/cm.².sec.; the others, 28,600/ergs/cm.².sec. (After Schönbohm, 1963.)

duced by light, polarized with the vibrating plane perpendicular to the cell axis, than if the vibrating plane is parallel to the axis. To induce the negative phototaxis, only polarized light vibrating parallel to the axis is more effective than cross-vibrating light. Besides the effect of far-red light, already mentioned above, it has also a general sensitizing effect on the cells if it is applied before the inducing blue irradiation (Fig. 11). This effect could partly be explained by the fact that far-red light cancels the after-effect arising from the pretreatment which is necessary to orientate the chloroplasts into the starting position for the experiment.

VARIATIONS IN RESPONSE TO RED LIGHT AS
GIVEN IN CONNEXION WITH BLUE LIGHT

The influence of long-wave (red) light on the different blue-light induced movements does not seem to be the same in all cases. For example, in the plastid movements in *Lemna trisulca*, Zurzycki (1962a) found an increase in the rate of the reaction if the movement induced by blue light took place in red light. For *Vaucheria sessilis*, Fischer-Arnold (1963) found that an increased response to blue light caused a negative phototaxis when red light was given simultaneously. Far-red light was without effect on *Vaucheria*, while, as shown by Schönbohm (1963; see above), far-red light strongly decreased the negative phototaxis induced by blue light in *Mougeotia* chloroplasts. In a later work, Schönbohm (1965) studied the effect of polarized red and far-red light on the reactions induced by blue light. It seems to be of no importance whether the light comes from the same or from the opposite direction as the induction beam. As far as the effect of far-red light is concerned, polarized light given together with blue-inductive light inhibits the response; light vibrating perpendicular to the cell axis is a little more effective than light vibrating parallel to it. Far-red light seems to have no influence if it is administered after the induction period; that is, during the chloroplast movement.

Red light vibrating perpendicular to the longitudinal cell axis inhibits the response when it is given before or after the inducing light period, while parallel vibrating red light is without effect. Transverse vibrating red light given during the induction period increases the response to blue light about three times, whereas parallel vibrating light inhibits the response. If far-red light is given after the inducing-light period, it changes neither the increasing effect of perpendicularly vibrating red light nor the inhibition of parallel vibrating red light.

These experiments seem to support the view that for the negative phototaxis of *Mougeotia* chloroplasts, physiologically active phytochrome (P_{730}) must be present. At rather low intensities of blue light even comparatively small amounts of P_{730} seem to be a limiting factor. One can also draw the conclusion that the effects of red light must be due to a strengthening or a weakening of a P_{730} gradient in the cell already brought about by the inductive irradiation. This gradient is established by blue light or by red light absorption in phytochrome (Schönbohm, 1967). If cells of *Mougeotia* are irradiated simultaneously with blue and red light coming from different directions it is possible to show that additional blue light acts tonically if absorbed in a yellow pigment and not if absorbed in phytochrome. This tonic effect of blue light seems to be independent of the vibration plane of polarized light. In this respect it differs from the effects of blue light on protoplasmic viscosity (Seitz, 1967). In establishing a gradient of P_{730} polarized blue light is more effective if vibrating perpendicularly to the cell axis than if vibrating parallel to it (Schönbohm, 1967). Certain combinations of intensities of blue and red light result in an almost even distribution of P_{730} throughout the cell. In this case the chloroplasts remain in the starting position. However, from these experiments it is too early to draw definite conclusions concerning the orientation and spatial distribution of the photoactive pigments.

THE MECHANISM OF MOTION

While our knowledge of the course of events following a light impulse, microscopically observable, is at least in some special cases rather comprehensive, the mechanism behind the movements is obscure. In his comprehensive review of the subject, Zurzycki (1962b) discusses the five main hypotheses which are available to explain the movement of the single plastids.

The peristromium hypothesis

Already in 1908 Senn had stated that the chloroplasts are surrounded by a layer of special protoplasm, the peristromium, capable of sending out pseudopodia and thus giving the plastid a possibility of performing amoeboid movements. The existence of such a peristromial layer has been questioned by several later research workers but has been demonstrated by Honda, Hongladarom & Wildman (1961) and Hongladarom, Honda & Wildman (1961), who were able to make cinematographic records of such movements. Although these findings may give a clue about the way in which the displacement takes place, it does not explain the mechanism of the movements. All that can be said is that if an amoeboid type of locomotion is the cause of the movement, the mechanism must have much in common with the similar movements of animal protoplasm.

The surface tension hypothesis

According to this hypothesis the movements are caused by differences in surface tension on both sides of the plastid. A local change of surface tension can easily produce a 'bulge' on a surface boundary causing a tendency to flow. A great many movable systems of this type have been described. They suggest a possible way of 'explaining' a movement, but as metabolic energy is required (see below) and as they do not give us any hint of how a directed movement can be explained, these hypotheses are of limited interest. The same can be said of the third hypothesis.

The electrokinetic hypothesis

According to this hypothesis the movement of the plastids would result from a change of electric charge under the influence of light. Such electric charges can also result from pH-changes during photosynthesis. One must agree with Zurzycki (1962 b), however, in his opinion that 'according to all the available information the phototactic movements are a phenomenon far too complex to be explained merely by the simple effect of electrokinetic attractions...'. It is true, however, that changes of external conditions sufficient to bring out phototactic movements are accompanied by some electrobiological effects.

The hypothesis of pulling fibres

This hypothesis is more or less intimately connected with the assumption of the existence of a peristromium. According to this hypothesis the plastids are fixed to each other by contractile fibres. In studies of the plastids of mosses the existence of extremely delicate threads reaching from one chloroplast to another and forming a photoplasmic net has been verified (Fig. 12). Also in *Caulerpa prolifera* such threads have been observed dragging the chloroplasts (Dostal 1929). According to Boresch (1914), however, they do not have any significance for the movements.

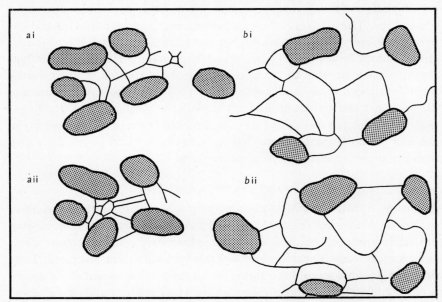

Fig. 12. Changes in shape of the protoplasmic net and of the position of the chloroplasts in a cell of *Funaria fascicularis*. *a*i and *b*i: initial conditions; *a*ii and *b*ii: after 27 min. (After Knoll, 1908.)

The hypothesis of plasmatic impulses

The chloroplasts in the protoplasm flowing out from incised cells of *Characeae* move round the shorter axis of an ellipsoid, making two or at most 4–5 rotations/sec. This phenomenon was first described in the middle of the last century. It shows that the movement of the plastids is active and independent of the plasmatic movements and that the plastids do not creep on the boundary surface of the plasma. Through the work of Jarosch (1956), it was established that there are submicroscopical fibrils in the drops of plasma capable of a lengthwise movement and able to propel the surrounding cytoplasmic medium. The fibrils have a tendency to assemble into larger bundles and are distributed homogeneously in a drop immediately after preparation only. According to Jarosch, the fibrillar substance is localized in the peripheral layer of the plasma and the pull exerted by these fibrils is the essential cause for rotating the protoplasm. When the chloroplasts get detached from the cortical layer some fibrils get stuck to them, and due to the ability of the fibrils to propel themselves they move the plastids. Whether these movements produced by plasmatic fibres are the natural cause of the phototactic movements of the chloroplasts is not known. It is of interest, however, to note that microscopically visible fibrils seem to disappear under the influence of strong light and appear again some time after the light is turned off (Jarosch, 1958).

Connexion with other phenomena

It has been postulated repeatedly that the light-induced movements of the chloroplasts depend on the physical state of the surrounding protoplasm, but the relationship is rather complicated. The phototactic movements of the plastids discussed above are clearly distinguishable from the passive movements of plastids commonly observed in plants with a protoplasm with low viscosity, which often shows rapid streaming. The most common examples of such passive movements are those found in the cells of some aquatic plants; for example, *Elodea*, *Vallisneria*. In these plants there is a phototactic movement of the plastids in darkness and in weak light when the main bulk of the protoplasm is at rest. Very soon after the onset of a light impulse, however, the physical state of the protoplasm itself is affected, and protoplasmic streaming results. In this streaming the chloroplasts often take part but the movement is passive. In terrestrial plants, and in most algae with a more viscous protoplasm and little tendency towards organized protoplasmic streaming, the phototactic movements are distinguished more easily.

The complicated relationship between phototaxis, photodinesis (protoplasmic streaming) and change in protoplasmic viscosity has recently been studied by Seitz (1967). All these phenomena are affected by strong light with practically identical action spectra (Fig. 13), showing the main response in blue light and possibly a small peak in the red region around 760 nm. The three phenomena show almost the same energy requirements in the blue region (360–500 nm.). This would indicate at the first glance that they are induced by the same photoreceptors, but other facts point to

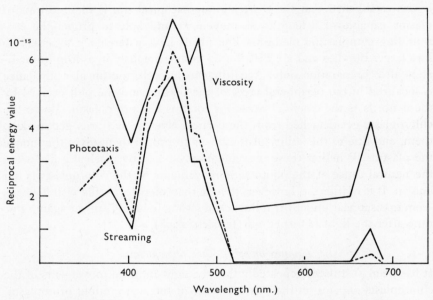

Fig. 13. Action spectra for the strong-light chloroplast movement (phototaxis), protoplasmic streaming and decrease in protoplasmic viscosity in cells of *Vallisneria*. Ordinate: reciprocal value for the energy (quanta/cm.^{2}. sec.) necessary to obtain 10 % reaction from an irradiation time of 20 min. (After Seitz, 1967.)

several photoreceptors. It was observed by Seitz (1967) that blue light, polarized parallel to the cell axis, has a much stronger effect on the protoplasmic viscosity than light polarized perpendicular to the axis. In the red region no such difference could be found. That variations in sensitivity to red and blue light are different and also seem to be mutually independent point to at least two primary processes, attached to different pigment systems. As far as the response to blue light is concerned, several facts point to riboflavin being the photoreceptor, probably common for all three responses. The red response, however, with a maximum at 679 nm. may depend on chlorophyll as the photoreceptor. This means that photosynthesis is responsible for the response and also for part of the blue-induced reaction.

ENERGY SUPPLY FOR THE MOVEMENTS

As far as the weak-light reactions are concerned, which are induced by a short light impulse but continue in darkness, one may assume that respiration or fermentation delivers the energy. The delivery of energy directly from photosynthesis can occur only if there is continuous irradiation throughout the reaction. Fetzer (1963) has shown that the irradiation of *Mougeotia* during anaerobic conditions does not affect the primary processes of the reversible response to red and far-red light. No response is obtained during anaerobic conditions, it is true, but the reaction starts when oxygen is supplied to the cells after the impulse is given (Table 4).

Table 4. *Effect of anaerobiosis on weak-light chloroplast movements in cells of Mougeotia*

Vertical arrows: second induction (1 min. of red light (100 ergs/cm.^{2}.sec.)). Horizontal arrow: O_2-treatment. The figures denote percentage of cells showing response. (After Fetzer, 1963.)

Time after first induction (min.)...	10	20	30	40	50	60	70
			↓				
Control	30	68	82	85	86	86	85
			↓				
N$_2$ (30 min.)	0	0	0	20	41	58	59
			↓				
N$_2$ (70 min.)	0	0	0	0	0	0	0

This response is also prevented by inhibitors of oxidative respiration such as CO, CN$^-$, NaN$_3$ and NH$_2$OH and by uncouplers of the oxidative phosphorylation such as 2,4-dinitrophenol. NaF and monoiodoacetic acid, which inhibit glycolysis, have no effect on the movement. If the cells are exposed to light during the whole period of the movement, inhibition brought about by anaerobiosis or by metabolic poisons can be reversed, provided the light energy exceeds a certain threshold value. This strongly points to the participation of photosynthesis in supplying the energy for the response, and suggests that photophosphorylations are involved. At least the weak-light reactions seem to get their energy from ATP, formed by photosynthetic phosphorylation. This would thus partly explain the similarity between the action spectra for chloroplast movements in some cases (*Lemna*) and for photosynthesis.

As far as the strong-light reaction is concerned, this is also strongly inhibited by anaerobiosis. But even after a change to aerobic conditions the inhibition remains for a comparatively long period of time. The fact that the reaction is affected relatively little by inhibitors of the oxidative phosphorylation shows that even in this high-energy process alternative energy-delivering processes are involved. Photosynthesis is probably working here also.

The connexion between chloroplast movements and photosynthesis in *Lemna trisulca* was further studied by Zurzycki (1966), and as far as photo-

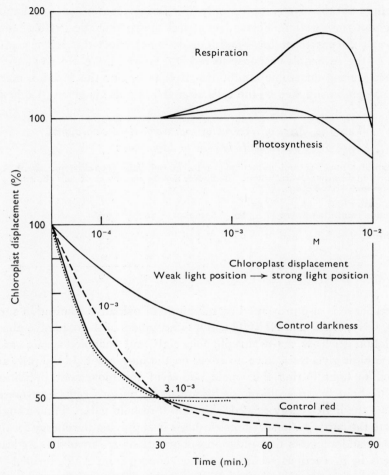

Fig. 14. Influence of ATP on photosynthesis, respiration and chloroplast displacements in *Lemna trisulca*. (After Zurzycki, 1966.)

taxis was concerned no direct correlation was found. The response is, as earlier discussed, confined to the spectral region of 350–530 nm., with the main peak at 450 nm. In the long-wave range (above 540 nm.) no photo-tactic response could be found, although there was an effect on the rate of displacement. This is the photokinetic effect of the light (Table 1, above).

Zurzycki (1966) showed that this reaction is affected by the same kind of poisons which inhibit photosynthetic phosphorylations. He also showed that the addition of ATP (10^{-3} M/l.) to the medium accelerates the displacement when the cells are kept in darkness and the speed of the chloroplasts approaches the value for their speed in strong red light (Fig. 14). This supports the idea of ATP being the energy source for at least the kinetic movement of the chloroplasts.

CONCLUSION

Chloroplast movements which are dependent on light are very complicated and are composed of at least three more or less independent photochemical primary processes. The action spectra for these are characterized by absorption spectra similar to those of the chlorophylls, yellow pigments (riboflavin) and phytochrome. The further chain of reactions is not known in detail, and our knowledge is very scanty on this point. Experimental evidence points to ATP being the energy source for some of the movements which require energy. As the movements of the plastids may be elicited by amoeboid movements of protoplasm surrounding the bodies and/or by contractions of fibril-like structures, it is justifiable to assume that the underlying mechanism is more or less the same as that found for contractile fibrils in animal protoplasm and thus of the same nature as muscle contractions.

REFERENCES

Bock, G. & Haupt, W. (1961). *Planta* **57**, 518.
Böhm, J. A. (1863). *Sber. Mat.-Nat. Kl. Kais. Akad. Wiss. Wien.* **22**, 479.
Boresch, K. (1914). *Z. Bot.* **6**, 97.
Butler, W. L. & Lane, H. C. (1965). *Pl. Physiol., Lancaster* **40**, 13.
Dostal, R. (1929). *Jb. wiss. Bot.* **71**, 596.
Fetzer, J. (1963). *Z. Bot.* **51**, 468.
Fischer, W. (1963). *Z. Bot.* **51**, 348.
Fischer-Arnold, G. (1963). *Protoplasma* **56**, 495.
Frank, B. (1872). *Bot. Ztg* **29**, 209, 225.
Haupt, W. (1958). *Naturwissenschaften* **45**, 273.
Haupt, W. (1959a). In *Encyclopedia of Plant Physiology*, vol. XVII, p. 278. Ed. E. Bünning. Berlin, Göttingen and Heidelberg: Springer Verlag.
Haupt, W. (1959b). *Planta* **53**, 484.
Haupt, W. (1960). *Planta* **55**, 465.
Haupt, W. (1963). *Ber. dt. bot. Ges.* **76**, 313.
Haupt, W. (1966). *Z. Pflanzenphysiol.* **54**, 151.
Haupt, W. & Bock, G. (1962). *Planta* **59**, 38.
Haupt, W. & Weisenseel, M. (1966). *Naturwissenschaften* **16**, 411.
Honda, S., Hongladarom, T. & Wildman, S. (1961). *Pl. Physiol., Lancaster* (Suppl.), **36**, xlviii.

HONGLADAROM, T., HONDA, S. & WILDMAN, S. (1961). *Pl. Physiol., Lancaster* (Suppl.) **36**, xlviii.
JAROSCH, R. (1956). *Phyton, B. Aires* **6**, 87.
JAROSCH, R. (1958). *Protoplasma* **50**, 93.
KNOLL, F. (1908). *Sper. Mat.-Nat. Kl. Kais. Akad. Wiss.Wien* **117**, 1224.
MOSEBACH, G. (1958). *Planta* **52**, 3.
MUGELE, F. (1962). *Z. Bot.* **50**, 368.
SCHÖNBOHM, E. (1963). *Z. Bot.* **51**, 233.
SCHÖNBOHM, E. (1965). *Z. Pflanzenphysiol.* **53**, 344.
SCHÖNBOHM, E. (1967). *Z. Pflanzenphysiol.* **56**, 282.
SEITZ, K. (1967). *Z. Pflanzenphysiol.* **56**, 246.
SENN, G. (1908). *Die Gestalts- und Lageveränderungen der Pflanzen-Chromatophoren.* Leipzig: Verlag von Wilhelm Engelmann.
STAHL, E. (1880). *Bot. Ztg* **38**, 297.
THIMANN, K. V. & CURRY, G. M. (1961). In *A Symposium on Light and Life*, p. 646. Ed. W. D. McElroy and B. Glass. Baltimore: The Johns Hopkins Press.
VIRGIN, H. I. (1954). *Physiologia Pl.* **7**, 343.
ZURZYCKA, A. (1951). *Acta Soc. Bot. Pol.* **21**, 17.
ZURZYCKA, A. & ZURZYCKI, J. (1950). *Acta Soc. Bot. Pol.* **20**, 665.
ZURZYCKI, J. (1962a). *Acta Soc. Bot. Pol.* **31**, 489.
ZURZYCKI, J. (1962b). In *Encyclopedia of Plant Physiology*, vol. XVII (2), p. 940. Ed. E. Bünning. Berlin, Göttingen und Heidelberg: Springer Verlag.
ZURZYCKI, J. (1966). In *Currents of Photosynthesis*, p. 235. Ed. J. B. Thomas and J. C. Goodheer. Rotterdam: Ad. Donker.

AUTHOR INDEX

Figures in bold type indicate pages on which references are listed.

SUBJECT INDEX

actin
actin
  activation of ATPase of myosin by, 18,
    33–7
  attachment of cross-bridges to, 81, 82, 84
  effect of, on binding of nucleotides by
    heavy meromyosin, 39, 40
  f-state of, as ATPase, 24
  fibrous and globular, 24, 51
  foetal and adult forms of, 13
  interaction of myosin and, 5, 6, 7, 8–9,
    17–42, 51–3, 72–81
  magnesium-polymer of, 212
  3-methyl histidine in, 13
  polarity of, 74, 83
  polymerization of, 23–4, 31, 51
  protein resembling, from myxomycete,
    204, 212
  ratio of myosin to, in insect flight muscle,
    75
  same in muscles from different sources,
    70
  in smooth muscle, 45, 48, 49, 50
  of smooth and striated muscle, com-
    pared, 51
α-actinin, 77
activity, adaptive response of enzyme
  composition of muscle to, 10
activity centre of nucleus (of *Polystictus*),
  see kinetochore equivalent
actomyosin, 6
  ADP exchange on, 22, 24–32, 81–2
  as ATPase, 18; regulated by actin, 33
  properties of, dependent on myosin
    component, 70
  protein resembling, in myxomycete,
    204; in surface membranes, 174
  from smooth muscle, 1, 50, 52
  superprecipitation of (*in-vitro* analogue
    of contraction), 24, 26–9, 52, 64
ADP (adenosine diphosphate)
  exchange of, on actomyosin, 22, 24–32,
    81–2
  in fibrous actin, 24
  interaction of heavy meromyosin with,
    37–40
algae, chloroplast movements in, 329
Allogromia, movement of, 163, 164, 165
Amoeba proteus
  changes in shape of isolated nucleus of,
    244–5
  chemotaxis of, 193
  electric potentials in, 181, 183, 186, 187
  movement of antibody on, 194

movement of cytoplasmic fraction from,
  153
surface membrane of, 171, 172
Amoeba striata, movement of, 162
amoebae
  large, amoeboid movement in, 151–61,
    166; pinocytosis in, 193; surface area
    of, 175
  small free-living, movement of, 161–2,
    166, 167
  testacean, movement of, 159–61
amoeboid movement, 169–98
  different types of, 151–68
amphibia, eggs of
  cleavage of, 312
  local contraction of surface of, 174, 192
anserine, in muscle, 13–14
antibodies
  for adult myosin, 12
  for cells of slime mould, 174
  for different segments of myosin molecule,
    78, 79
  fluorescent-labelled, as markers for cell
    surface membranes, 172–3, 174, 194
  location of tropomyosin in muscle by, 77
apostrophy of chloroplasts, 330, 331, 332
Arbacia, flagellar fibres from sperm of, 43
arteries, smooth muscle of
  actomyosin and myosin from, 1, 50
  calcium and magnesium requirements
    for contraction of glycerinated fibres
    from, 53
  tropomyosin abundant in, 51
ATP (adenosine triphosphate)
  actin-bound, 24, 30, 31
  in contractile system of muscle, 9, 18, 19,
    21–3; rigor in absence of, 18, 22, 73
  contraction induced by, in glycerinated
    cytoplasm, 154, 200, 203; in glyceri-
    nated muscle, 52, 58
  cross-bridges in presence and absence of,
    73
  dephosphorylation of, *see* ATPase
  effects of, in fibrils in myxomycete cyto-
    plasm, 204; on isolated nuclei, 244,
    245; on movement of chloroplasts,
    350–1
  in generation of mechanical energy, in
    moving cells, 246; in muscle, 81; in
    sperm, 105–6
  interaction of heavy meromyosin with,
    37–40
  not present in bacterial flagella, 216